MASTERPLOTS II

SHORT STORY
SERIES

MASTERPLOTS II

SHORT STORY SERIES

2

Cro-Gra

Edited by

FRANK N. MAGILL

SALEM PRESS

Pasadena, California   Englewood Cliffs, New Jersey

Library of Congress Cataloging-in-Publication Data
Masterplots II: Short story series.
    Bibliography: p.
    Includes index.
    Summary: Examines the theme, characters,
plot, style and technique of more than 700 nine-
teenth- and twentieth-century works by prominent
authors from around the world.
    1. Fiction—19th century—Stories, plots, etc. 2.
Fiction—19th century—History and criticism. 3.
Fiction—20th century—Stories, plots, etc. 4. Fic-
tion—20th century—History and criticism. 5.
Short story. [1. Short stories—Stories, plots, etc. 2.
Short story] I. Magill, Frank Northen, 1907-   .
II. Title: Masterplots 2. III. Title: Masterplots two.
PN3326.M27   1986   809.3   86-22025
ISBN 0-89356-461-3 (set)
ISBN 0-89356-463-x (volume 2)

LIST OF TITLES IN VOLUME 2

LIST OF TITLES IN VOLUME 2

MASTERPLOTS II

SHORT STORY
SERIES

CROSSING INTO POLAND

Author: Isaac Babel (1894-1941)
Type of plot: Impressionistic realism
Time of plot: 1920
Locale: Poland
First published: "Perekhod cherez Zbruch," 1924 (English translation, 1929)

> *Principal characters:*
> THE NARRATOR, the protagonist, an unnamed officer in the
>   Russian cavalry
> A JEWISH WOMAN, unnamed, in whose house the narrator is
>   billeted
> HER FATHER, who was killed in the recent fighting

The Story

To appreciate fully this very short story, apparently no more than a sketch, one must understand its context. Most significant is its position as the first of thirty-five related stories originally collected under the title *Red Cavalry* (1926). The stories all deal with the Russian campaign against Poland—from July through September, 1920—undertaken by General Semyon Budyonny's First Cavalry. The author, a Jew from Odessa who rejected Judaism to become a Communist, participated in this campaign (which was unsuccessful) as a propaganda officer and a war correspondent.

The narrator of the various *Red Cavalry* stories is apparently the same person throughout and autobiographical in essential features. Consequently, although little information is given about the narrator of the initial story, one learns from later stories that he is Jewish.

"Crossing into Poland" begins with a note that Novograd-Volynsk was taken at dawn. Now the rearguard is marching on the highroad from Brest to Warsaw, crossing into Poland over the twisting torrents of the River Zbruch.

The largely peaceful and brightly colored sights of nature—fields, flowers, streams, the sun, and finally the moon—are described as a prose poem often employing striking, disturbing, and contradictory imagery. Late at night, the narrator reaches Novograd and is billeted in a house where Jews live. He describes them as "scraggy-necked" and living in filth. He angrily orders the young pregnant woman of the house to clean up the mess.

Eventually he lies down on the floor, on a ragged feather bed, next to one of the Jews, who is lying huddled to the wall with his head covered up, evidently asleep. The narrator soon sleeps but then is awakened from a nightmare by the pregnant woman, who tells him that he has been crying out. Suddenly he sees that the old man, next to whom he has been lying, is dead: "His throat had been torn out and his face cleft in two; in his beard blue blood was clotted like a lump of lead." The woman laments the loss of her father, killed by Poles that day—and the narrator is shocked to silence as the story abruptly ends.

Themes and Meanings

In "Crossing into Poland" one may note at least three of the important themes to be developed in full detail throughout *Red Cavalry*. The first of these is disapproval of war—conveyed in this story through disturbing imagery and the gruesome description of a victim of war. One might conclude that the author is in fact a pacifist, but that he declines to voice that view explicitly on the grounds that subtlety and understatement will have a greater effect on the reader.

Yet the author also must have felt some ambivalence toward the Polish campaign, as a Communist and as a supporter of the Russian Revolution. Hence, there may be discerned in the stories a tentative (perhaps merely ironic) effort to seek justification for the sacrificial victims of the war. (Note that the old man may be seen specifically as a sacrifice because his throat has been cut, as in Jewish ritual slaughter of animals.) This second theme in "Crossing into Poland" occurs as little more than a suggestion, as the narrator, in describing the mess spread out over the floor of the Jews' house, refers to the "fragments of the occult crockery the Jews use only once a year, at Eastertime." This one reference to "Eastertime" (in Russian, "Passover" is also indicated, as the word for Easter and Passover is the same, *Paskha*) implicitly evokes the sacrifice of Jesus, with whom the old man, in retrospect, becomes tentatively associated. (One may think of him as a sheep or lamb offered to God.) Because this implicit comparison is in no way resolved, one is left with two ironic possibilities, depending on one's religious convictions: Either the old man may somehow benefit mankind as Jesus did, through his sacrificial death, or there is no such benefit at all, and the old man died in vain, as did Jesus.

It is important that the old man is presented as an exceptionally good person. He submits to death voluntarily (as the narrator learns from his daughter), pleading with the Poles, "Kill me in the yard so that my daughter shan't see me die." The daughter asks the narrator at the end: "I should wish to know where in the whole world you could find another father like my father?" An implicit comparison with Jesus is not unjustified. Meanwhile, the reader may believe in any case that Isaac Babel's story—as a kind of redemption through art—accords transcendent dignity to the sacrifice of the unknown Jew. There is even a hint at resurrection in the daughter's pregnancy.

A third major theme deals with anti-Semitism—rampant among the Russian cossack troops as well as among the Poles. In this story, the reader is invited to share in the apparent anti-Semitism of the presumably Russian cavalry officer as he describes the Jews skipping about (to his orders) "monkey-fashion, like Japs in a circus act." (It is their faintheartedness and passivity that seem to him especially objectionable.) Yet suddenly Babel brings the narrator—and the reader (originally a Russian reader)—face to face with the mutilated corpse and the weeping woman. The only decent emotion at this point is shame for having forgotten that all men are one under God. The fact that the narrator is himself Jewish (a fact deducible only in the later stories, but which does not prevent the reader from rereading "Crossing into Poland") merely adds poignancy to Babel's basic theme: A Jew also may experience the shame of anti-Semitism. In addition, one may suppose that the narrator must see himself, forever a Jew despite his atheism—and all other suffering Jews—in the sacrificed old man.

Style and Technique

Despite what at times appears to be stark realism in his works, Babel's literary art is often more concerned with style than content. Usually, however, one may perceive some basic relationship between the two, as in the following images from the opening section of "Crossing into Poland": " . . . the highroad . . . built by Nicholas I upon the bones of peasants"; "the orange sun rolled down the sky like a lopped-off head"; and "into the cool of evening dripped the smell of yesterday's blood. . . ." This imagery found early in the story is given an especially ominous character as it is contrasted, in the same opening paragraph, to bright visions of peace and serenity: " . . . on the horizon virginal buckwheat rose like the wall of a distant monastery"; "the . . . peaceful stream . . . wound weary arms through a wilderness of hops"; and "On the waves rested a majestic moon."

Yet, after all in the house have gone to sleep, and "faint-hearted poverty" has "closed in " over the narrator's bed on the floor, the reader is confounded by the following elaborately poetic line: "Only the moon, clasping in her blue hands her round, bright, carefree face, wandered like a vagrant outside the window." At this point, the narrator is already being assailed by a nightmare in which "the Brigade Commander's head" is pierced by bullets, and "both his eyes" drop to the ground. It is no doubt true that the clasped face of the moon and the commander's pierced head anticipate the wounds of the old man, but the imagery seems excessive (why the "bright, carefree" face?) and enigmatic (why the eyes dropping to the ground?). Yet the overall impressionistic effect is very satisfactory, even if somewhat puzzling. This highly colored style, characteristic not only of the early Babel but also of other Russian writers of the 1920's, has been referred to as "ornamentalism."

Babel's ornamentalism usually yields to meaning, or at least to some significant insight, perhaps not fully resolved, but disturbing and unforgettable. Such is the case, at the end of "Crossing into Poland," with the sudden and shocking revelation of the dead man by his grieving yet angry daughter.

The reader is not told what the narrator is thinking as the story ends but nevertheless knows the narrator's thoughts exactly, because the reader becomes him through Babel's astonishing "epiphany," or "showing forth," in which all the elements of the story seem to have coalesced. The literary epiphany, a conception brought into use by James Joyce, is one of Babel's most effective stylistic devices.

Donald M. Fiene

CRUEL AND BARBAROUS TREATMENT

Author: Mary McCarthy (1912-   )
Type of plot: Psychological realism
Time of plot: Mid-twentieth century
Locale: New York City
First published: 1939

> *Principal characters:*
> THE YOUNG WOMAN, an unnamed divorcée-to-be
> BILL, her husband
> THE YOUNG MAN, her paramour

The Story

In this, Mary McCarthy's first published story, the initial two sentences summarize the whole. The remainder of the narrative details the careful, ritualized process by which the protagonist makes her way from a clandestine affair to public disclosure and impending divorce. Mary McCarthy's satiric view of bourgeois society is never sharper than in this study of how a bored woman transforms her life from a series of "timekillers, matters of routine . . ." to one of "perilous and dramatic adventures," merely by ending her marriage in three steps. This is a story wherein the third-person narrative voice is orchestrated with a care matched only by the protagonist's own arrangement of events.

The young wife loves groups of three: the love triangle that she has brought into being, the three-times-a-week minimum for social outings during which she can "tremble . . . on the exquisite edge of self-betrayal," and above all the three-part sequence into which she organizes her drama of marital disintegration and from each of which she squeezes all the excitement she can before moving on to the next.

First, during the period of secrecy, the "subterranean courtship," there is the Public Appearances routine. Its main advantages come from its "outlawry," which tends to force the illicit lovers into an especially strong dependency and which gives the young woman intense feelings of superiority. This latter derives from her feeling that she has "bested" her husband and can feel good about her restraint in not gloating over the victory. Then too, she can feel superior to the callow Young Man, whose "imperfections" seem so clear under the pressure of his having to attend parties and act as if they were her "private theatricals." In this triangle she has power: "She was undoubtedly queen bee."

The second "preordained stage," made necessary when the possibilities of the first are "exhausted," the young woman calls the Announcement. It, too, has special characteristics which provide not only emotional stimulation but also feelings of superiority. To make the Announcement rids the lovers of the "morally distasteful" secrecy, and, more important, it allows her to satisfy her curiosity about What People Would Say. What good is a secret if it is never revealed? It is not only revealed to a wider and wider circle of friends, but also finally used to discover How Her Husband Would Take It (and to discover the full strength of his love by putting it "face to face with its own annihilation," and thus putting it into "the category of completed experiences"). Once again, the young wife's genius for arranging stage performances shows itself in the public *conférence à trois*, and her instincts for the ritualistic reveal themselves in her arranging "the confession in the restaurant and the absolution in the Park."

The final, Post-Announcement phase proves to be the shortest and least satisfying of the three: There is no triangle; there are only the "dull moments . . . she spent alone with the Young Man." For a person who finds pleasure in the flux of instability and manipulation, some method of breaking the stasis of pairing must be found. The young woman does not perceive the situation in these terms, however, and concludes that she is the "victim" of unconscious forces, "a sort of hypnotic trance." In the throes of a depression that is neither "dramatic" nor "pleasurable," she takes refuge in this vague sense of fate, wondering if it might be that she is "designed for the role of *femme fatale*," to be "a bad risk," to enjoy the "glamour" of the title Young Divorcée.

Just when her options seem to be gone, when she remembers the old fear of spinsterhood, when she realizes there is "no signpost to guide her"—just when, in other words, the story seems about to deliver something as artistically vulgar as poetic justice—she rallies and finds new improvisations, saving both herself and the narrative from a final triteness and exhaustion.

Themes and Meanings

The social and psychological themes of "Cruel and Barbarous Treatment" become clear after a moment's reflection: the superficiality of social friendships, the difficulty of understanding another human being, the battle of the sexes, and what Edgar Allan Poe once termed "the imp of the perverse," one's desire to throw over what in rational terms is in one's best interest for something more intense and passionate, though risky and destructive. The young woman, while manipulative and dishonest, is nevertheless, a very attractive character because of her energy, inventiveness, and ability to play her game with great dexterity. Though condemnations of her behavior spring to mind, nothing in the narrative itself announces or invites them. McCarthy's satire here is not of the heavy, moralistic sort. The husband, after all, does quite well without her, his social life so busy that he does not have time to see her off on the train to Reno. The wife has more than sufficient resources. Only the Young Man will be hurt, and his problems are never significant in the story except as comedy.

McCarthy herself referred to the story's main concern as "the quest for the self," which is also the unifying theme for the collection of short stories *The Company She Keeps* (1942), in which the story appeared as the first in a connected sequence about a woman who attempts to create a sense of who she is by means of dramatic and often scandalous actions. The cleverness of this protagonist in "Cruel and Barbarous Treatment," as in many of the other stories, is not to be seen as defining a self, but rather as a nervous indication that no identity has been found. The great insight into human character here is of the comic: People are unable to learn from their mistakes, and this fixity is the basis for the comedy that keeps the story from sinking into the didactic. What defines the protagonist is the need for excitement, the need to feel superior, and the essential triteness that this "quest" demands. Thus, the clichéd phrases which name the ritual phases of her progress are capitalized (Woman With A Secret, and so forth), and thus near the end of the story, she shows the essentially unimaginative quality of the quest when she takes refuge in the self-delusion and silly fatalism of such lines as, "If the Man [to replace her husband] did not exist, the Moment would create him." Yet she is, above all, consistent, as the comic stasis requires. McCarthy in her essay "Characters in Fiction" describes her desire "to be as exact as possible about the essence of a person," nicely underlining the idea of a static conception of character.

Style and Technique

McCarthy describes this story as a "stylization." The voice itself in this third-person-limited narrative stays for the most part very close to the vocabulary and mental forms of the character being described. The sequence of events, the capitalized divisions of the ritual, the mental improvisations within the tightly closed divisions, the carefully balanced parallels of a sentence such as, " . . . the deception was prolonged where it had been ephemeral, necessary where it had been frivolous, conspiratorial where it had been lonely," all describe a mind that loves, not free spaces, but securely fenced ones. All this evidence of symmetry and control supports the idea that this woman is not interested in wild abandon, or even passion, but rather in power (and in a very small arena).

This explains McCarthy's technique of condescension, for the reader is always made aware that there is a world bustling about outside this self-absorbed mind, that there is a great irony in the direct quotation marks as the protagonist announces to her silly Young Man that she should have been "a diplomat's wife or an international spy." In irony, the highest consciousness must be reserved for the implied author, and McCarthy here has taken it. The protagonist, clever rather than imaginative, is not "superior" as she believes herself to be, and the authorial consciousness shows this, in the protagonist's fear of what others will think of her lover once he is revealed, in her jealousy at her husband's warm reception by their mutual friends, and in her self-delusion concerning fate near the end of the story. The character's lack of self-knowledge reveals her inferiority to the consciousness that controls the story itself.

The protagonist is in the best sense a "flat" character, or to repeat McCarthy's own term, an "essence." Thus there is no development of awareness, or other evidence of change. The story is frankly analytic, depending on explanation of a fixed principle of character. The surprises result, not from revelations of hidden recesses, but from the virtuoso variations on the single theme: How much excitement, how much plot, can the young woman create for herself using such limited resources? All these variations reflect on the satiric mind behind the story's conception.

Kerry Ahearn

THE CRUISE OF *THE BREADWINNER*

Author: H. E. Bates (1905-1974)
Type of plot: Antiwar adventure
Time of plot: World War II
Locale: On the ocean off the coast of England
First published: 1946

> *Principal characters:*
> GREGSON, a large, heavyset man in his sixties, skipper of *The Breadwinner*
> JIMMY, the engineer of *The Breadwinner*
> SNOWY, about seventeen, the cook and chore boy on *The Breadwinner*
> KARL MESSNER, a German pilot
> AN UNNAMED RAF PILOT

The Story

   The Breadwinner is a small, rickety fishing boat that has been pressed into service by the exigencies of war to patrol the coast of England, complete with an unreliable engine and an ancient Lewis gun mounted on the stern. On the day of the story, everything is as usual: Gregson, the skipper, is impatient for Snowy, the cook, to bring his cup of tea; Jimmy, the engineer, is fretting over the balky engine; Snowy is in the tiny galley reluctantly making tea and wishing that something exciting would happen. Snowy becomes more interested when a squadron of Hurricane fighter planes leaves the coast looking for German aircraft. As always on these occasions, he thinks bitterly of the binoculars the skipper has been promising him for weeks. The routine of the day is suddenly interrupted by the noise of gunfire well out in the channel, and Snowy's keen ears detect the sound of Messerschmitts. For some time, the boat cruises uneventfully in the direction of the gunfire, until Snowy detects the sound of a whistle. Excitedly, the crew rushes toward a speck in the distance, which proves to be a downed RAF pilot in a dinghy. The pilot is unhurt and in good spirits, full of praise for the German pilot whose plane he believes he shot down. From him they also learn that his was not the battle they had heard earlier, so they head farther out to sea in case there are more pilots to be rescued. Sent to the galley to peel potatoes, Snowy is sullenly and bitterly angry at being away from the excitement and the glamour of the pilot. Moments later, Jimmy announces that another pilot has been sighted, a wounded German. As the English pilot brings him toward the boat, Snowy sees around the German's neck a leather binoculars case. War seems to him now wonderful and romantic.
   A few minutes later, while Snowy is in the galley making tea for the pilots,

he hears the deafening roar of a plane and a burst of cannon fire. Rushing on deck, he sees to his horror that Jimmy has been killed and the two pilots wounded. Gregson is too angry at the enemy to attend to the German, but the RAF man insists that he be treated decently. As Gregson nurses the Englishman, Snowy hopes the German will try to escape so Gregson can kill him and he can claim the binoculars. When rain begins falling, Gregson and Snowy move the wounded men to the cabin below. Snowy attempts to take Jimmy's place as engineer but discovers that gunfire has damaged the motor beyond repair. Gregson rigs a sail, but they must hurry as bad weather is brewing. Below, Snowy tries to administer first aid to the wounded German, whose name is Karl Messner, but the man is badly wounded. Snowy also tries to talk to the RAF pilot, a hero in his eyes, but the pilot downplays his actions and seems more concerned for Messner's welfare than his own. While they sail for home, first Messner dies, then the Englishman.

As *The Breadwinner* nears shore just ahead of the advancing storm, Gregson's face bears a look Snowy has not seen before. Suddenly the skipper bursts into an angry, cursing denunciation, "Why don't they let our lives alone? God damn and blast them—all of them, all of them, all the bastards, all over the world!" Snowy, clutching the binoculars, sees the older man's face wet with tears and feels grateful to be alive amid the horrors of war.

Themes and Meanings

As is so often the case in H. E. Bates's fiction, the theme of this story is a young man's fall from innocence. In this instance, Snowy's innocence is his belief that war is a romantic adventure, especially for fighter pilots. Like most adolescents, he sees his own life as dull and commonplace, and his almost childish desire for a pair of binoculars signifies his longing for something just beyond his reach. One by one, Snowy's illusions are stripped away, first by the sight of Jimmy's mangled body lying inert in a pool of blood, then by the strange camaraderie of the two pilots, and finally by Gregson's outburst against the nameless and faceless "them" who inflict war on ordinary, decent people. Snowy is left at the end of the story clinging halfheartedly to the binoculars, now a symbol of his former illusions, stunned into the realization that modern war is only organized, mechanized horror.

Style and Technique

In the early days of World War II, Bates was commissioned to write a series of stories under the pseudonym "Flying Officer X" to publicize the quiet heroism of the Battle of Britain pilots. By the end of the war, however, he had seen enough of war's destruction, and this story is indicative of his new perception. The "Flying Officer X" stories were not entirely romantic, but in "The Cruise of *The Breadwinner*," Bates employs his most grimly realistic manner to the subject of war and its dehumanization. Like his earlier stories, "The Ox" and "The Mill," this one is marked by Bates's unrelenting starkness of vision and style. In clear, pictorial prose, Bates describes the laughably fragile boat, the ineffectual Lewis gun, the devastation wrought by the strafing German airplane, and the lingering, painful deaths of the two young pilots, who might, except for the accidents of war, have become friends. In direct contrast to the passages of destruction and death are the descriptions of the characters. Gregson is first depicted as tough and confident, but his jingoistic patriotism, like Snowy's innocence, melts into common human caring because of the pilots' deaths. The two young pilots, only a few years older than Snowy, are presented as willing but tragic participants in a war they did not cause. Brooding over the events of the story is indifferent nature, which first provides a "good day" for flying, then a storm that threatens the lives of them all. In short, Bates employs his most incisive, vivid style to describe his characters and their sufferings, depicting all of them as victims of forces beyond their control.

Dean Baldwin

DADDY WOLF

Author: James Purdy (1923-   )
Type of plot: Dramatic monologue
Time of plot: The 1950's
Locale: New York City
First published: 1961

Principal character:
BENNY, a Korean War veteran

The Story

James Purdy's concerns about the vanquished in American society reach full cry in this monologue by a veteran of the Korean War. Speaking from a phone booth, apparently in the hallway of the rat-infested tenement in which he lives, Benny addresses someone who appears to be waiting to use the phone. He asks the person to be patient a little bit longer because he is attempting to get the operator to reconnect him with a woman with whom he has been talking. From his position in the phone booth, he also can see into his flat, the door of which has been left open.

The reader is in the position of the person waiting to use the phone: He or she must listen to Benny's litany, must hear about Benny's wife, who has given up trying to cope with life on the ragged edge of poverty and who has taken herself and their son out of the city. Economic hardships are a commonplace of Benny's existence, and he now works for little pay in a company that makes mittens. So hard-pressed has he been that his only food is a bowl of Cream of Wheat leavened with some brown sugar. In fact, he is about to be displaced in his linoleum-floored apartment by a mama rat and her baby, which emerge periodically from the holes in the floor.

Before his wife left him, she had gotten in the habit of calling someone named Daddy Wolf at a number described as the Trouble Phone number. She would talk to Daddy Wolf about her problems, and he would unfailing offer the same remedies: Stand by your man, go to church, and read uplifting books whenever sexual desire troubles you. Daddy Wolf was for ladies only, however, and Benny, desperate in his need for his own trouble phone, has picked a number at random from the phone book and has been pouring out his woes to a female voice that responds only occasionally with "I see."

Ground down by a system which offers platitudinous prerecorded messages, Benny and Mabel, the absent wife, represent the urban poor in America, victims of a system that they have had no part in creating and that they cannot control. Mabel, the reader learns indirectly, had to resort to prostitution in order to get money to provide food for the family. A report she heard about the increase of venereal disease in the city provided additional impetus for her flight. Daddy Wolf cannot save her, and in his own desperate search for someone to listen, to care, Benny pleads with the operator at the story's end to help him because his is an emergency phone call.

Themes and Meanings

The "quiet desperation" about which Henry David Thoreau wrote in describing the lives of the masses of men breaks out in the open in this tale of frustration and loneliness. The American dream of coming to the big city and there achieving the success which the system argues is due each hardworking person eludes Benny, who has served in the Korean War and returned unscathed to make a life for himself and his family. Trouble phones, crisis lines, and dial-a-prayer services are what pass for human compassion, for understanding. Mechanical and electronic instruments become the only means by which desperate people may attempt to make contact with those they believe could help them. Tenements, low-paying jobs, and unfulfilled promises are the legacies that Benny inherits from those who have gone before.

Benny is almost childlike in his recounting of the troubles that he has experienced; his frustration and anger come more and more to the surface as the story progresses, and by its end he is literally shouting at the operator, demanding and at the same time pleading that someone listen to him. Yet the trouble phone spins out its never-changing message: Be good; if you are good, God will love you.

Style and Technique

Because this is a dramatic monologue, Purdy uses several devices to involve the reader directly in the experience. Benny uses direct address as the story opens: "You aren't the first man to ask me what I'm doing so long in the phone booth with the door to my flat open and all." The reader is immediately involved in the situation and recognizes, almost at once, that he or she will be involved in what is about to happen, as a passerby is sometimes engaged by a stranger seeking alms of some kind. Like the monologuists who became staples of radio and television programs, Benny talks to the reader and to the unseen operator who may or may not be on the other end of the line. His voice is ceaseless; he hardly pauses for breath. Purdy lets the reader listen at first and then by the simple expedient of increasing the tone of desperation in Benny's voice, forces the reader, almost against his will, to listen as the broken pieces of Benny's life are spread out before him as on the linoleum floor of his flat. When the reader hears the anguish and discovers the pathos of Benny's situation, he is no longer in such a hurry to use the phone because he knows that it is indeed an emergency call which Benny is attempting to place.

Dale H. Ross

DAMBALLAH

Author: John Edgar Wideman (1941-   )
Type of plot: Psychological realism
Time of plot: The apex of the American slavery period
Locale: A cane plantation somewhere in the Deep South
First published: 1981

> *Principal characters:*
> ORION (Ryan), an intractable slave, alienated from both
>   blacks and whites and intent upon preserving his African
>   language and rituals
> AN UNNAMED SLAVE BOY, who is fascinated by Orion's strange
>   habits
> AUNT LISSY, one of Orion's detractors, the black cook in
>   charge of children too young to work in the fields
> THE WHITE OWNER, who is identified only as Master and who
>   has grown intolerant of Orion's defiance

The Story

Orion is the name of a brawny giant in Greek mythology, a slayer of all beasts, who became a constellation. In this story, his namesake is a physically beaten, emaciated African disavowed by all on the plantation except one slave boy; accordingly, his proud name has been truncated to "Ryan." The boy, contemptuous of his vapid chores and the animal stories often repeated to him, is eager to take his place alongside the field hands and to learn the subtleties of male conversation. Restless, he alternately laments both "the nothing always there to think of" in his mind and the bombardment of orders from others upon him, "so crowded and noisy lots of time don't hear his own voice." For this reason, Ryan, who maintains serenity while obstinately speaking "heathen talk," abstaining from American food, and meditating in the river, poses an irresistible attraction.

Despite a beating from Aunt Lissy, the black doyenne of Mistress' kitchen and the supervisor of the slave children, the boy follows Ryan every spare moment, hiding behind trees. He even memorizes a word that he has heard the man shout in his direction: "Damballah." Though the boy does not know that this refers to a powerful god in the African pantheon, the word's very sound engenders equilibrium in him. He senses that Damballah will permeate something latent and beneficent inside himself, like a sudden gleam "you knew all the time . . . was there" appearing in a tarnished spoon when he polishes Mistress' silver.

The boy suspects that Ryan, aware of his spying, longs to communicate with him, yet before the two can meet directly, Master loses his patience with the recalcitrant man. Frustrated and irate, Master requests a full refund for Ryan in a letter to the unscrupulous trader who sold him. Then at last Ryan does something powerful, worthy of the legendary Greek hunter but for him, a slave, unthinkable and fatal. He strikes an overseer from his horse with bone-breaking effect, incurring a punishment of death: Master and the other overseers torture and decapitate him. Not even death can stop Ryan from contacting the boy, however, and through Damballah's intercession Ryan transmits to the child the native stories that he had yearned to preserve. When his spirit finally departs, the boy tosses the severed head into the waters where the dead man used to stand.

Themes and Meanings

As John Edgar Wideman indicates in an epigraph to the collection of short stories commencing with "Damballah," the paternal sky deity of this name—"himself unchanged by life, and . . . at once the ancient past and the assurance of the future"—embodies the concepts of unity and history. Ryan's invocation to this god, then, belies how he and other slaves are scattered in strange lands, severed from their families, tribes, and cultures. In addition to this physical displacement, Wideman suggests how, brainwashed to view the gods of "wild African niggers" as inauthentic, the plantation-born blacks are estranged from real powers such as Damballah and in turn have embraced the bogus Christianity taught them by whites.

Aunt Lissy, for example, is appalled when Ryan shouts Damballah's name during a black preacher's sermon on "Sweet Jesus the Son of God." Her horror at what he has done reflects the typical longtime slave's attitude that anyone, black or white, who is not a Christian is hedonistic, savage, and insane. Yet she is the crazy one for accepting a Christianity that condones, rather than condemns, her enslavers' harsh treatments.

In fact, in his behavior Master himself is unchristian. He justifies as "my Christianizing project" his bondage of blacks, of which Ryan's in particular culminates with a murder by "ax and tongs, branding iron and other tools" wielded by several able-bodied whites. Though Master brags, "I concern myself with the spiritual as well as the temporal needs of my slaves," he actually is preoccupied with neither. He fornicates with slave women at random despite the full cognizance of his anguished wife, and he worries about his slaves' market values instead of providing them with properly sized clothes and undergarments. To these hypocrisies neither God nor Christ, as if nonexistent, replies.

On the other hand, when Orion alerts Damballah in the spirit world, power emanates. This response undercuts the religion of the slaves' owners even more, since as part of his ritual Ryan ironically traces a cross, a symbol associated with the triumph and might of Christianity. During one such rite "over the cross the air seemed to shimmer like it does above a flame or like it

does when the sun so hot you can see waves of heat rising off the fields."
Similarly, the boy has heard that the crossed cuts on a whipped slave have
attracted vengeful spirits who "had everything in they hands, even the white
folks." Thus, stressing the impotence of the Christian Father and Son, only
spirits and gods connected to the slaves are active and responsive.

Style and Technique

Wideman's deft shifts in point of view convincingly dramatize the alienation of slaves from owners and of both groups from Ryan. Yet whether the
boy finally hears Damballah's instructions and the murdered slave's stories or
merely has grown simpleminded is a question that the author resolves
through other techniques.

First, Wideman suggests a soul-link between boy and man by describing
their physical features and actions in related terms. Both Ryan and the child
resemble tall, gangly, aquatic birds, specifically storks or cranes, for example.
Similarly, just as the story opens with Ryan absently bathing and peering into
the shallows, so the boy himself spends much of his day dreamily studying his
image, "like his face reflected in the river," in Mistress' flatware. Thus, to the
careful reader, this child's communication with the dead old man is merely an
extension of a bond that always existed between them.

Also, because of references to versions of the Greek Orion myths sprinkled throughout this story, Ryan comes across as not a pitiful slave but an
extraordinarily gifted spirit. Three elements prominent in "Damballah"—
eyes, water, and a bull—play key parts in the ancient tales as well. The
Greek Orion, blinded by an angry king, regained his sight by looking directly
into the rising sun. Interestingly, black Ryan watches the morning sun illuminate the river, and the boy is struck by the penetrating quality of the man's
"hooded eyes." Further echoing a variant of the Hellenic tales, wherein the
appearance and disappearance of Orion's constellation signal impending rain
(the word "Orion" itself means "he who makes water"), the enslaved Ryan
senses a storm brewing, a harbinger of his death. Finally, while a bull is associated with the classical Orion's birth—his desperate father sacrificed one so
the gods would grant his wish for a child—in "Damballah" a sound like a
bull's scream comes from the barn on the night of Ryan's death. The graying
slave's thin body and distant air hence cloak a majestic soul searching for
someone worthy of his gifts, recalling the Greek gods and goddesses who visited so many mortals, including Orion's own parents, disguised as poor, ragged old couples. Since Ryan shares the legacy of a demigod, it is believable
that he can maintain a mystic rapport with the boy even after death.

Indeed, one particular thread from the Orion myths woven through
"Damballah" serves to do more than legitimize the boy's talks with a corpse.
His eyes put out by his lover's furious father, Orion impressed Cedalion, a
young blacksmith's apprentice, into service as his guide. Clearly in a similar

fashion the slave youth, drawn magnetically to the outcast, directs Ryan at the end of the story. Whereas Cedalion conducted Orion toward the sun and sight, the boy sees Ryan's spirit home to the light of freedom: "Orion talked and he listened and couldn't stop listening till he saw Orion's eyes rise up through the back of the severed skull and lips rise up through the skull and the wings of the ghost measure out the rhythm of one last word."

Barbara A. McCaskill

DANTE AND THE LOBSTER

Author: Samuel Beckett (1906-   )
Type of plot: Philosophical farce
Time of plot: The late 1920's
Locale: Dublin, Ireland
First published: 1932

> *Principal characters:*
> BELACQUA SHUAH, the protagonist, a student and idler
> SIGNORINA ADRIANA OTTOLENGHI, Belacqua's Italian teacher

The Story

As the story begins, Belacqua Shuah, the protagonist, is reading canto 2 of Dante's *Paradiso* and having difficulty understanding it. At noon, he lays his task aside and considers his schedule for the day, consisting of lunch, picking up a lobster for his aunt, and his Italian lesson. The preparations for his lunch are strange. First, he toasts bread, which must be blackened through and through to suit him. He succeeds in achieving the desired glassy texture, but he burns his wall in the process. He then applies a thick paste of Savora, salt, and Cayenne, wraps the "burnt offering" in paper, and goes out to buy cheese. Nothing would do but "a good green stenching rotten lump of Gorgonzola cheese." Warning the grocer that if he does not come up with rottener cheese in the future, he will take his business elsewhere, Belacqua, with his now completed Gorgonzola sandwich in hand, heads for the public bar for his daily two pints of stout, looking forward to his lesson with his Italian teacher, Signorina Adriana Ottolenghi, whom he idolizes.

Belacqua then goes to school, lunch having been "a notable success," far better than he had anticipated. The "pale soapy piece of cheese" had proved strong, and the toast had had the texture of glass: "His teeth and jaws had been in heaven, splinters of vanquished toast spraying forth at each gnash." His mouth still burning and aching from his lunch, he then goes to pick up the lobster, which he believes to be freshly killed, and proceeds to his Italian lesson. While he is with the signorina, a cat attacks his parcel, which has been left out in the hall, but the French instructress rescues the lobster before any harm is done. The lesson continues. When it is over, Belacqua takes the lobster to his aunt's house, where he is horrified to learn that the lobster is not yet dead and will have to be boiled alive. He comforts himself that at least it will be a quick death. The last line of the story is, "It is not."

Themes and Meanings

Belacqua Shuah, the prototype for many of Samuel Beckett's fictional heroes, makes his presence felt initially, in this the opening story of the author's first book of fiction, by means of a failure. He is unable to understand a passage from canto 2 of Dante's *Paradiso*. The story ends with another failure, Belacqua's misunderstanding of how a lobster is cooked. In the afternoon between these two incidents, typical scenes from what must be regarded as Belacqua's ordinary life are presented.

In contrast to the stupefaction which accompanies his failures, the demeanor to which Belacqua's afternoon activities give rise is intense, aggressive, fastidious, and perfectionist. By means of this contrast, the story satirically places activity above thought. Belacqua's round of time-killing appointments serves to distract him from the abyss of unknowing into which his mind, in its ignorance, can lead him. The vehemence and relish of Belacqua's encounters with the everyday are astutely and economically dramatized as overstatements. The air of triumph with which Belacqua concludes his business with the story's various, almost invariably anonymous tradesmen is misplaced and, in any case, ephemeral. The sense of completeness which attends these transactions is spurious, given that they occur between the twin inscrutabilities of Dante and the lobster. Thus, the story can be seen as a comedy of misperceptions and absurdly inflated responses, framed by what the mind cannot grasp (the passage from Dante) and by what it grasps so well that it cannot bear to contemplate (the fact that, to be cooked, lobsters must be boiled alive).

Dante and the lobster are extremes, in the presence of whose reality Belacqua becomes virtually speechless. As though to distract himself from the ineluctability of such extremes, Belacqua creates an extreme of his own, the story's celebrated Gorgonzola sandwich. The production of this concoction, which it is pleasant to imagine Belacqua uniquely capable of consuming, is a splendid comic set piece. In a way which Beckett's later work perfects, however, the sandwich ritual's excruciating humor has a directly conceptual, but obliquely narrational, bearing on the more distressing components of the story's framework. The tears which the preposterously spiced sandwich bring to Belacqua's eyes are tears of consummation. His mouth palpitates in the aftermath of the self-inflicted culinary assault, but his mind rejoices in the completeness which he has perpetrated. ("The lunch had been a noticeable success, it would abide as a standard in his mind.") Idea transcends experience, as is borne out by Belacqua's laughable tendency to idealize his Italian teacher, Signorina Adriana Ottolenghi.

It is the signorina, however, in a brief outburst of impatience and anxiety, who returns Belacqua to an awareness of immutability and a recognition of the unalterable nature of things. By this outburst and, earlier, by her questioning the desirability of translating Dante, the signorina, in effect, prepares Belacqua for the lobster's death. The preparation is, however, cerebral only; it does not prevent Belacqua from being shocked when his aunt (another of the story's anonymous characters) is about to carry out the crustacean's execution. In this instance, as in the opening case of the *Paradiso* passage, experience defies idea. Whatever cannot be understood, whatever retains its unamenable integrity, obtains to a different plane of reality than the repetitious features of the everyday—drinking porter, making sandwiches, and attending lessons (for the most part, Belacqua is a creature of habit). It may be that Belacqua's engrossing fidelity to a familiar daily round (hinted at by the circular shape of the bread for his sandwich) leads him to assume that the world is his oyster. His comically exaggerated sense of his own importance may be a dramatization of this assumption. Yet together, Dante and the lobster undermine such posturing.

In addition to being, by virtue of his idleness, related to a character of the same name in Dante's *The Divine Comedy*, Belacqua is a member of a long line of Irish fictional students. All these characters are notable for the varying degrees to which their makeup combines intensity, subjectivity, and vanity. As in the case of the line's most illustrious members (James Joyce's Stephen Dedalus immediately comes to mind), the challenge which Belacqua must face concerns the mind, its range and efficiency. The contrast in "Dante and the Lobster" between what can be effectively undertaken, or satisfactorily experienced, and what cannot, may be considered as a differentiation between the mind as a mechanism (responding to urges and appetites) and the mind as an organism (susceptible to evolution). Despite its philosophical inclinations, however, "Dante and the Lobster" should not be thought of as a philosophical argument.

On the contrary, Beckett impartially gives both conceptions of the mind equal attention. Belacqua embodies both but controls neither. He is a space where both models of mind come randomly into play. Beckett seems to do no more than establish the space and invoke the play. The two kinds of mind are permitted, or even perhaps encouraged, to collide with and override each other. The fact that one version of mind is being attended to at a given juncture in the story does not mean that its opposite (though it is also possible to say, its counterpart) is totally in abeyance. The story is so committed to a sense of duality that it may be suggesting that its two models of mind share a mutuality as well as an antagonism. Dante and the lobster, in different ways, produce a common effect. Yet, as Belacqua's flounderings reveal, it is possible, because of the ineluctable nature of time, to inhabit only one of the terms of the duality at once. Thus, the interplay between experience and idea succeeds in both substantiating and undermining its own conceptual structure.

Style and Technique

Much of the conceptual dimension of "Dante and the Lobster" is borne out by the story's stylistic variety. Beckett's later stylistic virtuosity may be seen in embryo here. The story's preoccupation with disruption, discontinu-

ity, interruption, and reversal is given its primary salience in the author's language. Veering from the mandarin to the demotic, from the platitudinous to the rarefied, from the language of Dublin to the language of Dante, Beckett provides a telling form of dramatic validation for Belacqua's experiences of finality and indeterminacy. The oscillations of style occur unpredictably, devoid of a sense of pattern or overall objective. Their reality, like that of everything else in the story, is ratified by Belacqua's failure to rise above them.

Supplementing the story's plethora of styles is an equally wide and unpredictable range of literary allusions. In addition to Dante, a greater influence on Beckett—James Joyce—subtly pervades the story. A reader gains an interesting perspective on Belacqua through noting his fear (mentioned on two different occasions) of "some brisk tattler. . . bouncing in now with a big idea or petition"; fear, that is, of a confrontation dramatized in Joyce's *A Portrait of the Artist as a Young Man* (1916). Similarly, it is amusing to compare the fitful Belacqua's lunchtime with that of steady Leopold Bloom in *Ulysses* (1922): Bloom lunches on Gorgonzola and burgundy. Besides cryptic references to Joyce's works, "Dante and the Lobster" directly invokes *Hamlet*, the Bible, and a number of nineteenth century Italian authors. Yet none of these references provides anything like an explanation or a rationale for Belacqua's many frames of mind. On the contrary, in context, the allusions seem inappropriate. Their effect, indeed, is to reinforce the sense of arbitrariness provided by the story's potpourri of styles.

The ultimate expression of the story's use of arbitrariness occurs toward the end: "Belacqua drew near to the house of his aunt. Let us call it Winter, that dusk may fall now and a moon rise." Here Beckett dispenses with and satirizes fiction's conventional pretense to consistency and uniformity. Since such criteria of credibility are repudiated by Belacqua's behavior throughout the story, and by the stylistic variety which communicates that behavior, Beckett's artistic deviation here hardly seems extravagant. Moreover, no sooner has the arbitrariness of invention been introduced than Beckett goes on to sketch an effective, twilight, urban pastoral. Invention may be arbitrary, but it is also final. By locating the juxtaposition of that antithesis in the story's technique, Beckett bestows aesthetic substance upon, and thereby legitimates, the interplay of opposites, contradictions, and antinomies which are discernible in the conceptual underpinnings of "Dante and the Lobster."

George O'Brien

THE DARING YOUNG MAN ON THE FLYING TRAPEZE

Author: William Saroyan (1908-1981)
Type of plot: Character study and social realism
Time of plot: The 1930's
Locale: San Francisco
First published: 1934

> *Principal characters:*
> THE WRITER
> THE LADY AT THE EMPLOYMENT AGENCY

The Story

"The Daring Young Man on the Flying Trapeze" is divided into two short, titled parts. The first and shortest (only three paragraphs long), called "Sleep," describes the dream images and thoughts of a young San Francisco writer before he awakens on the last day of his life. His sleeping mind is flooded with a series of unconnected impressions, including cities (Rome, Paris, Jerusalem), writers (Gustave Flaubert, Fyodor Dostoevski), political figures (Joseph Stalin and Adolf Hitler), animals (a reptile and a panther), and purely imaginary scenes ("the magnified flower twice the size of the universe").

The writer's sleep is ended in the second and longest section of the story, "Wakefulness." He is poor, having only one tie and drinking only coffee for breakfast. He reminds himself that in the unconscious world of sleep, from which a welter of images has just been presented, all human experiences are unified. In that death-in-life, one can experience eternity.

The real world which the writer inhabits is quite a different matter. The streets are cold and grim, and he walks noisily, as if to affirm himself in the face of an uncaring world. The lyrics of the popular song "The Daring Young Man on the Flying Trapeze" float through his mind and, throughout the story, he associates himself with the circus acrobat who so skillfully performs feats of daring. His amazing feat is merely to get through the day.

The writer finds a penny in the gutter, and realizing that he can buy almost nothing with it, fantasizes about what he would do if he had money; he would buy a car, visit prostitutes, but most important, buy food. He is reduced to meals of bread, coffee, and cigarettes, and now he has no more bread. There is no work for him at all, much less work for a writer. From a hill he looks at the city and thinks of it as a place from which he is denied admittance. He lives in a society in which the work he does is not respected. He plans to write *An Application for Permission to Live.* He thinks of the possibility of visiting a Salvation Army kitchen, but he decides instead to live his own life, and play out the part that he has chosen for himself. Once again he thinks of himself as the daring young man on the flying trapeze, but now he also considers that the landing place of the trapeze artist may be God or eternity, the eternity he glimpsed in sleep.

He continues his walk through the city, passing restaurants which he dares not look into, enters a building and visits an employment agency. When asked what he can do, he says he can write, and the clerk expresses no interest in this skill, asking further if the writer can type. There is no work even for a typist. He visits another employment agency with the same result, and department stores also have no jobs available. He visits the YMCA to obtain paper and ink to write his *An Application for Permission to Live*, but begins to feel faint from hunger and must go to a park to drink a quart of water and revive himself. He sees an old man feeding pigeons and almost asks him for some of the crumbs this man is tossing on the ground. The writer goes to the library near the park and reads, but again feels faint and has to drink water to recover.

The writer leaves the park and walks back to his room, thinking to go back to sleep, as there is nothing else left to do. Back in his room, he prepares coffee without milk or sugar, both of which he has run out of and for which there is no more money. He had stolen paper from the YMCA and hoped to finish his *An Application for Permission to Live*, but the act of writing is too difficult for him. He looks at the penny he found and wonders if he could get more pennies and thereby obtain enough money to go on living, but he inventories all the items that he has already sold and realizes that there is nothing left to sell. He has sold his clothes, his watch, and his books. None of these losses troubles him except that of the books, which he wishes he still had.

The writer looks at the details on the penny and considers its simple beauty. Now utterly weak, he falls on his bed, expecting to do the only thing left to do, sleep, but in fact the only thing left for him to do is die. His last conscious thought is that he should have given the penny to a child, who might have been able to buy many things with it. As he dies, he joins the unity which he had seen in sleep that morning. Like the trapeze artist, he makes a graceful exit, not from an acrobatic apparatus, but from his body. Now that he is dead he becomes "dreamless, unalive, perfect."

Themes and Meanings

During the Great Depression of the 1930's, when "The Daring Young Man on the Flying Trapeze" first appeared, many people were out of work and hungry, so the story had a strong impact for its initial audience as an account of daily life during hard times. Yet Saroyan does much more with his material than provide a naturalistic view of a day in the life of one oppressed man. Saroyan takes a phrase, "starving artist," which has become a cliché and almost a joke, and gives it new power by taking the reader not only into the life but also into the mind of a writer who is literally starving to death. The death of this man is doubly tragic, for as well as being a fellow human being, he is a person who is able to transform the apparently meaningless flow of circumstance, order it, and give it a meaning which might help others to understand their lives and thereby endure them. In a society primarily concerned with survival, however, art seems an extravagance. Depression America, or perhaps any society, does not recognize the role of the artist as a seer and healer. Throughout his last day, the writer sees details which no one else observes and of which he continues to try to make sense. His last conscious act is to look closely at the coin he has found and marvel at its beauty. He wants to bring his sense of joy and wonder to others, but the world does not respect his function, and he no longer has the energy to write. This tragedy is brought to focus in the only scene in the story in which the writer exchanges words with another person. When he tells the lady at the employment agency that he is a writer, she ignores this statement and asks him if he can type. There is no work for his mind, only for his hands. Finally, the writer finishes the task of assimilating all the myriad details he has been trying to capture and organize, not by explaining them, but by joining them in death.

Style and Technique

"The Daring Young Man on the Flying Trapeze" brought instant fame to Saroyan, establishing him as an important talent, not only because of its timely subject and timeless conclusions about the life of an artist, but also because of its arresting style and view of the subject. The story combines a stream-of-consciousness account of the interior monologue of the artist with a detailed, realistic view of the outside world he inhabits, thus uniting two of the major technical approaches of modern literature. The bizarre images that tumble through the writer's mind as he sleeps both accurately reflect the strange world of the dream and alert the reader that this story is something different, something which will demand full attention. The enigmatic dream images also involve the reader in the story by giving him a glimpse of what the writer's life is like: The writer's dream is as bewildering to the reader as are the details that the writer encounters as he walks through the streets of the city, and as the writer must take up the hard work of organizing the details of everyday existence, so must the reader work to piece together the elements of the story. Little by little, the reader must infer that the writer is dying in part from integrity, because he refuses to be anything less than an artist, a role with dignity, in a society which does not respect that dignity. Because this bitter truth is inferred by the reader, its impact is more stunning than if it had been directly stated by the author.

Ironically, the psychological style and bleak viewpoint of this story, which made Saroyan a celebrity, are not at all typical of his work. Saroyan preferred direct, open, declarative statements and affirmed the positive value of human experience in spite of tragedy, qualities which are seen in such stories as "The Summer of the Beautiful White Horse."

James Baird

THE DARK CITY

Author: Conrad Aiken (1889-1973)
Type of plot: Psychological fantasy
Time of plot: Early twentieth century
Locale: The suburbs of a large city
First published: 1922

> *Principal characters:*
> ANDREW, the protagonist, a business executive
> HILDA, his wife
> MARTHA,
> MARJORIE, and
> TOM, their children

The Story

Aiken's "The Dark City," a slice-of-life account that focuses on a commuter husband, actually involves only those events which occur between late afternoon and bedtime. The story begins on the commuter train that carries Andrew from the city to the suburbs, where he works in his garden, plays with his children, eats, takes a post-dinner stroll, plays chess with Hilda, his wife, and then prepares for bed. Aiken, however, does not restrict himself to the external plot, which is prosaic in its typicality, but instead includes his protagonist's inner life, which indicates that Andrew has, at best, a tenuous grip on his sanity.

In the first part of the story, Aiken presents Andrew as an executive who attempts to put the "staggering load of business detail" behind him as he "devours" the evening newspaper on the train. When he reaches his station, he begins his walk home and thinks about "news amusing enough to be reported to Hilda." He sees his children playing, and after engaging them in banter about being needed in his garden, he jokes with his children and wife about having lost the flannel trousers that are apparently part of the "uniform" he wears as he readies himself for the gardening ritual.

Gardening is a welcome respite for Andrew, for whom the "order" is a welcome change from business. With his children, particularly Martha, Andrew has a series of ritualized games in which the actors have clearly assigned roles: The children hide his hoe; he declares himself a slave to the children and to the garden; the children and he personify the plants; the children and he regard caterpillars as enemies and carefully circumvent the toad, "obese, sage, and wrinkled like a Chinese god." If the garden affords Andrew with the chance to play with his children, it also provides him with the opportunity to drift off into a world of his own, where he can meditate about the meaning of his activity and of his existence. For example, his transplanting of strawberry plants becomes, for him, an analogue to "resurrecting" them and giving them "life" through, presumably, his role as a godlike creator.

At dinner Andrew shares his philosophizing with his family, which is more concerned with "beany" bread pudding and with unripe strawberries. In mock exasperation, he wonders why he and Hilda married and paraphrases William Wordsworth's "London, 1802," suggesting that their powers have been "wasted" by "feeding and spanking." After dinner he strolls on the lawn, and in the gathering darkness he sees, apparently not for the first time, the "dark city, the city not inhabited by mortals." Despite the city's "immense, sinister, and black" appearance, he does not seem upset by his vision. When he reenters the house, he wakens Hilda, who says that she has been dreaming about Bluebeard. He assures her that he is instead intent on the upcoming chess game, which he soon wins. When Hilda asks him about the "dark city," he gives her an elaborate description of not only the city but also the "maggots of perhaps the size of human children" that inhabit the city. Hilda understandably suggests that he is "going mad," to which he laughingly responds that he is "gone" and that his "brain is maggoty." They then close up the house for the night.

Themes and Meanings

In "The Dark City" Aiken depicts two "dark cities," the one in which Andrew toils and from which he attempts to escape, and the one that exists within his tortured mind. Aiken is not concerned with the literal city, which he dismisses in a phrase: "the staggering load of business detail, under which he had struggled all day in the office." Andrew "instantly" forgets this city (or believes that he does) as he reads the newspaper as "prelude" to "his greatest pleasure in life," which comes with the dusk at home in his garden or with his family. The suburbs, with their suggestion of rural innocence, initially seem to offer Andrew a conventional refuge from the grind of the job and the city, but Aiken suggests that in this Edenic garden paradise there is also a darker, more corrupt reality: "at the core so vile a secret. . . ."

When he first describes Andrew's dark city, Aiken clearly indicates that it is a bleak vision: "the dark city, the city submerged under the infinite sea, the city not inhabited by mortals." There is no entrance to the city with "immense, sinister, and black walls," walls that are as "old and cold as the moon." When Andrew describes the city to Hilda, however, he embellishes that description with details about the inhabitants of the city:

> Its people are maggots—maggots of perhaps the size of human children. . . .
> What horrible feast is it that nightly they celebrate there in silence? On what carrion do they feed? It is the universe that they devour; and they build above it, as they devour it, their dark city like a hollow tomb. . . .

Andrew's additions are significant because they suggest an identification between the maggots and children (and, by extension, the family) and because the real world, including Andrew, is seen as dead.

Clearly Andrew has ambivalent but strong feelings about himself and his family. Andrew's "greatest pleasure in life came always at dusk," and after gardening he has, "for a moment, an extraordinary satisfying sense of space." (This "moment" is, however, transient, and Aiken suggests that Andrew will lose his "space"—another writer might have used "peace" instead—and will be hemmed in again.) Yet dusk also brings his dark vision, at once repulsive and fascinating, and his half-joking remark about his madness. In fact, Andrew typically relies on humor to escape or conceal his true feelings. He jokes, "Spare your neurotic father," and his Wordsworth parody about "wasting" his "powers" because "our kids are too much with us" may reveal his other, darker view of his children. Even his attitude toward Hilda is suspect. If Hilda notices his neurotic, compulsive behavior and senses the hostility which motivates it, then her remark about dreaming of Bluebeard, the wife murderer, is grimly appropriate. When Hilda mentions that he resembles Bluebeard, Andrew typically laughs it off and then comments enigmatically, ostensibly about the chess game, that "queens die young and fair." The reader senses that beneath the clever banter and the superficial camaraderie there is an undercurrent of hostility and suspicion.

Andrew's behavior oscillates between compulsive haste and meditative calm. Until he reaches the garden, he rushes, hurries, and runs; in the garden, however, he is in "profound meditation" before the order of the rows. Through his "methodical" hoeing with the rising and falling hoe-blade, he is "hypnotized" with his thoughts in a "rhythm." As he "resurrects" the strawberries, the gardening becomes a religious ritual. He "enshrines" a flame, and the cloud of smoke seems like "incense." Then, after Martha's comic interruption, he comments, "O Lord, Lord, what a circus we are."

Andrew's wry observation is indicative of his plight, for he is aware of both the potential, represented by "pilgrims who struggle upwards in the darkness for pure love of beauty," and the reality, represented by the feasting maggots which also work in darkness. Despite the hylas which sing of "peace," Andrew lives in a world of corruption, decay, and death, and his own destruction is suggested by his comment about his "maggoty" brain. While Andrew and Hilda avoid any further discussion of madness, they live in a volatile situation, one in which murder and suicide are a distinct possibility—and the reader is reminded that Aiken himself saw his father kill his mother and then take his own life.

Style and Technique

Aiken uses the third-person point of view in "The Dark City" and uses Andrew as the "central intelligence" through whom the events are screened. That literary device enables readers to understand Andrew thoroughly, for readers share his thoughts through the stream-of-conciousness technique. To indicate Andrew's delicate balancing act, Aiken also distances himself from his protagonist and under the guise of objective description reveals the contradictions within Andrew. For example, reading a newspaper should relax Andrew, thereby allowing him to escape from the bustle of the city, but Aiken's diction implies that even a sedentary activity involves repressed aggression for Andrew. Aiken has Andrew "devour" with "rapacious eyes" the newspaper, and the activity "consumes" time—the imagery would be more appropriate in financial situations in the city. In his refuge at home, replies become "missiles," a metaphor readers may regard as part of Andrew's "comic rage," but that "rage" is not altogether "comic." Even the setting sun assumes destructive force: "The red sun . . . was gashing itself cruelly on a black pine tree." When he returns from his evening walk, Andrew says, "He had no watch, and his trousers grew like grass," an enigmatic and apparently innocuous comment, but in its allusion to the watch, the object of earlier musings, and to the lost trousers, the comment serves to tie up loose ends for Andrew, who needs to retain his "grip" in a situation that is steadily deteriorating. In a very real sense, Aiken's protagonist is a symbol for modern man.

Thomas L. Erskine

THE DARLING

Author: Anton Chekhov (1860-1904)
Type of plot: Parody
Time of plot: The 1880's
Locale: A provincial town near Moscow
First published: "Dushechka," 1899 (English translation, 1915)

> *Principal characters:*
> OLENKA PLEMYANNIKOVA, the protagonist, a village housewife
> IVAN KUKIN, her first husband, a local entrepreneur
> VASILY ANDREICH PUSTOVALOV, her second husband, manager
> of the local lumberyard
> VLADIMIR PLATONICH SMIRNIN, her lover, a veterinarian
> SASHA SMIRNIN, the son of the veterinarian, a ten-year-old
> student

The Story

Olenka Plemyannikova is a lonely spinster who is constantly in love with someone or other. She finds it difficult to live without loving someone; she turns pale, loses weight, and is unable to form opinions of her own. When the reader encounters her at the beginning of the story, she has been infatuated with her French teacher, loved her father dearly, and is now ready for marriage. She is young, healthy, and well liked by all, men and women, young and old.

Ivan Kukin, the manager of the local theater and amusement park, lives by Olenka and converses with her regularly. He constantly complains about the indifference of the ignorant public to good theater, the rain and poor weather which keep people from the outdoor amusement park, his financial worries, and life in general. Olenka feels sorry for the hapless Kukin and gradually falls in love with him. They marry, and Olenka begins to help him in his business affairs. Because she has no opinions of her own, she merely repeats whatever her husband says about the public's relation to good theater and she faithfully echoes his other complaints. She states her feeling that the theater is the most important thing in the world and necessary for all people. Optimistic Olenka prospers in her new life and radiates health while her incurably pessimistic husband continues to complain.

During Lent, Kukin goes to Moscow to book acts for his summer repertoire at the theater. Olenka is beside herself without her husband; she is unable to sleep and compares herself to a hen in the henhouse without a rooster. Kukin dies unexpectedly in Moscow; Olenka returns from his funeral and enters a period of deep mourning, sobbing so loudly that her neighbors can hear her grief.

Three months later, Olenka walks home from church with Vasily Andreich Pustovalov, and a friendship blooms. At loose ends without someone to love, Olenka now fills a void in her life as the courtship progresses. Olenka and Pustovalov marry and the dutiful wife begins to assist her husband in his duties as manager of the local lumberyard. Her conversation is now filled with references to lumber, lumber prices, and the difficulties of managing the yard. Lumber now replaces the theater as the most important and necessary thing in the world. In fact, her previous opinions concerning the exalted nature of the theater are completely reversed, since her new husband, a very stolid businessman, has no use for the theater and views it as a trivial amusement for people of no serious interests. When her husband is away on trips to buy lumber, Olenka becomes bored and restless; she cannot live without her husband, just as she was unable to be apart from her first husband, Kukin. Olenka and Pustovalov lead a very respectable and sedate life for six years, until Pustovalov dies suddenly after catching a cold. Once again Olenka plunges into deep mourning.

A military veterinarian, Vladimir Platonich Smirnin, has rented a room from Olenka, and soon the two become fast friends. Friends and neighbors become aware of the closeness of the relationship when Olenka begins to repeat the opinions of the veterinarian concerning animal health and veterinary inspections in the town for domestic animals. Marriage in this case is an impossibility, however, as the doctor has an estranged wife and child living elsewhere. When the veterinarian is transferred to a distant town, Olenka's life is changed once again; although no death has occurred, she has been deprived of the source of her opinions. Her physical appearance worsens, she becomes listless, and even her house begins to fall apart, reflecting a general degeneration. The author of the story makes it very clear, however, that her greatest loss is the inability to have opinions and consequently to have conversations with her neighbors.

A few years later the veterinarian, now a civilian, returns with his wife, with whom he has reconciled, and his child to settle down in the small provincial town. At Olenka's invitation, the family moves into her house, while she herself moves into the small outbuilding which Smirnin formerly occupied. The wife soon leaves the family, Smirnin himself is often absent on business, and Olenka becomes the *de facto* mother of the child. She now springs into life, for she has discovered a new purpose, a new person to love. She begins to repeat the opinions of the ten-year-old student as if they were on the same level as those of the male adults whom she loved. She complains to neighbors about the amount of homework the students are receiving, the difficulties of the academic program in the classical high school which little Sasha is attending, and she sympathizes with the sleepy boy when he has to get up in the morning. Olenka's demeanor changes and her old radiance and vivaciousness return. The story ends as Olenka lovingly listens to the boy talking in his sleep.

Themes and Meanings

Anton Chekhov, considered by most students of Russian literature to be the foremost Russian writer of short stories, often uses exaggeration to point out a human foible. Olenka's total inability to think, speak, and form opinions of her own is rarely, if ever, met in this world, but there is a kernel of truth in this caricature. Chekhov wishes to poke fun at people who rely upon others to form opinions instead of forming their own, people who prefer to follow the crowd rather than question and probe. In a number of stories the author uses the same technique with different types of examples to make the same point—too many people are prisoners of conformity and prefer to eschew critical thinking. Olenka's complete lack of self-worth is evident as she goes through life repeating the opinions of other people, even a ten-year-old schoolboy.

The theme of love is also present in this story. The reader can find a pattern in Chekhov's stories which concern love, a pattern which may reflect the skeptical and world-weary author's own feelings about the subject. Love rarely works out to the satisfaction of the parties involved. Love is usually illusory. Either the love is not reciprocated, or two people who love each other are not aware of the other's love through a lack of communication, or two people marry and become unhappy. In this story love seems to be successful, but fate intervenes to remove the two husbands and one lover. Olenka does not live happily ever after with a husband, but is forced to transfer her enormous capacity for love to a child. Although the reader leaves Olenka at the end of the story in a very happy and contented state, it is also clear that the child will grow up and go his own way, once again leaving Olenka alone and probably very unhappy.

Style and Technique

Unlike many other well-known Russian authors, such as Leo Tolstoy and Fyodor Dostoevski, Chekhov is famed for an economy of words and a sparing use of detail. Almost every word is important and is used to convey a single impression of a person or situation. Chekhov portrays Olenka in three very different romantic situations with the identical result; the reader cannot fail to grasp the point. The fourth situation occurs when the time for romantic love has passed, yet the love for the boy, Sasha, produces the same result: complete adoption of the opinions of the person loved. In the limited space of the short story the various characters are well-defined, demonstrating the ability of the author to impart much information in a very small space.

Philip Maloney

THE DAUGHTERS OF THE LATE COLONEL

Author: Katherine Mansfield (Kathleen Mansfield Beauchamp, 1888-1923)
Type of plot: Psychological realism
Time of plot: Early twentieth century
Locale: England
First published: 1921

> *Principal characters:*
> JOSEPHINE "JUG" PINNER, one of the two protagonists, the
> older daughter of Colonel Pinner
> CONSTANTIA "CON" PINNER, the other protagonist, the sister
> of Josephine Pinner
> KATE, the insolent young maid

The Story

"The Daughters of the Late Colonel" is an account of the activities and thoughts of two spinster sisters during the week after the death of their dictatorial father. Although the sisters think of themselves as having been extraordinarily busy that week, it is obvious that most of their efforts have been psychological. They have agonized over the one necessary decision—to bury their father—and they have accomplished that, not without misgivings. Yet they are still unable to assert themselves, even in the most mundane areas of life.

The story is divided into twelve sections. In each section, Mansfield concentrates on one area of the sisters' preoccupations, penetrating the mind of one sister or the other, or of both, alternately, reproducing their churning thoughts. Most of the sections take place on the Saturday which marks a week after his death; there are flashbacks, however, to the death, to the funeral, and to an earlier visit by a grandson.

Although the prime tyrant of the sisters' lives was their father, the incidents related in the story show their fear of Kate, the bad-tempered young maid, of Nurse Andrews, and of public opinion. In the first section, they worry about the propriety of wearing colored dressing gowns and slippers during the mourning period, when Kate or the postman might see them. In the second section, they cannot summon up the courage to ask Kate for more jam or to restrain Nurse Andrews from gobbling up their butter. Later, although they have proved to themselves that Kate snoops in their bureau, and although they are the victims of her consistent impertinence, they cannot summon up the resolution to dismiss her.

If Constantia and Josephine Pinner are unable to confront people, they are even more emotionally crippled by the possibilities of demands on them for action. When the vicar of Saint John's, Mr. Farolles, offers to bring

Communion to them at their home, it is the possibilities that frighten them. What if Kate came in? What if the bell rang? What would they do? It is easiest to reject any new situation, rather than dealing with their fears of decision.

Naturally, the sisters are preoccupied with the death of their father; they find it difficult to believe that he is really dead and not somewhere waiting to criticize them. In the third section, they are haunted by the deathbed scene, particularly by the fact that he opened only one eye before he died. Accustomed as they are to assuming that everything their father did was significant, generally involving blame for them, the sisters cannot dismiss that single-eyed glare. In fact, they torment themselves with thoughts of his reappearing to scold them for burying him and to go into a fury about the expense of the funeral. A third worry involves disposing of the Colonel's clothes. Two days after the funeral, Constantia and Josephine attempt to go through his possessions. Merely opening the door to his room without knocking takes almost more courage than they possess. Even Josephine, who seems to be the braver sister, cannot open the chest of drawers. Typically, the decision that Constantia makes, and which she considers one of the boldest of her life, is a denial of action: She locks up the wardrobe and thereby postpones real action. To Constantia and Josephine, however, it is like locking up their father.

Sections 7 through 9 have to do with two relatives, their brother Benny Pinner and their nephew Cyril Pinner. Evidently, both men have escaped the Colonel's domination, Benny by going to a distant part of the Empire, Cyril by spending his time in London. Josephine and Constantia must decide which of the men should have the Colonel's gold watch. Constantia's imagination sends the watch by runner to Benny, but then she begins to worry about its getting there safely. Deciding to deliver it to Cyril instead, the sisters remember his last visit, when they sacrificed to buy him treats for tea, which he refused, and when Cyril unwillingly saw his deaf, irascible grandfather and escaped by inventing an appointment. Remembering only a problem about time, the sisters are certain that Cyril needs a watch.

After two sections in which the sisters admit Kate's imperfections but cannot resolve to dismiss her, there is a long section which contains a brief flicker of hope for Constantia and Josephine. When they hear the barrel organ, they realize that they are free to hear the music as often as they like. Their father is truly dead. The sun comes into the room, and both sisters begin to speak about the future. Yet the sentences are never finished. Again, the thought that might have led to action is stifled, and as a cloud covers the sun, both the sisters say that they have forgotten what they began to say.

Themes and Meanings

Like many of the stories of Katherine Mansfield and of her major influence, Anton Chekhov, "The Daughters of the Late Colonel" deals with the theme of captivity. Josephine and Constantia have been imprisoned in a world with two objectives: to avoid displeasing a testy old father and to stay out of his way. Their lives, then, have been directed toward negatives, rather than toward positives. Over the years, they have become imprisoned not only in their father's house but also in their own passivity. The causes of their condition are touched on in the story: their mother's death, their father's habit of command and unconcern for their social life, and their own timidity. After his death, the sisters are still imprisoned by their habitual responses of fear and obedience, which make decisions impossible for them.

Yet, throughout the story there are impulses toward freedom. The very fact that the imaginations of the sisters are not dead, that they can summon forth the runner moving toward Benny, that they can respond to the sunshine and the barrel organ, that Constantia has yearned in the moonlight and by the sea, suggests that they may be able to escape from their prison, now that their father is dead and they are still alive.

The final section, however, makes it clear that there will be no escape. The sisters cannot even confess their impulses to each other. When they repress their impulses to speak of the future, the sun is symbolically covered by a cloud, and it is clear that captivity has conquered.

Style and Technique

Because Mansfield's stories are primarily psychological, point of view is particularly important. In her journals, Mansfield makes it clear that she sees her characters from the inside out, that she assumes their identities as an actor assumes a role, while at the same time making the reader aware of the authorial judgments upon them. "The Daughters of the Late Colonel" is especially complex in point of view because there are two protagonists, and Mansfield alternates between them, except for a brief passage where she penetrates the mind of Cyril. Yet sometimes she treats the two sisters as a single entity, as in the first paragraph. In one of the most interesting passages, in the seventh section of the story, she gives their imaginations the same subject, the runner on his way to Benny with the watch, but then she reveals the divergent images in their minds. At the end of the story, the single point of view is thematic. If one of the sisters could have contemplated a future, there might have been hope for both; their very unanimity dooms them.

In a story such as "The Daughters of the Late Colonel," in which there is almost no real action, slight events become symbolic, but the symbolism is used in various ways. Actions may be symbolic: The fact that Kate hands the sisters an empty jam pot indicates her domination of them; the fact that Nurse Andrews questions the taste of the marmalade shows her contempt for her former employers. Sometimes Mansfield uses symbols to indicate an authorial comment, as when the cloud blots out the brief sunlight at the end of the story. Often, however, the symbols are used to reveal the characters' feelings. In their father's white room, the sisters feel cold, thinking of death. Throughout the story they see images of freedom, such as the flapping tassel of the blind, the sunlight on the photographs, the moon, and the sea. The Buddha suggests to Constantia the unknown in life, which she will never experience. At times there is even an identification with pitiable, vulnerable creatures, such as the mice which Constantia fears will find no food, or the sparrows whose crying outside the window becomes a crying inside Josephine's heart. Finally, a symbol may be used ironically. To Constantia and Josephine, the locking of their father's wardrobe seems like a triumph, a real defiance of the tyrannical old man; actually, it is an admission that they cannot lock out his memory by dealing with it. Thus, the final imprisonment is theirs.

Rosemary M. Canfield-Reisman

DAWN OF REMEMBERED SPRING

Author: Jesse Stuart (1907-1984)
Type of plot: Psychological realism
Time of plot: The 1930's
Locale: Rural Kentucky
First published: 1942

> *Principal characters:*
> SHAN, a rural adolescent, the narrator
> MOM, Shan's mother

The Story

Left to his own devices for the day, Shan decides to seek revenge on snakes for the bite received by his friend Roy Deer, whose family Shan's mother visits to pay a condolence call. Given his freedom, the boy states, "I would like to be a man now. . . . I'd love to plow the mules, run a farm, and kill snakes." Much of the action of the remainder of the story involves Shan's playing at being a man, a common adolescent fantasy. He breaks a club from the wild plum thicket close to his home and wades the creek to search for water moccasins to kill.

His knowledge of his prey is rich beyond his years, attesting his experience with nature. For example, he plans his strategy for slaughter by relying on the knowledge that it is impossible for the water moccasins to bite him while their heads are beneath the water. Too, the snakes will raise their heads above the surface if the water is muddy, a fact that he turns to his advantage by stirring up the bottom frequently. Though he experiences fear concerning the danger of his hunt, not once does the boy exhibit any pity or compassion for his victims. One of their kind has bitten his friend without cause, and Shan takes upon himself the duty of wreaking revenge on the whole race of poisonous serpents. Stealth and knowledge serve him well, and by the end of the afternoon he has killed fifty-three water moccasins. On his way home, after leaving the creek, Shan comes upon two other poisonous snakes, copperheads.

These two snakes are wrapped around each other and pay no attention to him. The boy believes that the copperheads are fighting, and he plans to kill them too if they fail to kill each other. From a passing neighbor he learns the truth: "It's snakes in love!" Uncle Alf Skinner tells him. The neighbor quickly fetches his wife to see the spectacle; soon a small crowd assembles to witness the event. Shan's mother returns and joins the group and, because of the danger he was in, she is angry with Shan for going on his unescorted hunt.

Before he is sent away by his mother, Shan notices the changed expressions of the adults who remain to witness the mating of the copperheads. Their smiles puzzle him and he observes that "their faces were made over new." The boy persists in his notion that the snakes are fighting, and the crowd finds his innocence amusing. In the end, as he leaves, he is baffled by the laughter of the adults. He cannot quite figure out how the grown-ups in a rural community plagued by poisonous serpents can smile and laugh at such a sight, and their laughter seems to follow and haunt him as he walks home alone.

Themes and Meanings

"Dawn of Remembered Spring" is a complex story of fear, hate, and love. On the surface, it appears to be nothing more than a boy's boast about the number of snakes he has killed, but although Shan's action on the snake hunt takes up much of the space of the story, the title shows that the focus of the tale is really not on its simple plot.

What is the reader to make of the title? None of the story takes place at the hour of dawn, neither Shan nor his mother seems to dwell on remembering anything, and even if the story takes place during springtime (though this is not at all certain) very little is made of the importance of the season to the action of the story. Because a literal interpretation of the title is so unproductive, investigating it figuratively may prove more profitable.

The dawn which Stuart seems to have in mind is more in the sense of beginnings and awakenings than an actual hour of the day—much in the manner in which Henry David Thoreau uses the idea of dawn in *Walden* (1854). The remembrance of the title suggests that the story is a recollection by an adult of an incident from his youth, and what is remembered is his spring, the period of his adult awakening, an emergence from the chrysalis of adolescence into the lush, green atmosphere of sex and love. For the narrator, this was a very important period in his life, a time when he made a discovery that influenced him deeply. Though Shan seems to discover nothing from the incidents related in the story while it is actually taking place, the narrator, through the selection of the title, gives readers a strong clue to the meaning of the narrative.

Shan's action, his snake hunt, is in one sense an act of bravery and manhood. With his strength and intelligence, he seeks to rid the world of an ancient evil. His story, like almost all boasts, relates his acts of heroism, as do heroic stories from both the Angle-Saxon and Greek precursors of modern fiction. In "Dawn of Remembered Spring," however, it is not the heroism itself that teaches the hero what he needs to know to further his existence. Instead, it is the unimportance of his actions in comparison to something else that furnishes him with a new value that allows him to progress into maturity. In effect, he has discovered (though not during the actual time related during the story) that courage and cunning by themselves are not the sole admission-price into the cherished state of maturity. It is at this point that the story diverges from its ancestor, the heroic narrative, and it is at this point also that Shan finds out that his society places higher values on love and the creative urge than it places on simple acts of heroism. His mother is on the whole displeased by his undertaking, and the neighbors who assemble to watch the courting of the copperheads are not at all impressed by his hunt.

"Dawn of Remembered Spring" is a coming-of-age story, a pattern that Stuart had used earlier in his better-known narrative "Split Cherry Tree." Yet whereas "Split Cherry Tree" exhibits the pattern in its complete form, with the young man reaching a new level of maturity, "Dawn of Remembered Spring" uses only the beginning and middle elements of the coming-of-age form. Stuart's decision to forgo the narrator's realization of the importance of love and procreation over heroism complicates the story. While Stuart's decision invariably makes the tale more true to life, it nevertheless makes the story's meanings and themes more obscure.

Style and Technique

In the creation of his character Shan, Stuart uses psychological realism to elevate this coming-of-age story above its ancestor, the heroic boast. The narrator's inability to speak of what he has learned from watching the faces of his neighbors and hearing their laughter is much more true to life than anything Shan might have thought to say about what he has witnessed. Shan resists the lesson he has learned at the end of his day of snake killing: that love is more powerful, more compelling, more appealing to humankind than hate, revenge, and death. The boy is really not quite as puzzled as he seems; he simply refuses to believe what his elders tell him about what the snakes are doing, but in his heart he knows that they are right. Stuart's delicate handling of this matter raises Shan above the level of the stereotypical youngster, giving his central character the depth and dimension necessary to make a story of this complexity and delicacy believable.

A further example of Stuart's psychological realism occurs in the beginning and middle portions of the story. Shan repeats three times that a snake bit his friend, but none will bite him. The reader knows full well that the boy is in danger, and this is one of the main reasons that he or she continues to read further—to find out whether Shan will actually escape harm. Through repetition, the author both shows his main character's fear and endows him with a very human characteristic, the ability to hold a belief in spite of what one really knows to be the case. This complex structuring of character easily eludes the careless reader, but for those who read Stuart's story deeply, such craftsmanship serves both as preparation for the ending and as a guide to the understanding of human ways of thought.

Charles Hackenberry

THE DAY STALIN DIED

Author: Doris Lessing (1919-   )
Type of plot: Psychological realism
Time of plot: March 5, 1953
Locale: London
First published: 1957

> *Principal characters:*
> THE NARRATOR, a writer
> JESSIE, the narrator's cousin
> EMMA, Jessie's mother, the narrator's aunt
> JEAN, a Communist Party associate of the narrator
> BEATRICE, an old friend of the narrator from South Africa
> THE HOST, the manager of a photography studio
> JACKIE SMITH, his friend and assistant

The Story

The day begins badly. The narrator receives a letter from Aunt Emma in Bournemouth, reminding her of a promise to take her cousin Jessie to have her picture taken that afternoon. Aunt Emma, Jessie's mother, wants the photos because she intends to show them to a television producer who visits his older brother in the boardinghouse where she and her daughter live. Aunt Emma hopes that Jessie will prove sufficiently photogenic to induce the producer to whisk her off to London to be a television star. Jessie is a broad-shouldered girl of about twenty-five who looks eighteen.

The narrator, forgetting all about the promise, has made other plans, which she is now obliged to cancel. She quickly tries to call off a date that she made with an American screenwriter named Bill. Bill, it seems, had some trouble with the House Committee on Un-American Activities, was black-listed, and could not find work in the United States. He is also having difficulty getting a permit to live in Great Britain. The narrator is trying to help him find a secretary and has gotten in touch with an old friend from South Africa, Beatrice, who is out of a job. The date was arranged to introduce the two. The narrator believes that these friends will get along, since both have been involved in left-wing causes. (As she subsequently discovers, they prove not at all compatible.) It takes the narrator an hour to get in touch with Bill, only to discover that he has forgotten about the appointment. She then sends Beatrice a telegram, since Beatrice has no phone.

Having freed the afternoon for Jessie, the narrator starts to get some work done in what is left of the morning. She has just begun when she is interrupted by a call from one of her Communist Party comrades, who says that she wants to see the narrator at lunchtime. The caller, Jean, is the narrator's self-appointed "guide or mentor towards a correct political viewpoint." Jean is the daughter of a bishop and has worked unquestioningly for the Party for the past thirty years. Having divorced her husband when he became a member of the Labour Party following the Nazi-Soviet Pact, she now lives alone in a sitting room with a portrait of Joseph Stalin over her bed. Jean is disturbed about a remark that the narrator made the week before at a Party meeting, that "a certain amount of dirty work must be going on in the Soviet Union." Jean arrives, bringing her sandwiches with her in a brown paper bag, and berates the narrator for flippancy. She tells her of the necessity of "unremitting vigilance on the part of the working class." She says that the only way that an intellectual with the narrator's background can gain a correct, working-class point of view is to work harder in the Party to attain "a really sound working-class attitude." Jean recommends reading the verbatim transcript of the purge trials of the 1930's as an antidote to a vacillating attitude toward Soviet justice.

Jean's visit leaves the narrator, "for one reason or another," depressed. Yet there is not much time to brood; no sooner has Jean left than a call comes from Cousin Jessie, who asks if the narrator can meet her in twenty minutes outside a dress shop, as she has decided to buy new clothes in which to be photographed. The narrator therefore quits work for the day and takes a cab to her rendezvous.

Jessie is waiting outside the dress shop when the narrator arrives; she is already wearing her new dress, but it does not seem any different from the clothes she usually wears. Jessie, almost by way of greeting, announces, somewhat aggressively, that her mother, Aunt Emma, is coming to the photography studio with them. Aunt Emma then emerges from a corner tearoom, and the three of them set off to take a bus to the studio. Between Aunt Emma and Cousin Jessie there is a constant tension, which sends off "currents of angry electricity into the air around them." Aunt Emma's bulldog eyes are "nearly always fixed in disappointment on her daughter." Whatever their divisions, however, mother and daughter share a mutual detestation of the lower classes, with which they carry on incessant guerrilla warfare. This form of entertainment, the narrator explains, is conditioned by their extremely dreary lives. Their conversation on the bus therefore is a constant running battle against the lower classes and each other.

They get off the bus; the entrance to the studio is not far away. As the three women hurry down the street, their heads under Aunt Emma's umbrella to protect them against the cold, drizzling rain, the narrator notices the announcement on a newsstand bulletin board that Stalin is dying. She stops and buys a paper but has only a brief moment to exchange words with the vendor, as Aunt Emma is obviously annoyed at being held up. Aunt Emma has more important things on her mind: "What do you think, would it have been better if Jessie had bought a nice pretty afternoon dress?" The studio is on the second floor. The stairs have a plush carpet and striped gold-

and-mauve wallpaper; upstairs is a white, gray, and gold drawing room with a small crystal chandelier, the prisms of which tinkle from the reverberations of Igor Stravinsky's *The Rite of Spring*. The studio is run by two very effeminate men, one of whom, the host, is a disturbingly outspoken racist.

The highly charged atmosphere makes all three women ill at ease, especially Jessie. "You don't look relaxed," the host tells her gently. "It's really no use at all, you know, unless you are really relaxed all over." To break the ice, the host suggests "a nice cup of tea" so that "our vibrations might become just a *little* more harmonious." Aunt Emma tries to steer the conversation in another direction and blurts out that Stalin is dying, or "so they would have us believe." The subject of the great man's demise produces only more trivialities. The host comments that he does not know much about politics but that "Uncle Joe and Roosevelt were absolutely my pin up boys" during the war, "But absolutely!" All this chitchat does nothing to calm Jessie's nerves. She now demands that they get "this *damned* business over with." The host happily agrees and asks for what use the photos are intended: dust jackets, publicity, or "just for your lucky friends?" Cousin Jessie answers that she does not know and does not care. Aunt Emma insists, "I would like you to catch her expression. It's just that *little* look of hers...." Jessie clenches her fists at her mother. The narrator suggests that she and Aunt Emma absent themselves for a while, and Jessie goes into another room to be photographed.

Aunt Emma starts to ask about all the exciting things that the narrator has been doing that day. The only incident which the narrator thinks might be of interest to her aunt is that she had lunch with the daughter of a bishop. The conversation is interrupted by the reemergence of Cousin Jessie, who is more distraught than ever. She says that she is simply not in the mood and then has the whole session called off. Aunt Emma has never been more ashamed. Jessie could not care less. The three women leave the studio. The narrator leaves behind the newspaper that she has just bought. They say good-bye outside. Aunt Emma and Jessie get into a cab; the narrator gets on a bus.

When the narrator returns home, she receives a phone call from Beatrice, who says that she received the telegram and then says that Stalin is dying. The narrator says that she knows, and tries to change the subject. Beatrice's call is followed by one from comrade Jean, who announces that Stalin is dead. Jean is crying and says that it is obvious that he was murdered by capitalist agents. The narrator remarks that it is not unusual for death to come naturally to people who are seventy-three. Jean tells her that they will have to pledge themselves "to be worthy of him." The narrator replies mechanically, "Yes, I suppose we will."

Themes and Meanings

The narrator is an author, a writer of short stories, who cannot work on the day that Stalin dies because of constant interruptions by members of her family and by her associates in the Communist Party. Such impositions on her time are apparently commonplace and are a constant source of tension and depression. The narrator finds it impossible to say no.

Yet the frustration goes deeper. The narrator finds it difficult to reconcile her involvement with the Communist movement and various other left-wing activities with the independence of judgment and spirit necessary to practice her craft. A Party hack, such as Jean, has a special commitment to trivializing the author's talent, reducing it to the level of the class struggle. With obvious delight, she says condescendingly that intellectuals such as the narrator are under "greater pressure from the forces of capitalist corruption than any other type of party cadre." Clearly, no middle ground can exist between orthodox Communism and a free spirit. There is no possibility of compromise. Jean is in effect saying that one cannot have it both ways, while the narrator apparently believes that it is possible.

On this conflict between independence of mind and the quest for political-social identity is built a pedestrian story. The motives that prompted the narrator to join the Communist Party are not stated directly, but it seems certain that these motives, ostensibly idealistic, have something to do with a strong impulse to belong and to serve: those traditionally feminine characteristics that condition her to respond to any request, no matter how trivial. It becomes clear, for example, that her presence at the photography studio is completely unnecessary.

The death of Stalin is symbolic. It dramatizes an important change in the author's life, a change that has been a long time in coming. The news of the Communist leader's death is disturbing at first, since he is so closely linked to the past from which the narrator has derived stability and identity. She is annoyed when the reactions of other people are so superficial and trivial. By the end of her wasted day, however, it is clear that the defection from Stalinism and the adjustment to a new relationship with people has been well established.

Style and Technique

Much of Doris Lessing's work is autobiographical. Although the narrator is unidentified in this story, her attitudes presumably mirror the author's own. Like the narrator, Lessing was at one time associated with the Communist Party and subsequently broke her ties with it. Her disaffection probably did not occur as she describes it in this story, but some of the issues she raises and the conflicts she relates no doubt figured in her decision. Stalin's death is the occasion for the parting of the ways, not the cause of it.

Lessing is particularly effective in revealing character through dialogue and in describing the way people speak. Jessie, for example, "always speaks in short, breathless, battling sentences, as from an unassuageably inner integrity which she doesn't expect anyone else to understand." Another technique of Lessing is to relate her main character's values through that character's reactions to the comments of others, including those she hears by eavesdropping on the conversations of strangers. In the bus, a middle-aged couple are arguing about fish, "all those little fishes," says the man. "We explode all these bombs at them, and we're not going to be forgiven for that, are we, we're not to be forgiven for blowing up the poor little fishes." The narrator says, "I had known that the afternoon was bound to get out of control at some point; but this conversation upset me." The reaction masterfully reveals an intellect troubled by surroundings from which it had previously drawn support.

Wm. Laird Kleine-Ahlbrandt

THE DAY THE FLOWERS CAME

Author: David Madden (1933-   )
Type of plot: Psychological realism
Time of plot: The 1960's
Locale: Rolling Hills Homes, an upper-middle-class subdivision in an
    unnamed city
First published: 1968

> *Principal characters:*
>> JAY D. HINDLE, known as "J. D.," the protagonist, second
>> vice president of an insurance company
>> CAROLYN HINDLE, the protagonist's wife, mother of his
>> children, Ronnie and Ellen
>> BILL HENDERSON, a friend of J. D. known for his practical
>> jokes

The Story

After a night of solitary, heavy drinking, the protagonist, J. D. Hindle,
wakes up on the couch in the living room of his house in a subdivision called
Rolling Hills Homes. He has trouble getting his bearings. There are two
glasses next to the empty bottle of Jack Daniel's on the coffee table, but
J. D. remembers being alone. He seems to have fallen asleep reading *True*
magazine; the voices of a man and woman on television, actors in a situation
comedy, at first seem to be talking to him. The sunlight coming through the
window hurts his eyes, and J. D. pulls the drapes to darken the room. The
doorbell is ringing, and it takes him a few moments to remember that it is
Labor Day and that his wife, Carolyn, and children, Ronnie and Ellen, are
away in Florida. When he answers the door, he finds a deliveryman from a
florist with a basket of roses and a printed card which reads, *"My deepest
sympathy."*

This opening situation is charged with implications which the unfolding of
the story's plot confirms. While J. D. convinces the man from the florist's
shop, at least initially, that "there's been no death in *this* family," the deliveries of flowers continue. There are visits from neighbors and friends bearing
food and expressing sympathy, for they have seen a newspaper account of the
deaths of Carolyn Hindle and her children in Daytona Beach. Their deaths
were caused by Hurricane Gloria. J. D. telephones the Breakers Hotel and
Mr. Garrett, the local newspaper editor; a telegram sent from Florida that
morning, obviously delayed by the weather, lets him cling to the belief that
his wife and children are alive. He even accuses his friend Bill Henderson of
engineering the whole affair as an elaborate practical joke.

J. D.'s unwillingness to accept the truth, implied by the details of the opening situation, arises from more than normal shock at the news of an accident. As the story develops, other details reveal that J. D.'s marriage was in trouble, and that this is the reason Carolyn took the children and left for Daytona Beach. As he stumbles around the house between telephone calls and trips to the door to receive deliveries of flowers, J. D. reveals his unfamiliarity with his home. He does not know how to operate the kitchen stove, where to find razor blades in the bathroom, or where his clean clothes are kept. Carolyn has always had things ready for him. In this house, their fourth since they were married, he is virtually a stranger. "As second vice-president, perhaps he spent more time away now, more time in the air. Coming home was more and more like an astronaut's re-entry problem."

J. D.'s isolation from his family becomes permanent with the deaths of Carolyn, Ronnie, and Ellen. Acceptance of this fact comes hard. When Mr. Garrett calls back, reporting that the Associated Press confirms all three deaths, J. D. turns on his friend Bill Henderson, who has suggested that J. D. is responsible for the fact that Carolyn and the children were in Florida. Still denying reality, J. D. tells Mrs. Merrill, the P.T.A. president, that Carolyn and the children will be home soon: "They're having a wonderful time in Florida." He also loses control at a call from Gold Seal Portrait Studios, which is trying to sell him a package deal on family photographs; he throws the flowers that have been delivered all over the front lawn; he attempts to break the doorbell with his fist. Finally, he turns off the electric current to stop the chimes, now ringing continuously, and collects the flowers on the lawn before stretching out on the living room carpet for a nap.

Rather than obliterating the facts that he wants to avoid, this period of sleep reconciles J. D. to the deaths of Carolyn and the children. The climax of the story occurs when he recalls something his wife said on the way to the airport the day before. Trying to explain her need to go away, Carolyn told him, "Something is happening to me. I'm dying, very, very slowly; do you understand that, Jay? Our life. It's the way we live, somehow the way we live." He had not understood her words at the time. His feeling then was relief at the prospect of being alone in the house for a few days. Turning on the electric power again, thereby reactivating the doorbell, J. D. goes to the door of his home and looks at the houses in the darkened subdivision spread below him. He looks up at the moon, but he cannot see the face of the man in it. Continuing to look at the heavens, however, he sees the faces of Carolyn, Ronnie, and Ellen in the stars. At this moment, in September, "snow began to fall, as though the stars had disintegrated into flakes."

Themes and Meanings

In the imagery of that star-filled sky, Madden objectifies J. D.'s realization that his wife and children are dead and that he is fundamentally alone in the universe. This isolation, with its overtones of existential philosophy, is different from the unself-conscious isolation J. D. had experienced in the last few years of his marriage to Carolyn. Like his wife, J. D. is dying inside, and the cause of the problem is the way he has chosen to live his life. Having put career before marriage and material measures of success before emotional ones, J. D. embraces the middle-class success ethic that Madden indicts in the story. It is ironically appropriate that "The Day the Flowers Came" takes place on Labor Day.

In one sense, the story is about J. D.'s death and not the deaths of his wife and children. When he picks up the flowers he has hurled all over the front lawn, he "took them into the house and laid them in his leather easy chair." The nap he takes on the carpet puts him at a level below that of the flowers. When he awakens, therefore, J. D. rises metaphorically from the grave. He contemplates the darkened exterior world from inside his home, now fully lighted, and sees with real intensity the full moral and psychological dimensions of his situation. This final episode reverses the lighting system of the opening of the story, when J. D. closed out the light of day and resisted facing the truth in a darkened house.

The cold, wet whiteness of the snow with which the story ends reveals J. D.'s capacity to feel grief for the deaths of Carolyn, Ronnie, and Ellen. Paradoxically, he is closer to them at this moment than at any other point in the story. The tension between J. D.'s sense of isolation and his newfound capacity to feel close to his family defines the ending of Madden's story.

Style and Technique

Madden's style in "The Day the Flowers Came" is straightforward, even colloquial in places. He uses a limited third-person point of view to get inside J. D.'s mind and to show how J. D. sees his own situation, but much of the story is rendered in dialogue between J. D. and his various visitors. The narrator does not comment on J. D.'s thoughts and actions. Their meaning emerges from the juxtaposition of events and from the implications that arise from Madden's handling of them.

Aside from the use of light and darkness to underscore J. D.'s changed perspective of himself, the chief images are the doorbell chimes and the flowers referred to in the title. The chimes have the single function of calling J. D. to his door to confront a reality he does not begin to accept until the end of the story. The flowers serve a dual function. They are the literal expression of the sympathy of J. D.'s friends and neighbors, and they are also symbols of life's impermanence. The day the flowers come is a turning point. It is the day on which J. D. is first able to see life clearly and to recognize his place in the universe.

Robert C. Petersen

THE DEAD

Author: James Joyce (1882-1941)
Type of plot: Ironic naturalism
Time of plot: 1904
Locale: Dublin, Ireland
First published: 1914

>   *Principal characters:*
>   GABRIEL CONROY, a university-educated teacher and
>   journalist who considers himself a writer and sophisticate
>   GRETTA CONROY, his wife, a country girl from the west of
>   Ireland
>   KATE MORKAN, Gabriel's aunt, who is old and feeble and who
>   gives piano lessons for beginners
>   JULIA MORKAN, Kate's sister, an organist and the mainstay of
>   the family
>   MARY JANE, the only niece of the Morkan sisters; she lives
>   with them and teaches piano
>   MOLLY IVORS, Gabriel's friend and colleague, a teacher
>   dedicated to the ideals of Irish nationalism and the Gaelic
>   League
>   LILY, the caretaker's daughter, who works as the Morkan
>   housemaid
>   FREDDY MALINS, a forty-year-old houseguest, given to drink
>   MR. BROWNE, another socially awkward houseguest, an
>   expert on opera singers of years past
>   MRS. MALINS, Freddy's mother, who is visiting Dublin from
>   Glasgow, where she lives with her daughter
>   BARTELL D'ARCY, a well-known, second-rate tenor "full of
>   conceit"
>   MICHAEL FUREY, a Galway boy who died at the age of seven-
>   teen but whose memory dominates Gretta Conroy's
>   consciousness

The Story

James Joyce's "The Dead" begins one way and ends another. The shifting nature of the story is balanced by the shifting perception of the protagonist, Gabriel Conroy, a teacher who wants to be considered a writer, though his writing seems to be confined to journalism. The opening exposition suggests that the story mainly will concern a social event, "the Misses Morkan's annual dance," held during the Christmas season, at which the Morkans' favorite nephew, Gabriel, and his wife, Gretta, are significant guests, since

Gabriel serves as master of ceremonies. The impact of the story, however, comes much later, after Gabriel has left the party and is confronted with new information about his wife and her past.

The cast of characters at the Morkan house is large and representative of many Irish stereotypes: the Morkan sisters, Kate and Julia, who are musically inclined spinsters; their musical niece, Mary Jane; and other assorted characters, ranging from Miss Molly Ivors, the Irish nationalist, to Freddy Malins, whose sobriety is a matter of continuing concern. Upon his arrival, however, Gabriel is defined as the focal character, a man who is a little too proud of his education and sophistication, foolishly smug and superior, but aware nevertheless of his social awkwardness. Gabriel is expected to perform as an after-dinner speaker and is condescending in his assessment of his audience. Gabriel is destined, however, to learn a lesson in humility before the story is over.

Gabriel Conroy is bored by his country, his relatives, and his colleagues and their provincial ways. Molly Ivors criticizes him for his lack of interest in Irish politics, for writing for *The Daily Express* (the slant is "West Briton" rather than properly Irish, she asserts), and for his preference for traveling to France and Belgium rather than to the native Aran Islands, a focal point for Irish nationalism. In response to these charges, Gabriel embarrasses himself by telling her that he is "sick" of his own country. Molly Ivors is so upset by his bluntness that she leaves the dance before dinner is served. Gabriel knows that he is responsible for her "abrupt departure." Joyce provides ample evidence that Gabriel is insensitive and cannot control his rudeness. In his own way he is a social misfit, offending people without intending to offend them.

Gabriel gets through his hypocritical after-dinner address without apparently offending anyone, extolling the virtues of traditional "warmhearted courteous Irish hospitality," flattering "the Three Graces of the Dublin musical world," Kate, Julia, and Mary Jane, and then toasting them. As the party is breaking up, Gabriel notices his wife, standing on the stairs, listening in rapt attention as Bartell D'Arcy, accompanied by Miss O'Callaghan at the piano, sings a traditional Irish air, "The Lass of Aughrim." Gabriel romanticizes the moment and imagines his wife to be the subject of a painting that he would entitle "Distant Music." His blood is warmed by her shining eyes and the color in her cheeks.

Gabriel remembers the intimate moments of their courtship, and the spark of romance kindled in him by Gretta begins to flame. He then takes his wife to a hotel, feeling "that they had escaped from their lives and duties, escaped from home and friends and run away together with wild and radiant hearts to a new adventure." Little does he know. The problem is that Gabriel does not understand his wife's emotional state, for hearing "The Lass of Aughrim" has reminded her of a boy she had known and loved in Galway,

Michael Furey, who, at the age of seventeen, died of a broken heart when Gretta left Galway to come to Dublin.

Learning of the dead Michael Furey causes Gabriel to reassess his relationship with his wife, his own petty vanity, and his self-image. The result is frustration and disappointment. He is forced to realize that his wife experienced a deeply felt romantic loss that had nothing at all to do with him. Gabriel aspires to be a writer, but he has failed to know and understand the person with whom he is most intimate. This is the subjective epiphany that provides the ironic reversal which Joyce uses to conclude the story. Gabriel is finally forced to realize that he has "never felt like that himself towards any woman," that he himself is incomplete and unfulfilled; his illusions about himself are destroyed; the truth he discovers is painful.

Themes and Meanings

"The Dead" is the most obviously autobiographical story in the *Dubliners* (1914) collection in that Joyce offers through the character of Gabriel Conroy a speculation concerning the sort of person Joyce himself might have become had he chosen to build a career for himself in Ireland. Gabriel is a vain and frustrated man who can find no genuine joy or pleasure in a nation that can look only to its past and constantly cherish, as Gabriel proclaims in his after-dinner speech, "the memory of those dead and gone great ones." Can a nation so obsessed with its past look forward to a promising future?

"The Dead," then, offers the reverse image of Joyce's optimistic (though also ironic) reflection of himself posed by Stephen Dedalus in *A Portrait of the Artist as a Young Man* (1916), an untested but confident artist who leaves his family and his country to escape the environmental ties that would surely impede his artistic development. Joyce was working on "The Dead" at the same time he was transforming his fragmentary *Stephen Hero* (1944) into the more carefully controlled narrative that was to become his *A Portrait of the Artist as a Young Man*. No doubt his mind was playing upon two extreme alternatives during this period following the most important decision he had made in his life to that point. "The Dead" can be seen as Joyce's portrait of the failed artist as an older man (though not necessarily a wiser one).

There can be no doubt that the source of this story is autobiographical. Richard Ellmann devotes chapter 15 of his biography *James Joyce* (1959) to the genesis of "The Dead." As a young girl in Galway in 1903, Joyce's wife, Nora Barnacle, had been courted by Michael ("Sonny") Bodkin, who suffered from tuberculosis. When Nora decided to leave Galway for Dublin, Sonny Bodkin left his sickbed in rainy weather to bid her farewell and to sing to her. After Nora arrived in Dublin, she heard that the boy had died. Knowledge of this courtship nettled Joyce, a jealous man by nature. The courtship letter that Gabriel quotes in the story is nearly a verbatim transcription of a letter that Joyce wrote to his wife, Nora, in 1904.

Ellmann offers an impressive list of biographical detail to support his point further. Every year, the Joyce family would gather for a Christmas party at No. 15 Usher's Island, where the writer's great aunts lived—Mrs. Lyons, Mrs. Callanan, and her daughter, Mary Ellen. According to Stanislaus Joyce, the writer's brother, their father would perform the annual ritual of carving the goose, as Gabriel does in the story, and would address the dinner guests in the same florid style that Gabriel affects after dinner.

Like Gabriel, Joyce wrote book reviews for *The Daily Express*. Gabriel shares Joyce's own disdain for west country provinciality and for the Gaelic League, represented by Miss Molly Ivors in the story. He shares Joyce's frustration over having to compete with a dead man, idealized in his wife's romantic memory, for his wife's love and affection (though one suspects that this dilemma, heightened in actuality by the writer's jealousy, was exaggerated in the story so that the futility of the dilemma would be more effectively dramatized).

Gabriel's ego is bruised and his cultured self-image of superiority undercut when he learns that Michael Furey was employed by the "gasworks," forcing upon him the realization that there is no necessary connection between a man's employment and his sensitivity. The man of learning may not in all respects be superior to the man of feeling.

The major themes of the story, then, are jealousy and intellectual pride, both major sins in Roman Catholic theology, and both of these sins attach to the character of Gabriel, who is as callow and unfeeling, as insecure and insensitive in his own way as Stephen Dedalus seems to be in Joyce's *A Portrait of the Artist as a Young Man*. The theme of escape is understated in the story but insinuates itself into the basic fabric of Gabriel's character. Gabriel's frustration is shaped and exacerbated by his career decision to remain in Dublin and work there. His interests obviously tend elsewhere—toward England and the Continent. Yet the story suggests that he can still learn important lessons through the intelligent exploration of native Irish culture and that he has been out of touch with the natural virtue and goodness that Michael Furey represents to his wife and with the instinctual understanding that makes his wife superior to him. Gabriel learns an existential moral lesson through his revelation and humiliation.

As a young man, Joyce scorned the provincial limitations of Dublin and the enthusiasm of the Irish nationalists for native culture and folkways. As an older and more mature writer, Joyce continued to draw upon those elements, dominant in his memory and imagination, for the rest of his creative life. Joyce never really lost touch with the fact that he was Irish and Catholic by birth and background. Although the stories of *Dubliners* all document the spiritual impoverishment of Irish life, and "The Dead" is no exception in that regard, Gabriel is stunted in his human potential mainly because of his arrogant rejection of the culture in which he has chosen to live. His character shaped by frustration, rancor, and disappointment, this teacher still has much to learn about his country, his family, and himself.

Style and Technique

"The Dead," Joyce's capstone story for his *Dubliners* collection, represents the most complex application of his device of the epiphany, defined by Stephen Dedalus in *A Portrait of the Artist as a Young Man* as a moment of revelation in which a new perception of reality is suddenly achieved, illuminating "the soul of the commonest object" or the "whatness of a thing." These naturalistic narratives involve realistic characters trapped by their environment, but the revelation is symbolic and, in the case of "The Dead," imagistic, as demonstrated by the snow that is constantly falling.

Joyce structures "The Dead" so as to offer twin epiphanies that are internal and external, subjective and objective, specific and general. The subjective epiphany is Gabriel's new insight into his wife's past, which places his own significance in their relationship into a new light. The objective epiphany, grasped by the reader, is Joyce's revelation about the nature and quality of life in Ireland.

The wonderful achievement of this story is the way in which Joyce raises the stylistic device of the epiphany to a complex symbolic level, and the way in which the subjective epiphany (Gabriel's perception that his wife has loved another man, idealized and immortalized in her memory) combines with the objective epiphany, the reader's realization that the Dublin of Joyce's imagination is a city of the dead, its citizens dwelling in the past and held captive by the memory of those who had gone before them. The snow that is "general all over Ireland" suggests that the whole country is gripped by the cold hand of death. Joyce creates the chilling impression that the dead are more vital and interesting than the living who carry on with their dull routines. The most for which any Irishman can hope, Joyce seems to suggest, is to be immortalized by death, thereby establishing a hold on the living.

The atmosphere of the story also shifts from the external to the internal. Outside, winter, the season of death, is symbolized by the snow. Contrasted to the cold, sterile exterior setting is the interior setting of the Christmas gathering, suggesting warmth, hospitality, and human companionship, but this celebration is dominated by the "distant music" of ancient voices, such as that of Aunt Julia, who was in her prime as a singer thirty years before. The celebration is set, moreover, in a household ruled by two sterile old women.

The symbolism of the story is multiplaned and complex. Gretta has been wooed by two angels—Gabriel, the archangel who will awaken the dead on the final day, and the more militant Michael, whose last name, "Furey," suggests a natural, west country passion that the educated and more intellectual Gabriel lacks. The "journey westward" mentioned in the final paragraph perhaps alludes to a literal journey, with Gabriel granting his wife's desire to return to visit Galway, but there are also traditional symbolic associations between traveling westward and man's natural progression toward death.

Certainly the most complex symbol the story has to offer, however, is the unifying metaphor of the snow, representing isolation and coldness. The disclosure of Gretta's secret gives Gabriel a new insight into her character and his own, but this is a moment of personal insight for the character, when he realizes another man has kindled in his wife a memory of poetry and romance. The epiphany for the reader is that the dead have a hold over the living, and that snow-covered Dublin is a city of the dead.

The story's dramatic impact depends on the ironic reversal of Gabriel's new perception of his wife and, consequently, of himself. Dramatic irony also comes into play as Gabriel reveals himself to the reader through his thoughts, words, and actions. The subjective epiphany is one of self-realization for Gabriel. His newfound self-knowledge puts him in communion with the living and the dead.

The very length of the story, as well as its placement, is indicative of its importance to Joyce. In "The Dead," as well as in *A Portrait of the Artist as a Young Man*, Joyce demonstrated that he had mastered the technique of ironic distance. Simply put, "The Dead" represents the finest achievement of Joyce's early naturalistic fiction, offering an exquisitely structured sustained experiment in extended symbolism and effective irony.

James M. Welsh

A DEAL IN WHEAT

Author: Frank Norris (1870-1902)
Type of plot: Naturalism
Time of plot: c. 1900
Locale: Kansas and Chicago
First published: 1902

>   *Principal characters:*
>   SAM LEWISTON, a Kansas rancher who loses his land during a
>   bear market in wheat and moves to Chicago to find work
>   EMMA LEWISTON, his wife
>   MR. TRUSLOW, a wealthy speculator and "great bear" in
>   wheat who never directly appears in the story but to whom
>   characters constantly refer
>   MR. HORNUNG, a wealthy speculator who leads the bull
>   market in wheat
>   HORNUNG'S BROKER, a critic of Truslow who wants the bulls to
>   destroy the "great bear"

The Story

   The price of wheat is the thread holding together this episodic short story. As Sam Lewiston hitches up the buckboard, he and his wife, Emma, anxiously wonder if wheat is still selling for sixty-six cents a bushel. Like so many Kansas farmers, they face economic disaster if the price does not rise. Regardless of the market, Sam must sell his wheat today, and if the bears still rule in Chicago, he and Emma will lose the land they love. Both sense that their worst fears are about to be realized. Looking out across the prairie and into an uncertain future, Emma reminds Sam of his brother Joe's offer of work in Chicago. Sam resists the idea of giving up, but as he kisses Emma good-bye and rides off to town, the reader knows that hope is all but gone.

   Upon entering the office of Bridges & Co., Grain Dealers, Sam gets the bad news from Bridges himself. Wheat is at sixty-two cents. "It's Truslow and the bear clique that stick the knife into us," laments Bridges, who is powerless to help his farmer friends. Sam Lewiston is ruined, and so are many of his neighbors. It costs them a dollar a bushel to raise the wheat, and few, certainly not Sam, can afford to store it any longer. Dazed by this sad turn of events, Sam goes home to Emma. "We'll go to Chicago," he tells her. "We're cleaned out!"

   The second episode takes place some months later when Mr. Hornung and the bulls have driven wheat up to $1.10 per bushel. The bears, led by the once dominant Truslow, are on the run. Indeed, the scene opens with Hornung agreeing to sell a hundred thousand bushels of wheat to Truslow, working out the deal with Mr. Gates, one of the great bear's minions. Hornung wonders if he has done the right thing. Truslow has paid dearly for the wheat, which he apparently had to have in order to cover overseas commitments, but Hornung's broker warns that the bulls should have taken full advantage of the great bear's distress to destroy him. Only then would the bull market be safe.

The third episode shifts ahead several days to the frenetic pit of the Chicago Board of Trade. The bulls still hold the corner in wheat, with Hornung setting the price at $1.50. Suddenly, one of the bears, a new man named Kennedy, begins selling wheat in thousand-bushel lots, and the bulls cannot figure where Kennedy is getting it. Had Hornung not held firm and kept buying at $1.50, the market might have broken, and that would have given the bears their chance to drive the price down. Who was behind the raid? Truslow is the prime suspect, but for weeks he had made no move, and rumor had it that he was in Wisconsin, bass fishing at Lake Geneva.

The fourth episode solves the mystery. Cyrus Ryder, a detective, tells Hornung and his broker that he dressed as a hobo and rode the Belt Line around Chicago looking for the source of Kennedy's wheat. Truslow, who owns the Belt Line, was shipping the very grain he had bought from Hornung out of Chicago and back to his elevator as thought it were new wheat fresh from Kansas. Truslow had been trying to break the bull market by selling back to Hornung at considerable profit the very wheat he had purchased from the latter and pledged to ship abroad. The broker is incensed at Truslow's chicanery, but Hornung laughs it off as a brilliant ploy and makes plans to recoup his losses and outmaneuver Truslow by raising the price of wheat to two dollars.

The fifth episode begins in a breadline behind a South Side bakery. It is cold and drizzling and almost 1:00 A.M. Dozens of hungry men have been there for hours waiting for the usual handout of day-old bread. One of them is Sam Lewiston. He has left Emma in Topeka and gone ahead to work for brother Joe. The reader learns that Joe's hat factory has failed, in part because of the repeal of tariff duties on cheap imports, and Sam has found little work since. The breadline is a godsend to him and others like him who are out of work and have nowhere else to go and nothing else to eat. Sam looks into the bewildered faces of the men standing with him and is consoled by the knowledge that the bread will keep them from starving. He likes to think of the breadline as a small platform that for now keeps those on it safely above the dark and threatening waters of complete despair swirling below. Suddenly, the bakery door opens and someone tacks up a sign. Groans are heard, and Sam and others push forward to read that because wheat is two dollars a bushel, the bakery will not be distributing free bread. The platform is gone, the price of wheat has ravaged him once again, and Sam walks away stunned by the loss, a hapless victim of a capricious fate.

Yet even as he wanders aimlessly, Sam's fortunes are changing. The reader is told that Sam finds a job the next day cleaning the streets. He works hard, sends for Emma, and gets promoted first to shift-boss, then to deputy inspector, and finally to inspector. Sam sees things more clearly after that night. Learning from the papers of Truslow's scheme against Hornung, he recognizes that he and countless others are powerless victims in the battle between the Bear and the Bull. The speculators carelessly ruin both farmers and workingmen and gamble with the nourishment of nations. Only they—the powerful bears and bulls—remain prosperous and unassailable. It is a chilling insight, but one based on painful experience, and the reader is left with the impression that understanding this harsh reality somehow helps Sam Lewiston survive.

Themes and Meanings

"A Deal in Wheat" clearly reflects the influence of naturalism and its leading European practitioner, Émile Zola. Some critics call Norris the first naturalistic American writer; others hotly disagree, citing his devotion to and identification with Romantics such as Rudyard Kipling. In fact, Norris combined elements of both Romanticism and naturalism in much of his writing. Perhaps the purest naturalistic piece he ever wrote, "A Deal in Wheat" sets forth in coldly analytical terms several themes which he first introduced in *The Octopus* (1901) and would develop further in *The Pit* (1903). As in the two novels, the overriding theme in this short story is that of economic struggle against almost irresistible forces. "A Deal in Wheat" is especially important because it marks a significant shift in Norris' thinking away from the optimistic determinism of *The Octopus* and *The Pit*. The story ends on something of a positive note, but it is dominated by a sense of pessimistic determinism.

Sam and Emma Lewiston are representative types. Good and wholesome, hardworking, they lose their Kansas ranch because of the rivalry between the bears and the bulls in Chicago. There is absolutely nothing they can do; they are victimized by circumstances well beyond their control. As for the speculators, they are battling not for survival but for wealth, and their economic warfare takes on a rationale of its own; it is a contest of wits. The injustice of it all is an underlying theme basic to much naturalistic writing. The speculators, however, are not vicious men; they are simply the haves in an amoral system that compels the haves to exploit the have-nots.

The story is bleakly depressing, yet in the very capriciousness of human existence, there shines a glimmer of hope. As he is about to sink into complete despair, Sam Lewiston finds a job and makes the most of it. The good man wins out in the end, but it is not so much because of who he is or what he has done. Inscrutable Fate, for reasons of her own, has smiled upon him. Sam understands this, and that is Norris' final point.

Style and Technique

Norris was much more committed to the method of Zola than to the latter's philosophy; he found in naturalism the tools to probe mankind and the natural world and to convey the "truth" of what he discovered to the reader. Hence, Norris tells his story coldly and concisely, giving it much the quality of a documentary drawn directly from life. The realism is enhanced by pertinent details which add to the mood of impending doom or increasing despair. The descriptions of Sam hitching the wagon and of Emma twisting her apron around her arms, for example, accentuate the commitment and concerns of two desperate people. Tying everything together is the wheat itself. An artful paradox is at the very heart of the story: Low wheat causes Sam to lose the ranch; high wheat almost takes his life.

The five episodes of the story progressively emphasize the helplessness of Sam the farmer and worker on the one hand and the power of the speculators on the other. Truslow's deception and Hornung's response to it bring matters to a head. These events serve to emphasize the speculators' fundamental lack of concern for anything but their own pursuit of wealth. Sam's reappearance in the last scene serves as an interesting contrast and makes clear the impact upon ordinary people of the games the speculators play. Although Norris cared little for the short-story form, he achieved in this work a remarkable unity of character and purpose that was sadly lacking in his novels. "A Deal in Wheat" represents the momentary triumph of naturalism over Romanticism in the writing of a man who was strongly influenced by both.

Ronald W. Howard

DEATH AND THE CHILD

Author: Stephen Crane (1871-1900)
Type of plot: Symbolic realism
Time of plot: The Greco-Turkish wars
Locale: Greece
First published: 1898

> *Principal characters:*
> PEZA, a young correspondent whose father was Greek
> THE LIEUTENANT
> THE CHILD

The Story

In "Death and the Child," a young man enters upon "a great venture toward death" that initiates him progressively into the experience of war and life. The central character, a university-educated correspondent named Peza, arrives upon the scene of a mass exodus of peasants who flee an approaching battle between Greek patriots and Turkish invaders. Although assigned to cover the event for an Italian paper, Peza identifies with the Greek people because his father was a Greek. Moved by the sights of war, he wishes to become immediately involved in fighting rather than in merely observing. His adventure, however, carries him through a moral process that changes his feelings about the war and himself.

Divided into seven sections, each of which focuses on a crucial event in Peza's transformation, the story begins by establishing the pattern of the events into which Peza is drawn. It opens with the great human torrent that sweeps down the mountainside away from the threatening booms of artillery. Moving counter to this wave of refugees, Peza walks up the mountain. Overcome by pity and awe at the sight of such misery, Peza is inspired to join the fight. A young lieutenant returning to the front agrees to become Peza's guide into the war. The contrast between these two characters foreshadows the difficulty Peza will have in his attempt to become involved in the war's action. Although young like Peza, the lieutenant has already experienced battle and knows it is not the romantic adventure that Peza imagines it to be; he finds Peza's fervent patriotism and heroic innocence at once amusing and contemptible.

The second section of the story, while not directly concerned with Peza, introduces the child whose image will bring about Peza's ultimate transformation. The child has been left behind by his parents in their rush to escape. He plays tranquilly at his homesite on a mountain overlooking the plain on which the fighting rages. Though the lines of battle are moving imperceptibly closer, the boy shows only minimal interest in such distant action. It is too childish an affair for one who, like himself, is "dealing with sticks" in a pretend-game of sheepherding. Unlike Peza, who is caught up in causes—in ideals and abstractions—the child's involvement in his play is direct, immediate, and concrete.

Sections 3 through 6 follow Peza as he further engages the experience of war. At the beginning of section 3, he is struck by the war's failure to erase the "commonness" of familiar objects. The "immovable poppies," images of nature's endurance in the midst of human upheaval, also impress him. Seeing that the torrent of peasants has now become a stream of fatigued and wounded soldiers, Peza discovers that "pity ha[s] a numerical limit"; he is no longer moved by the sight of the wounded, but instead his vision becomes "focused upon his own chance." At this moment, the lieutenant parts company with Peza, leaving him alone and unguided to "wander helplessly toward death." Unable to see the troops for the trees, Peza moves blindly forward. When a shell shatters a nearby tree, he perceives the previously "immovable" natural world now "astounded," "bewildered," and "amazed" at its own vulnerability. He realizes that he is in this spot not primarily because of his conscious decision or noble ideals, but "because at a previous time a certain man [the lieutenant] had smiled."

As section 4 opens, Peza inflates his influence upon the war, personifying it as a "barbaric deity" that he must "surprise" so as not to give it pretext for further vengeance. His arrival at a company of peasant soldiers, however, inspires no extraordinary act. The soldiers ignore him, while he imagines them as dumb puppets ignorantly carrying out the superior will of great men. Approaching a captain of the battery, Peza reasserts his desire to fight, but the officer and soldiers only want from him political news of the war. In the midst of their civilized conversation, shells fly overhead and far beyond their position. Peza is elated that the shells "kill no one" and that "war ha[s] turned out to be such a gentle business." It is as though he were "having coffee in the smoking room of some embassy where reverberate the names of nations," rather than the guns of battle.

Sections 5 and 6 take Peza into the front lines of battle where his romantic notions are shattered and where death becomes an actuality. As he climbs toward the high infantry position, he encounters a soldier whose jaw is half blown away. Running from this "spectre," he happens upon a squadron positioned in trenches. From this vantage, Peza sees for the first time the Turkish battalions as they move steadily against the Greek lines. Fearing that they will "take the position," Peza runs again, this time into the rifle pits near the front. Here, he announces to an officer his desire to fight for the fatherland. When the officer instructs him to take a gun and ammunition from a corpse, however, Peza shrinks back. A soldier performs the task for him and, donning the bandolier, Peza feels himself strangled by death and drawn into its "mystic chamber." Terrified, he bolts for the rear, hardly noticed by the

soldiers who continue to fight. At the beginning of section 7, the child
reappears. Weary of his game and hungry, he realizes that he is alone. The
battle, now obviously closer, captures his attention for the first time, and he
weeps at its incomprehensible mystery. Distracted by a nearby noise, the
child sees a man covered with dust and blood—Peza—drag himself over the
crest of the hill and fall to the ground panting. The child approaches him,
looks into his eye, and asks a simple question: "Are you a man?" The question strikes at the heart of Peza's dilemma, his attempt to define himself in
relation to the war. As he gazes up into the child's face, however, he sees a
power beyond the personal—he sees "the primitive courage, the sovereign
child, the brother of the mountains, the sky, and the sea, and he knew that
the definition of his misery could be written on a wee grass-blade."

Themes and Meanings

Throughout the story, there occurs an emphasis on eyes and vision. When
Peza first appears, he "look[s] at everything," specifically the fleeing peasants, "with . . . pitying glances." His protestations of patriotism to the lieutenant are described as the overflow of emotion "which heretofore had been
expressed only in the flash of eyes." At every step along his journey, his eyes
are assaulted with the sights of war. He often imagines eyes gazing at him,
mostly horrifyingly when the "two liquid-like eyes" of a corpse seem to stare
into him. When he encounters the child, he "roll[s] his eye glassily" toward
him and "gaze[s] up into his face." Compelled again and again to open his
eyes to the immediate facts of the world, Peza undergoes a literal visual
awakening through which his vision is successively cleansed of his mind's
romantic and theoretical attitude toward war and life.

In the first phase of this visual evolution, Peza is struck by the disturbing
sight of the refugees as they course wildly down the mountain. This image
arouses his physical emotions, the feeling of pity and consanguinity that culminates in his patriotic vision of the war. As he ventures farther and the
images of jaded soldiers replace those of the miserable peasants, he experiences an aesthetic perception. The soldiers' oversaturation with the tragedy
and ferocity of war he compares with a visit to a picture gallery where his
mind had become so glutted with "all the strength of Argus-eyed art" that he
had come away feeling "a great hollow quiet." When, at the battery position,
he is besieged by questions concerning the politics of the war, Peza's vision
becomes further abstracted from its immediate dangers. Not until the soldier
with the broken jaw appears does Peza's intellectual perspective radically fail
him. Rapt by the "mystic gaze" of this specter, Peza begins to feel the immediacy of death that climactically consumes him when the corpse looks at
him with liquid eyes, and he runs.

Peza's mystical vision culminates in the imaginative vision of the child.
Throughout his "grand venture," it is the image of death that Peza has been

seeking; the gradual stripping away of the intellectual scales from his eyes reveals not death, the grand abstraction, however, but life, in the concrete image of the child, as the source of his moral transformation. When he comes to see the child "as some powerful symbol," it is not merely as a figure of suffering humanity and thus as an intellectualized reflection of his personal misery. Rather, Peza sees the child's unanalyzable union—his brotherhood— with the profound forces of nature—the sky, the sea, the mountains—so that the child's image bears within it the entire potential of the visible creation. It is the child's emergence, out of the war, as an imaginative event—a "symbol" of new possibilities—that takes Peza beyond the need to define himself and man through death and opens him to the greater venture of life.

Style and Technique

In keeping with Peza's evolution beyond the tragic self, Crane employs a self-effacing style. The "author" as an authority over his story becomes submerged within an action whose central interest is the narrative process itself, the visible rendering of change. Consequently, there is no clearly identifiable point of view, no self-conscious first-person narrative or authorial omniscience. The narrator, as inextricably involved in his narrating as the child's image is symbolically united with the elemental powers of nature, becomes simply the shifting visual perspective through which events rise into view, run their course, and issue into new events.

An important instance of the narrative's shifting visual perspective occurs when the child weeps. First, the narrator shows the scene from the child's vantage point:

> The child took seat on a stone, and contemplated the fight. He was beginning to be astonished. . . . Lines of flame flashed out here and there. It was mystery.

Then, he renders the same moment from the correlative perspective:

> If the men struggling on the plain had had time, and greater vision, they could have seen this strange, tiny figure seated on a boulder, surveying them while the tears streamed.

The "symbolic" value of the child, so central in Peza's evolution, originates precisely in this imaginative shift in perspective. Moreover, the author's self-effacing narrative generates the moral equivalent in style of the impersonal natural forces that impel Peza into his venture, that operate within the war, and that illuminate the child's image.

S. Elaine Marshall

DEATH IN MIDSUMMER

Author: Yukio Mishima (Kimitake Hiraoka, 1925-1970)
Type of plot: Psychological realism
Time of plot: c. 1950-1952
Locale: Tokyo and an inn on the Izu Peninsula
First published: "Manatsu no Shi," 1952 (English translation, 1956)

> *Principal characters:*
> TOMOKO IKUTA, the focal character, a wife and mother
> MASARU IKUTA, her husband
> YASUE IKUTA, her sister-in-law, a woman past the age for
> marrying

The Story

Staying at an inn near the southern tip of the Izu Peninsula, Tomoko Ikuta escapes the summer heat by taking a nap in her room. She sends her daughter Keiko, age five, and her sons Kiyoo and Katsuo, ages six and three, to play on the beach under the supervision of her sister-in-law Yasue. Proud of the whiteness of her skin, Yasue does not want to tan, so she remains under a beach umbrella while the children play near the edge of the water. Keiko and Kiyoo are caught in an undertow and pulled under the water; Yasue hurries toward them but collapses in the water from a heart attack. People on the beach pull her out and take Katsuo and Yasue's body back to the inn. They do not know that there had been three children with her.

Awakened with the news that Yasue has had a swimming accident, Tomoko hurries to the lawn and finds a man administering artificial respiration to her sister-in-law. She sees Katsuo in the arms of a local fisherman. Four hours pass before the doctor gives up the effort to revive Yasue, and only then does Tomoko find out from her youngest son that the other two children have drowned. "Katsuo looked up at her timidly. 'Kiyoo . . . Keiko . . . all bubbles.' He began sobbing." It is already after sunset, but young men begin to dive to locate the children's bodies. Tomoko waits until nearly morning before she sends her husband, Masaru, a telegram advising him that Yasue is dead and that Kiyoo and Keiko are missing.

Masaru leaves Tokyo immediately for the inn on the Izu Peninsula. When he arrives, both Tomoko and he play the roles expected of them. Tomoko kneels before her husband and says that the accident was her fault, and Masaru expresses understanding and sympathy. The two bodies are found the next day, and both parents begin to experience the emotions associated with so traumatic a loss. Tomoko resents her husband's grief over the death of Yasue, for example, thinking that it somehow diminishes his feelings for his dead children. She masters her feelings and does the conventional thing when Masaru's parents come up from Kanazawa for the funerals. She assumes responsibility for the accident again and apologizes to her husband's father and mother. To her own parents, however, Tomoko complains, "But who should they feel sorriest for? Haven't I just lost two children? There they all are, accusing me." In the days and weeks following the accident, Tomoko struggles with ambivalent feelings. At times she seeks punishment for her guilty sense that by leaving the children under Yasue's control, she is genuinely responsible for their deaths. At other times she seeks sympathy for her loss and seems to nurse her sorrow.

Tomoko also fears that another accident will occur. Masaru had had an accident with the car shortly before she had gone on vacation with Yasue and the children, and she will not ride in the car with her husband if Katsuo is going with them. Visiting Tama Cemetery to see the lot Masaru has bought for the burial of his sister and children, Tomoko will not allow Katsuo to drink from a public water fountain. She is afraid of germs and carries boiled water for him to drink. On the way back from the cemetery, Tomoko buys her son a toy from a vendor in the train station, and for a moment, thinking that Kiyoo and Keiko have been left at home, wants to buy something for the other children, too. Despite such occasional tricks of the mind, Tomoko adjusts to her loss but with great difficulty. For a time she keeps herself busy going to plays and concerts; later she takes up sewing. Both activities allow her to cut off her emotions at will and to experience periods of time when she does not think about the accident.

That winter Tomoko learns that she is pregnant once more, and with this change "forgetfulness came as a natural right." Both Masaru and she feel like spectators, rather than participants, in the events of the summer. The accident comes more and more to seem like something that happened to other people. Tomoko finds it possible to reduce the incident to the clichéd statement that one must watch children constantly at the beach. The past seems to be closed with the birth, the following summer, of a daughter named Momoko; when the new baby is a year old, however, Tomoko expresses the wish to go back to the beach on the Izu Peninsula. She does not want to go alone. As the entire Ikuta family stands on the beach, Masaru sees in Tomoko's face an expression familiar since the accident. She looks out to sea as if she were waiting for something, the implication being that she is waiting for Kiyoo and Keiko to return.

Themes and Meanings

The sea is an appropriate image of the timeless reality which Tomoko comes to perceive behind the surface of her comfortable, middle-class life. The essence of that reality is the fact of death's constant threat. Mishima shows Kiyoo and Keiko, shortly before the accident, aware of the power of death but too young to recognize it. "They had a secret all their own, the feel of the sand as it pulled away from their feet." It is significant that Tomoko is asleep when the accident occurs, for she too is innocent about death. Mishima's description of her sleeping form stresses its youthful, girlish quality; unlike Sleeping Beauty, however, she is not awakened to reality by a loving Prince but through the agency of the sea which takes both her children. It is important to Mishima's thematic point that Tomoko not be present during the accident and that Yasue experience death as her surrogate. Tomoko both participates in the children's deaths and is removed from them, and she thereby becomes aware of the universal fact of human mortality.

Initially, Tomoko has no such awareness. She reacts to the accident in purely personal and social terms by worrying about how she can face Masaru and his parents. Her husband has similar reactions: He responds to the telegram from Tomoko by making sure that he is carrying enough money to deal with the expenses of the emergency. He takes upon himself the organization of the funeral and arrangements for the burials in Tama Cemetery. For Masaru, the deaths of Kiyoo, Keiko, and Yasue present him with largely practical problems. Mishima concedes that he feels genuine grief but claims that his emotions are more sentimental than Tomoko's and more easily survived. Tomoko's feelings, initially centered on herself as the victim of fate, change over the course of the story. Her understanding of life at the end of "Death in Midsummer" is deeper, and more frightening, than Masaru's.

Despite the emotional growth Mishima attributes to her, Tomoko is not an easy character to like. The treatment of her feelings is too uncompromisingly honest for that. Mishima requires that the reader acknowledge that her self-centered reaction to the deaths of her children is true to human nature.

Style and Technique

Despite the dramatic intensity of the opening pages of the story, it is Mishima's manipulation of the third-person narrative point of view which gives "Death in Midsummer" its chief effects. The narrator of the story exhibits unlimited omniscience and both enters into the minds of nearly every character in the story and comments on their thoughts and actions from a position to be identified as the author's viewpoint. The story succeeds or fails, therefore, to the degree that a reader accepts or rejects the narrator's commentary.

Mishima's use of the narrator is most effective in the handling of the secondary characters in the story. He manages to convey the feelings of the children Kiyoo, Keiko, and Katsuo by combining brief dramatized incidents and deft commentary. He shows the insecurity that causes Yasue to accept the domination of the younger Tomoko, and he makes convincing the vanity that causes her to leave the children alone near the water. Mishima's narrator is less convincing in the characterization of Masaru. Tomoko's husband comes across as a stereotype of the modern Japanese husband. He is more wedded to job than wife, and the affection he seeks from her is as much maternal as conjugal. Masaru is more talked about by the narrator than shown in action. His grief for his dead children may be sentimental, as the narrator claims, but little in his behavior confirms the statement.

Mishima's treatment of Tomoko, like that of Masaru, combines dramatized action, summary of thought, and narrational commentary. Since she is the focal character of the story, there is both more dramatization and more summary of her thoughts than is true of any other character. The narrator succeeds in conveying the complexity of the feelings of a woman who has lost children in an accident and who feels at least partly to blame for their deaths. Nevertheless, Tomoko remains more a type than an individual. She is used by Mishima to make a metaphysical point; her development is a schematic of the ideas about death he seeks to illustrate in the story. As a result, Tomoko seems more a function of the narrator's perception of her than a character genuinely independent of the narrational voice.

Robert C. Petersen

DEATH IN THE WOODS

Author: Sherwood Anderson (1876-1941)
Type of plot: Psychological realism
Time of plot: Probably the late nineteenth century
Locale: Illinois
First published: 1926

Principal characters:
MRS. GRIMES, whose death forms the center of the story
JAKE GRIMES, her husband
THE UNNAMED NARRATOR, who remembers the story
HIS BROTHER, who shares his experience

The Story

"Death in the Woods" ostensibly concerns a farm woman, Mrs. Grimes, who, although only in her early forties, seems old and probably demented. She has no first name in the story, and, indeed, very little is known about her at all. The narrator, a man who remembers and re-creates the story's events from his childhood, tries to put together the few things that he actually does know. Through this re-creation, he searches for meaning and for completion. He needs the events to make sense.

"The old woman was nothing special," the narrator remembers. "She was one of the nameless ones that hardly anyone knows, but she got into my thoughts." In her youth, the woman had been a bound girl, practically a slave to a harsh German farmer and his wife. Her job was to feed the stock and to cook for the couple. Her life with them was very unhappy. "She was a young thing then and scared to death," the narrator says. In addition to the demands of her work, she was sometimes the victim of the farmer's sexual advances. One day he had chased her into the barn and torn away the front of her dress before he was stopped by the sound of his wife's returning. In such a situation, the girl looked desperately for any means of escape. Thus, when Jake Grimes, the wastrel son of a failed sawmill owner, offered to marry her, she accepted.

The woman's new life, however, was hardly an improvement over the former. Settled on a new farm, she again became a servant, first to her husband and later to her son. She soon withdrew into silence and routine, a deadly existence in which she was abused by her family and ignored by all others. "They left everything at home for her to manage and she had no money," the narrator says. "She knew no one. No one ever talked to her in town."

The central episode of the old woman's story occurs on a cold winter day. As is her custom, she makes her solitary trek into the village for the meager supplies for which she can barter and the scraps of liver and dog meat that the butcher sometimes gives her out of pity. On her way home, toward the end of day, the snow begins to fall, and by the time she reaches the woods, she is exhausted. Struggling along the forest path, she comes to a clearing and stops there to rest, despite the danger of the cold. Soon she falls asleep and slides quietly toward death.

Accompanying the woman on her journey are a pack of dogs. As the night comes on and the moon rises, these animals undergo a change. "Such nights, cold and clear and with a moon, do things to dogs," the narrator says. "It may be that some old instinct, come down from the time when they were wolves and ranged the woods in packs on winter nights, comes back into them." The scene takes on a magical quality as the dogs begin to run in a circle in the moonlit snow. If the old woman awoke before her death, she would have seen that queer, wonderful sight, or so the narrator imagines. She soon dies, however, and then all rules, all expectations and unspoken agreements between man and beast conclude. The dogs nudge, then tear at the backpack containing the meat. They drag her body into the center of the clearing, and, in doing so, rip away the top of her dress so that she is exposed to the night. Not one of the animals touches her body, however, and she is left undisturbed in the snow.

When the body is found several days later by a rabbit hunter, he is mystified and frightened. In town he tells everyone that he has seen a "beautiful young girl" dead in the snow. A crowd of men led by the town marshal hurry to the site, and with them go the narrator, then a young boy, and his brother. Together they follow the men into the woods. It is again night when they reach the clearing. Standing by the tree under which the woman died, the two boys see the body, now magically transformed by the snow and the moon. "She did not look old, lying there in that light, frozen and still," the narrator remembers. "One of the men turned her over in the snow and I saw everything. My body trembled with some strange mystical feeling and so did my brother's. It might have been the cold."

The town blacksmith respectfully covers the old woman's body with his own coat and carries her gently into town. The next day her body is identified, and she is again soon forgotten, except, that is, by the boy—now the man telling the story. He has listened to his brother recount the events that they have witnessed, but this telling has not seemed sufficient. Facts alone do not adequately explain the mystery of the events. "The whole thing, the story of the old woman's death, was to me as I grew older like music heard from far off. The notes had to be picked up slowly one at a time. Something had to be understood."

Thus, he returns to the story again and again, mystified, compelled to probe at the essence of the woman's life and death. "A thing so complete has its own beauty," he says, and it is that beauty that haunts him.

Themes and Meanings

The most obvious theme of the story is found in the narrator's emphasis on feeding, on giving of oneself to satisfy others. The old woman's job was always to feed others—the German farmer and his wife, her own husband and son, the animals which surrounded her. "Horses, cows, pigs, dogs, men"; the narrator numbers them off, the men undifferentiated from the beasts in the woman's mind.

One aspect of this "feeding" is sexual in nature. Certainly the farmer's desires for her are basic, brutal, and animal-like. He tears away the top of her dress, paralleling the action by the dogs in the clearing—although, ironically, the dogs treat her with greater respect than do the humans. When she runs off with Jake Grimes, she tells him that the farmer never actually possessed her, but she gives herself to Jake without resistance, at least in the narrator's imaginative reconstruction of the scene. Sex is, for the woman, simply another form of feeding, and she is relieved when, grown bent and wasted by hard work, she is no longer attractive to Jake and no longer has to satisfy him in this way.

In her deathly transformation, however, the woman once again regains her youthful sexuality. She becomes a young girl, untouched and pure. When the body is discovered, and as the young boy and his brother watch, the woman's breasts are revealed. The narrator remembers that he "saw everything" and that his body "trembled with some strange mystical feeling," which he attempts to attribute to the cold. Still, it is clear that at least part of the reaction is sexual. The boy sees and feels an aspect of existence which has heretofore been hidden from him. The weird connection of sex and death is ironic and, no doubt, disturbing, but, as the adult narrator realizes, there is an unknowable quality, a shared "mystical" reality in them both. At this moment, the boy gains awareness. He cannot truly understand what he feels, but his life is forever changed by the experience. He can never return to his own innocence; he can only wonder at the mystery of life and death.

Style and Technique

As is so often the case in a work by Sherwood Anderson, the means of telling the story can be as compelling as the story itself. Such is the case with "Death in the Woods." Anderson wrote several versions of the tale before he felt that he had come close to telling it adequately, and one of the most obvious narrative devices employed in the story is the narrator's apparent difficulty in saying exactly what he means, in capturing in words the truth of the event. The "story" is simple, but the feelings evoked by it are very complex.

It may be argued, in fact, that the story is concerned more with the narrator than with the old woman whose death serves as inspiration, or catalyst, for the narrator. The unnamed narrator is a grown man looking back to his childhood, and there is considerable ambiguity concerning the actual events that he recounts. At one point he wonders how he could know some of the details that he is relating, and clearly there are many aspects of the story that he could not know. Later he tells the reader that he is drawing on events in his own life to help make sense of, give structure to, and fill the gaps in the old woman's life. For example, he remembers having himself worked on the farm of a German who abused the hired girl. He also had "a half-uncanny, mystical adventure with dogs in an Illinois forest on a clear, moonlit winter night." In addition, he had once stumbled onto the woman's old, run-down farmhouse, inhabited now only by "tall, gaunt" dogs, the kind that he has imagined as accompanying Mrs. Grimes on her journey.

The point is that the narrator is admitting to the reader that he is creating the story in an attempt to make sense of the central event—the discovery of the old woman's body and its magical transformation. He is not satisfied with the way that others have told the story; thus, he adds to it selected events from his own life, from snatches of overheard conversation, and from "small-town tales." These he has put together with the actual events of that night, the ones he could factually know, in order to create the larger, more reso-nant, more universal story of life and death.

Thus, "Death in the Woods" can be seen as an explanation of storytelling: What causes the teller to repeat his tale; in what manner does he draw on fact, fantasy, and personal experience to transform the basic events of the world into the wonder of imaginative creation? Like the old woman's body, become that of a lovely young girl, the story, seen in the mystical light of the moon, transfixes the reader with its hidden magic and touches him with its revealed beauty.

Edwin T. Arnold

DEATH IN VENICE

Author: Thomas Mann (1875-1955)
Type of plot: Symbolic character study
Time of plot: 1911
Locale: Venice
First published: "Der Tod in Venedig," 1912 (English translation, 1925)

> *Principal characters:*
> GUSTAVE VON ASCHENBACH, a distinguished German writer
> with an international reputation
> TADZIO, a Polish boy of perfect beauty

The Story

The opening pages of the novella brilliantly foreshadow the theme of death by cholera in Venice, a city whose history of sensual self-indulgence has led to moral decline and physical collapse. The first of three symbolic messengers of death—a distinctly exotic figure with straw hat, red hair, snub nose, prominent Adam's apple, and glistening white teeth laid bare to the gums—suddenly appears in the Byzantine-style mortuary chapel (a parody of St. Mark's Basilica in Venice) while Gustave von Aschenbach is walking near the North Cemetery in Munich. This disturbing apparition weakens Aschenbach's repressive self-control, stimulates his visionary dream (which represents the source of the Asiatic cholera in the moist swamps of the Ganges delta), and inspires his voyage to Italy.

This thematic prelude and the revealing sketch of Aschenbach's dignified and repressed character establish the intellectual framework, suggest the inevitability of his tragic fate, and lead to a series of encounters with menacing and vaguely theatrical figures. The goat-bearded "circus director" sells Aschenbach a ticket across the northern Adriatic from Pola to Venice and seals their satanic pact with sand that warns of human mortality. Charon, the second messenger of death, conveys Aschenbach, against his will, from the dock to the Lido in a coffinlike gondola and, with a cryptic warning, suddenly vanishes.

When Aschenbach, in the grand hotel, encounters Tadzio's perfect beauty, delightful charm, and expression of pure serenity, he does not see him as an actual boy of fourteen, but as an embodiment of Greek art, transmuted and gilded with mythic significance. The irony of Aschenbach's futile attempt to idealize his pederastic passion is emphasized by the parallel development of his degrading love and of the cholera that insidiously infects the city. Aschenbach, the highly respectable widower with a married daughter, changes from a purely aesthetic admirer of Tadzio's beauty to a man who suddenly realizes that the acute pain he felt during his quite sensible attempt to leave the city (fortuitously prevented by the loss of his trunk) was entirely attributable to his rapturous though unacknowledged feeling for the youth.

Aschenbach's passion is like a crime, and the city's evil secret of the cholera mingles with the one in the depths of his heart. A sanitary inspector greets Aschenbach's ship as it approaches Venice, the lukewarm air of the sirocco breathes on him as he is rowed to the Lido. He smells the stagnant odor of the lagoon when he opens his hotel window, the sickening exhalations of the canals nearly drive him from the city, and the pungent smell of carbolic acid and municipal placards warn him of the dangers of certain intestinal infections. The blustering street musician, the third messenger of death, laconically confides that the oppressive sirocco is not good for the health. Even when the English clerk in Cook's travel agency advises him to leave immediately, he cannot tear himself away from the grip of the pestilence or the spell of his beloved.

Tadzio's poor teeth connect him with the aged and garishly dressed homosexual that Aschenbach has observed on the ship to Venice. This symbol of his anemic disease and human mortality is pleasurable to Aschenbach because it equalizes youth and age, beauty and ugliness, and diminishes Tadzio's godlike power over him. The writer is possessively jealous of the youth's perfect form, and wants him to die at the height of his beauty, before he is ravaged by decay and old age.

Overwhelmed by passion and disgusted by his aging body, Aschenbach submits to the cosmetic attentions of the hotel barber, who transforms him into a grotesque replica of the repulsive old invert on the ship. In the little square where he had once conceived the plan of his abortive flight, he eats the overripe strawberries that infect him with the fatal cholera.

The doomed Aschenbach then returns to the hotel to discover that Tadzio is leaving. When he rushes to the beach for a final glimpse of the beautiful boy, he finds that Tadzio's friend Jaschiu is avenging himself for his long weeks of subservience. Jaschiu challenges Tadzio to a fight and presses his face into the sand, symbolizing both degradation of beauty and spiritual forbearance in the face of fate. After witnessing this scene, Aschenbach is "summoned" by Tadzio to his death.

Themes and Meanings

Mann makes Aschenbach a homosexual for several reasons. On one level, his inversion is a manifestation of strain and disorder, a release from psychological repression that results in the vulgar and degrading passion of an elderly gentleman for a rather cruel and unworthy boy. Aschenbach abandons his will, conspires with pseudoartists such as the equivocal musician and the cosmetic barber, sadly deludes himself about his relationship with Tadzio, and condemns himself—and probably his beloved—to death.

More important, Aschenbach's homosexual pursuit symbolizes the artist's noble but tragic quest for perfection. Mann's imaginative artist, who para-doxically creates in his work a life that he is unable to live in reality, must maintain a perilous balance of feeling and thought, and cannot surrender to either without losing his capacity to write. In the doomed love of the suspect and antisocial pederast, Mann found the perfect pattern for the artist's des-perate struggle to recapture the ideal form of sensual beauty, and to unite passion with thought, grace with wisdom, the real with the ideal. The theme of the novella is the seed of self-destruction inherent in creative genius.

Style and Technique

The novella is structured by a series of polarities and contrasts: north-south, age-youth, health-sickness, art-life, reason-instinct, reality-illusion, order-chaos. Once Aschenbach breaks free from his northern restraints, he is unable to establish the proper balance between his Germanic culture, intel-lect, discipline, and serenity, and Italian passion, license, freedom, and deca-dence.

Mann also uses the structural device of the leitmotif: the repetition of a certain phrase in different contexts, which he associates with a particular theme. His allusions to the composers Richard Wagner and Gustav Mahler, the musicians in the gondola and the street, and Tadzio's name, which sounds like a musical description (*adagio* means "slowly"), all suggest that art can arouse dangerous emotions. The demonic tempters and messengers of death all have the same physical features and bad teeth; the black gondola, black-ened corpses, and snapping black cloth of the camera symbolize death.

Mann's style changes from coolly objective to intensely passionate as Aschenbach moves from a passive to an active lover and is gradually over-whelmed by moral and physical degeneration. Aschenbach first sees Tadzio as would an intellectual connoisseur, changes to a sympathetic and paternal view, realizes that he is staying in Venice for Tadzio's sake, and compares their relationship to that of Socrates and his favorite pupil, Phaedrus. As he approaches death, Aschenbach is overcome by panic, hysterical desire, de-monic frenzy, and orgiastic dreams, driven as he is into the bottomless pit of excess and damnation.

Jeffrey Meyers

DEATH OF A HUNTSMAN

Author: H. E. Bates (1905-1974)
Type of plot: Romance
Time of plot: Mid-twentieth century
Locale: A rural area outside London
First published: 1957

> *Principal characters:*
> HARRY BARNFIELD, the protagonist, a middle-aged
>   businessman
> KATEY, Harry's shrewish wife
> EDNA WHITTINGTON, an old flame of Harry
> VALERIE, Edna's nineteen-year-old daughter

The Story

"Death of a Huntsman" involves its protagonist, Harry Barnfield, in a love triangle; strangely enough, his wife is not one of the three "corners." It is one measure of the sterility and joylessness of his marriage, in fact, that when Harry has an affair with young Valerie Whittington, he hardly considers his wife to be an issue or obstacle. The third corner of the triangle is occupied by Valerie's mother, Edna, an old flame of Harry.

The story begins with Harry shown in his accustomed routine: perpetually late, running to catch his commuter train out of London, short, aging, and vaguely clownish, the butt of good-natured jokes by his fellow commuters. The reader soon sees why he is always late: His rural home, lovely as it is, is hardly the sort of place one would make a special effort to reach, for Harry's wife, Katey, is a more vicious shrew than her namesake, Katherina, in William Shakespeare's *The Taming of the Shrew.*

Rather than try to tame Katey—their marriage has been sour for too long, the reader senses, for there to be much hope of that—Harry takes solace in Valerie, a girl he accosts for riding her pony, without permission, across his property. Valerie is everything that Katey is not: young, vivacious, sensitive, and, most of all, caring toward Harry. Harry's fondness for her is hardly lessened when he learns that her mother, Edna, is the same who many years ago initiated him into the joys of sex. Edna, in fact, would very much like to strike up the match again, Katey notwithstanding.

For more than two months Harry and Valerie meet for walks and horseback rides in the woods, but the situation is too volatile to continue forever. The crisis comes at the Hunt Ball, an autumnal rite involving much dancing and drinking. Edna pressures Harry into taking her and, as an afterthought, Valerie. There, Harry and Valerie's feelings for each other become evident even to Edna. Edna tells Valerie to go home. Valerie refuses and dances with and openly kisses Harry before her dangerously calm mother. After the ball,

Harry drives mother and daughter home. Harry and Edna have a discussion in the car, during which Edna warns that Valerie will have to be told everything about their past. Enraged, Harry strikes Edna and drives wildly off with her down the twisting lanes, screaming that he will kill her. Edna leaps out, shaken but unharmed. The car crashes, and Harry is killed.

The story ends with Harry's funeral, attended by friends, neighbors, and fellow commuters—but attended by no one who loved him.

Themes and Meanings

A brief summary of the story's plot may seem to indicate that things would have worked out fine for Harry and Valerie, that true love would have triumphed, had not old Edna insisted on getting in the way. On the contrary, a closer reading indicates that the affair was doomed from the start, doomed by the lovers' very natures.

"Death of a Huntsman" is, in fact, a variation on the ancient *senex amans* pattern of comedy, that is, an old man made foolish by love for a much younger woman. Harry and Valerie's age difference is emphasized throughout. To his fellow commuters, Harry looks a decade older than his forty-three years. Harry is surprised, on the other hand, to learn that Valerie is nearly twenty rather than the fifteen or sixteen that he takes her to be. The difference between fifteen and twenty is greater than only five years: It is—emotionally, for Harry—the difference between having an affair with a young woman and having an affair with a schoolgirl. Indeed, a feeling of unease, of things being not quite right, pervades the story from the start. Bates manipulates the reader by favoring dramatization rather than idyllic and serene scenes of love in the woodlands—moments when things go wrong, when doubt enters Harry's mind.

Indeed, the feeling of unease emanates primarily from Harry. It is he who feels that there is something "disturbing" about Valerie. Exactly what is disturbing he cannot say, but it is associated with Valerie's ridiculously long legs dangling from her pony and her husky, woman's voice appended to a girl's body. Obviously, Harry is disturbed by the age question—is she old enough, or too young?—and its thinly disguised sexual implications. The unease only increases as the story progresses, culminating at the Hunt Ball. Harry is afraid that Valerie will go to the ball dressed in her schoolgirl uniform. When she emerges wearing a very mature dress and gloves, however, his discomfort hardly abates but turns into a "turmoil of fright and indecision." Is Valerie a girl or a woman? Harry says that he will dance with her if she does not mind being stepped on—but he had almost said, "If your mother will let you." Valerie pours Harry a glass of sherry, but she herself is not allowed to drink. Most telling (or damning) of all, at their happiest moment at the ball, Valerie actually reverts to baby talk: "You're the bestest good one," she tells Harry. "The most bestest good one in the world."

That Harry should have "seen" more clearly the consequences of his folly is evident from a "sight pattern"—a motif of images denoting eyes, vision, or the lack thereof—that runs throughout the story and includes not only Harry but Edna, Katey, and Valerie as well. Harry, for example, wears thick glasses which he polishes with "scrupulous short-sightedness." The reader is assured early in the story that Katey does not see Harry very well—because of her drunkenness, overtly, but more fundamentally because she is totally insensitive to his emotional and physical needs. Valerie's eyes, on the other hand, are "too big for her face," like Harry's, connoting a similar straining to see (because of a similar short-sightedness). More telling, at almost every crucial juncture in the story, Harry's glasses fog over, blinding him—an objectification of his being blinded by passion for Valerie. The sight pattern intensifies at the ball, where Edna, with her "ice-gray microscopic" eyes, sees everything all too clearly. At the same time, Harry must continually rub away at the mist fogging his glasses, and Valerie—after declaring Harry to be the "most bestest good one in the world"—finds her eyes "drowned in tears of happiness." The happiness is only momentary. The ugly scene between Harry and Edna in the car ensues, at the climax of which Harry hits Edna with a blow that "partially blinded her" and she counters with one that breaks his glasses. Blinded, he wrecks the car and dies.

All of them were blind all along. None saw clearly enough the realities of the situation until it was too late. Bates reemphasizes the foolishness of the aging man's passion by noting the mourners at his funeral. Many of them were "very bald."

Style and Technique

The *senex amans* pattern mentioned earlier is generally a comic one; indeed, with merely a few twists of the plot "Death of a Huntsman" could have been comic. Even before the situation begins to sour, however, the reader knows that events are moving toward tragedy, not comedy, because of a rich pattern of foreshadowing—perhaps the most interesting technical feature of this otherwise simple story.

The most obvious example of foreshadowing, one that hardly warrants analysis, is the title. Subtler examples, however, follow. It is the nature of foreshadowing that any one instance taken in isolation might seem insignificant, but repeated instances affect the tone of the story and the reader's expectations. In the first scene of "Death of a Huntsman," for example, Harry's fellow commuters gleefully anticipate Harry's nightly "race with time." No special significance seems implied by the phrase at this point. (Even here, however, the thoughtful reader might ask himself, "Who ever wins, ultimately, the race against time?") When the reader is told a page later that sometimes before Harry arrived "a final door would slam with doom," the implications become much more pointed.

The most obvious example of foreshadowing involves one last fruit of a quince tree, which both Valerie and Harry take as a symbol of their love. At the climax of their happiest moment together, the quince falls with a thud. The idyllic mood is broken. Immediately thereafter, Valerie reminds Harry that tomorrow is the night of the Hunt Ball and that he must dance with her. The scene ends with Valerie humming a tune in anticipation of the dance, but for Harry, "he remembered the sound of the quince dropping into the reeds, the last vanishing phial of the summer's honey, filling his mind like an ominous echo."

In the last brutal exchange between Harry and Edna in the car, the reader realizes that "ominous" is turning to "fatal" when, to Harry, Edna's drawn face seems "skeletonized," her mouth "almost cadaverous." Ironically, it is blind, foolish Harry who is about to die.

Dennis Vannatta

DEATH OF A TRAVELING SALESMAN

Author: Eudora Welty (1909-   )
Type of plot: Psychological realism
Time of plot: The 1930's
Locale: Rural Mississippi
First published: 1936

>   *Principal characters:*
>   R. J. BOWMAN, a traveling salesman
>   SONNY, a country farmer, about thirty years old
>   A COUNTRYWOMAN

The Story

The crucial action of "Death of a Traveling Salesman" takes place in the mind of the protagonist, a shoe company representative, in the last hours of his life. Feverish and weak, R. J. Bowman has sought shelter in the home of a simple country couple. His initial misperceptions about them eventually give way to a recognition that they possess some vital knowledge about life, knowledge which he has been denied.

Bowman has been a traveling salesman for fourteen years, living alone in hotels as he drives from one city to the next with his sample case of shoes. As the story begins, he has recently recovered from a serious case of influenza, during which he was cared for by a hotel doctor and a trained nurse. Although he had believed himself to be cured, Bowman finds himself oddly tired and anxious during his first day back at work. By midday, he has lost his accustomed road, and finds to his horror that he has driven his car to the edge of a ravine. He is able to get out before the car topples over. To his surprise, the car does not crash, but is caught by a tangle of vine leaves and sinks to the ground unharmed.

As Bowman begins to walk toward the only house in view, he feels his heart beat rapidly and wildly, so much so that he has difficulty thinking or speaking. He feels better after he has entered the house and has been seated in the cool living room. He finds himself uneasy, however, with the taciturn woman of the house. She is a big woman, still and slow-moving; Bowman estimates her age to be about fifty. He is relieved when she refers to Sonny, who will be able to help him pull his car out of the ditch. In fact, Sonny is able to do so with the help of his mule. While Bowman and the woman wait for the powerful young man to complete his task, Bowman feels a surge of unaccustomed emotion. He interprets his pounding heart as a protest against the lack of love in his life, as a plea that his empty heart should be filled with love. Somehow, he imagines, these people know more than he does about the meaning of life. He wonders what secret they shelter.

Prompted both by his fascination with the life of these country people and by his own fatigue, Bowman asks if he may spend the night there. Permitted to do so, he observes more of the habits of his hosts. They obtain their fire by going to a distant neighbor and carrying back a burning stick. They make their own illegal whiskey and bury the jug in the yard. As they sit down to eat dinner, Bowman makes a startling discovery: The woman is not fifty, as he had thought, but young, the same age as Sonny; Sonny is her husband, not her son as he had supposed. Finally, the reasons for her large, shapeless body and ponderous movements becomes clear: She is pregnant. Bowman is stunned to realize that this couple's secret is simply the possession of a ful-filled marriage.

Trying to sleep before the fire later that night, he listens attentively to the many sounds of a country night. As he hears the couple breathing in the next room, he wishes that he could trade places with Sonny and be the father of the baby soon to be born. Something propels him then to leave the house and return to his car. First, however, he empties his billfold and leaves the money under a table lamp. Then, running out to the car, he feels an explo-sion in his chest; he covers his heart to muffle the loud noise that seems to be coming from within. Bowman has arrived at the moment of his death.

Themes and Meanings

This quiet story offers an indirect portrait of sickness and health in both a physical and a psychological sense. Weakened by illness, Bowman comes to recognize that his life has never been strong or whole in an emotional sense. He has never before regretted his own failure to settle down and rear a fam-ily. Now, just before his death, he learns what he has missed. Yet it is difficult to define exactly what quality of the young couple's life Bowman envies. His admiration for their existence goes beyond the simple yearning to have a child, important though that is. Even before he realizes that the woman is pregnant, Bowman is drawn by her composure and by the way she responds to Sonny's every action. For example, he senses her wordless pride while Sonny works to pull the car from the ravine and in the way she points out that Sonny had made the whiskey offered to Bowman. The quiet bond between them contrasts with his own memories of indistinguishable women and faded hotel rooms. As a salesman, Bowman has developed a line of con-versational patter that he uses with his customers. With his hosts, however, he finds it difficult to get beyond the first few words of his usual line. Their silence compels his respect.

The theme of the story depends upon the contrast between Bowman's progressively deteriorating health and the young couple's strength and pur-posefulness. Although Bowman is superficially more sophisticated and know-ledgeable than Sonny and his wife, their lives have a meaning his has been denied.

Style and Technique

"Death of a Traveling Salesman" focuses on the last hours of the protagonist, and the story's style emphasizes the psychological changes of illness. In particular, the imagery used to describe Bowman's thoughts suggests his unconscious recognition of his approaching death. As the last day of his life progresses, his mind fills with images of comfort, rest, and letting go. For example, early in the story, Bowman remembers his grandmother and wishes that "he could fall into the big feather bed that had been in her room." Soon afterward, he notices a cloud that "floated there to one side like the bolster on his grandmother's bed." When his car goes into the ravine, a tangle of grapevines catches it and "rock[s] it like a grotesque child in a dark cradle." All these images indicate Bowman's unconscious readiness for the sleep and shelter he received as a child.

These images of rocking motion and safety carry over even into Bowman's thoughts about his failing heart. When his heart begins to beat erratically, it surges powerfully and then falls "gently, like acrobats into nets" and is "as quiet as ashes falling." Bowman's entire world falls under this gentle spell; even when he drops his bags they seem to "drift in slow bulks gracefully through the air and to cushion themselves on the gray prostrate grass near the doorstep." His former impatience gives way to a calmer demeanor, and he attributes this to his illness, when he learned to submit to the ministrations of the nurse.

The calm and receptive mood that overtakes Bowman, as suggested by the examples of the earlier imagery, makes it possible for him finally to recognize his hosts for what they really are. In his initial quick judgment of the woman, he had wrongly assumed that she was old and tired. He had associated her stillness with fatigue. Yet once his own impatience is transcended, he sees that her quiet attitude stems from her pregnancy and her happy marriage.

Ironically, Bowman's perception of the couple's happiness makes him wish to return to his former vigorous life. This desire is ironic, because Bowman's life is, in fact, nearly over. When the moment of his death arrives, the images of comfort give way to harsher images: For example, "his heart began to give off tremendous explosions like a rifle, bang, bang, bang." Earlier in the story, the abruptness of his death had been hinted at by descriptions of his heart leaping "like a little colt invited out of a pen" or his pulse leaping "like a trout in a brook." These images of quick motion contrast with the images of slowness and comfort. Perhaps Bowman's death must be thought of as combining the two poles: Although it comes upon him with suddenness, he is ready for the peace it brings.

Diane M. Ross

THE DEATH OF IVAN ILYICH

Author: Leo Tolstoy (1828-1910)
Type of plot: Domestic realism
Time of plot: The 1880's
Locale: St. Petersburg and nearby provinces
First published: "Smert Ivana Ilicha," 1886 (English translation, 1887)

> *Principal characters:*
> IVAN ILYICH GOLOVIN, a Russian magistrate
> PRASKOVYA FYODOROVNA GOLOVINA, his wife
> PIOTR IVANOVICH, Ivan's nearest acquaintance and colleague
> VASYA, Ivan's son
> GERASIM, Ivan's servant

The Story

This story begins with the news of Ivan Ilyich's death reported by his closest acquaintance from law school, Piotr Ivanovich. When his coworkers hear the news, their immediate reaction is one of self-centered concern over their possible promotions and other changes that Ivan's death might bring about in their own lives. Only after these considerations do the dead man's so-called friends think of the tiresome duties of attending the funeral and consoling the widow.

Giving up his usual nap to attend the wake, Piotr, meeting his bridge partner at the widow's house, takes the time to arrange for their regular game that evening after viewing the body. Then Ivan's widow, Praskovya Fyodorovna, escorts him into a room for a private talk, in which she, too, dwells on her own concerns, telling him how much she suffered through Ivan's screaming for the three days before he died. Her main interest in speaking with Piotr, however, is to find out whether and how she might get extra money from the government because of Ivan's death. On hearing his opinion that there is nothing she can do, she loses interest in their conversation, and Piotr takes his leave.

This opening chapter (the story is divided into twelve chapters) sets Tolstoy's tone, which mixes grotesque humor with the somber reality of death coming to a respected minor functionary—an ordinary death of an ordinary man (the name Ivan Ilyich is as common in Russian as is the name John Smith in English). In describing the family's and friends' reactions to Ivan's death, the narrative concentrates on their obsession with their own lives and petty comforts and their disregard for the deceased.

The next section, chapters 2 through 5, recounts the life and career of Ivan. The second and most successful of three sons of a minor official, he had risen to the position of examining magistrate and married a proper girl as the "right thing" to do. His married life did not, however, meet his expectations: His wife turned unaccountably jealous and ill-humored, and several of his children died. Ivan retreated steadily into his work, becoming progressively more aloof at home.

Finding his only consolation in the dignity and social activities attached to the official world of the magistrate, Ivan suffered a particularly heavy blow when, despite the fact that he was held in high esteem by his colleagues, he was passed over for several prestigious appointments. His ensuing financial difficulties catapulted him into a severe depression, and Ivan resolved to seek a post that would pay him sufficiently and relieve him from a department which had ceased to appreciate his talents.

By chance, a friend was in a position to help him to a new post two stages above his former colleagues. After this promotion, Ivan's relationship with his wife and family improved, and he secured a beautiful new home and had it decorated exactly like the homes of others in similar positions. He gave typical parties to which he invited only those of the proper social position, and cultivated only the proper acquaintances, keeping his real life separate from his official life. Ivan and his family, having achieved middle-class success, were happy: "And everything went on in this way without change, and everything was very nice."

In the process of having the new house decorated, Ivan had slipped on a ladder while hanging curtains and injured his side. At first, he had made light of the injury, but his illness kept getting worse, and the family discord returned. The doctor's original nebulous diagnosis eventually changed to that of a floating kidney and vermiform appendix. Ivan finally realized it was a matter of life and death. Facing death, he came to hate his wife, and she, pitying herself for having to put up with his bad temper, reciprocated the feeling.

The final section, comprising chapters 6 through 12, recounts Ivan's suffering through his terminal illness and his contemplation of life and death. At first, Ivan accepts the truism that all mortals will die, but only as an abstraction not applicable to himself. He thinks of how terrible and stupid it is for him to lose his life for a curtain. He is irked by the deception of others who console him, saying his illness will go away. Only his faithful servant Gerasim comforts him and helps him by holding up his legs. He believes that the only other person to pity and understand him is his son Vasya. His daughter Lisa is annoyed that his illness interferes with her social life.

Ivan alternates between despair and hope and finally no longer leaves the sofa. The only joy he can recall is that from his youth, and he begins to question whether his life might somehow have been wrong. He finally sees clearly that he has lived a life of self-deception, evading the meaning of life and death. He confesses his sins to a priest and takes communion.

Ivan's last three days are spent in agony. He screams as he feels himself thrust into a dark hole. He clings to the belief that his life has been good, and this belief seems to hold him back. At the moment that his son kisses his hand, Ivan falls through and sees the light; he realizes that, though his life has not been what it should have been, it can still be rectified. He pities his wife and the others and loses his fear of death. Then, as he looks for his former fear of death, he finds instead light and joy. His suffering continues for two more hours, and he dies

Themes and Meanings

As the title indicates, Tolstoy's story concentrates on the death of a very ordinary middle-class person. The second chapter opens with the sentence, "Ivan Ilyich's life had been most simple and most ordinary and therefore most terrible," which has been called one of the most frightening sentences in all literature. Ivan's life has been lived according to those middle-class values set by his society. Ivan has always done the correct thing to achieve success; while in school, he did things which disgusted him until he noticed that those in good positions did the same things and did not consider them wrong.

In working at his career, he is punctilious, reserved, completely honest; when he has affairs, they are with women of the best society. He marries, not really for love but because this is what society expects him to do. Everything Ivan does is according to what one should do to rise in society; his values are material values exemplified by his remodeling his house to look exactly like the homes of others in his social position. His relations with people have the semblance of friendliness, but he never develops any close or deep relationships.

It is not until his fatal illness that Ivan ever questions his values and his life. Even the cause of his illness—a freak accident that occurred as he was hanging curtains—is insignificant. Ivan comes to the realization that his life has been wasted. It is only with his death that he comes to a joyful revelation that, though his life had been wrong, it can still be rectified. He dies at peace with himself and the world.

Style and Technique

Tolstoy's first draft of this story was written in the first-person point of view with Ivan interpreting the events. Probably because of the importance of the theme of the story, Tolstoy later changed to an omniscient point of view, which more clearly shows the attitudes of the other characters toward Ivan's death. In the opening section, Tolstoy emphasizes the others' lack of concern over their friend's death. In describing Piotr's interview with Praskovya Fyodorovna, he concentrates on the little details of her shawl catching on the end of the table and Piotr's discomfiture in sitting on a pouf with broken springs, showing their distractions from the important event of Ivan's death. He thus prepares the reader for the simple, ordinary, and "most terrible" life that Ivan led, as is described in the second section of the story.

The second section is simply a prelude to the climactic death throes of the third part. Ivan's life is detailed in a straightforward narrative emphasizing his aloofness both with his family and official associates, and, one might say, with his own feelings. All of his attitudes and values seem to come from without, from what society considers the proper thing to do.

Fully half the chapters of the story are devoted to the fatal illness and Ivan's reactions to his family, friends, and doctors, as they all come to the realization that there is nothing they can do for him and that he is fatally ill. Here, too, Tolstoy describes the alternating feelings of home and despair that Ivan experiences and the exasperation of his acquaintances with his annoying behavior. The doctors' treatments are described as perfunctory after they realize that there is nothing they can do; they prefer not to understand his questions. His daughter, dressed in evening clothes, becomes impatient with his illness and resents that he causes her feelings of guilt as she attends the theater. Praskovya Fyodorovna asks after his health not to learn about it but because it is expected of her. Everyone comes to resent him for reminding them of their own mortality.

In the last section, Tolstoy turns to giving Ivan's reactions to his illness, to describing his feelings and his questioning of the meaning of life and death. In this way, he emphasizes the epiphany which Ivan experiences at the moment of death.

Roger Geimer

DE DAUMIER-SMITH'S BLUE PERIOD

Author: J. D. Salinger (1919-   )
Type of plot: Psychological realism
Time of plot: 1939
Locale: New York City and Montreal, Canada
First published: 1952

> *Principal characters:*
> ROBERT (BOBBY) AGADGANIAN, JR., the narrator's stepfather
> DE DAUMIER-SMITH, the narrator and protagonist, an aspiring
>   art instructor and aesthete
> YOSHOTO, the director of Les Amis De Vieux Maitres
>   correspondence art school, the protagonist's employer

The Story

The essential plot is a memoir of events recalled by the narrator in the year 1952. The narrator indicates in the initial paragraph that he wants to dedicate the following autobiographical account "to the memory" of his "ribald" stepfather, the late "Bobby" Agadganian, who married his mother after her divorce from his father in 1920.

After the Wall Street crash, Agadganian ceased being a stockbroker and took up a new occupation as agent-appraiser for a group of independent American art galleries. This necessitated, in 1930, a family move to Paris. Thus, the narrator had lived for more than nine years in Paris when he moved back to New York with his stepfather in the spring of 1939.

The cultural and social feelings of dislocation are considerable for this bright, bilingual nineteen-year-old boy as he attempts to come to terms with rude bus conductors, New York crowds, and art instruction at a school that he "loathes." In his spare time, he draws countless self-portraits in oils. The rapport between the narrator and his stepfather begins to deteriorate as they are "both in love with the same deceased woman" and both living in the cramped space of the same New York hotel room.

The narrator, after enduring life with Bobby for ten months in the Ritz Hotel, answers an ad in a Montreal paper for an instructor at a correspondence art school. Bilingual instructors are apparently being hired to coincide with the opening of the June summer session.

"Instantly, feeling almost unsupportably qualified," the young aspirant applies, enclosing examples of both academic and commercial art work ("lean, erect, super-chic couples" in evening clothes and "laughing, high-breasted girls"). He falsifies most of the biographical information in his personal and career resumé, pretending to be related to the French painter Honoré Daumier and feigning a close friendship with Pablo Picasso. His application accepted, "De Daumier-Smith" prepares to entrain for Montreal and informs Bobby and Bobby's girlfriend at dinner in the hotel dining room. De Daumier-Smith imagines that Bobby's companion is attempting to seduce him; actually she seems intent only on piercing his almost impenetrable egoism.

Self-consciously overdressed (gabardine suit, navy-blue shirt and yellow tie, brown-and-white shoes), De Daumier-Smith arrives in Montreal and is met by school director Yoshoto, whom he describes as "inscrutable." The school itself occupies the second floor of a run-down building in the slums of Montreal.

The rest of De Daumier-Smith's account relates the events of 1939 at the art school, Les Amis Des Vieux Maitres, in the succeeding months.

The narrator chronicles his problems with the director and his wife, Madame Yoshoto, who apparently is the only other instructor. He cannot find an ashtray; he is kept awake by the moaning of the sleeping Yoshotos; he is unaccustomed to the Japanese cooking, which disagrees with him, as does the banality of his duties, which are for the most part merely routine translation.

Finally, he is assigned three students, but two of them appear to be without much talent. Only the third student is promising and inspires De Daumier-Smith to initiate an animated correspondence. His excitement over the work of Sister Irma, a talented nun who lives in a convent near Toronto, prompts him to write to her, suggesting a possible visit. He also writes letters to the others, discouraging them from continuing to pursue a career as artists. Unfortunately, the mother superior writes that Sister Irma can no longer continue the course, and De Daumier-Smith, crushed, goes to a fashionable restaurant for a solitary meal to assuage his depressed thoughts.

Returning toward the school on foot and at twilight, De Daumier-Smith notices a light in the display window of the orthopedic appliances shop on the ground floor. Earlier, he described himself as doomed to live his life as "a visitor in a garden of enamel urinals and bedpans with a sightless wooden dummy-deity standing by in a marked-down rupture truss." There is a well-built girl among the surgical hardware, changing the window display. Her confusion at the sight of De Daumier-Smith in his dinner jacket, watching her, causes her to fall as he tries to reach through the glass window to avert her fall. These actions, in turn, trigger a mystical experience, and the narrator is conscious of a brilliant light traveling toward him and the transformation of the surgical display into a field of "shimmering . . . exquisite, twice-blessed enamel flowers."

Liberated by his experience ("a borderline case of genuine mysticism"), De Daumier-Smith walks back to his room, rests, and then writes letters to the students he has dismissed, reinstating them.

In a postscript, De Daumier-Smith reveals that the school survived only a week more and that he joined his father briefly in Rhode Island before returning to art school. In a whimsical final statement, he reveals that he had no further correspondence with Sister Irma but that another student, Bambi Kramer, had later turned her talents to designing her own Christmas cards. ("They'll be something to see, if she hasn't lost her touch.")

Themes and Meanings

Salinger's early stories, which appeared first in *The New Yorker* and were later collected under the title *Nine Stories* (1953), all concern children or adolescents. Salinger seems to believe (with William Wordsworth) that the young are the true visionaries of society and that their consciences are untainted and unencumbered with the hypocrisy and evasions that are common to the daily activities of the adult world. Salinger's stories also emphasize the quest for meaning and for an understanding of existence characterized by Zen Buddhism and the approach to Satori (oneness with all things, enlightenment, and ultimate acceptance and awareness of self). Salinger's characters are often self-deprecating but nearly always self-analytical as well. They typify a type of behavior, popular following World War II, of disengagement and disaffection, a refusal to participate fully in the adult social apparatus but a less than complete withdrawal from these habits as well. The involved yet uninvolved upper-middle-class teenager of the 1950's can be seen to perfection in the character of Salinger's most famous adolescent, Holden Caulfield, the hero of *The Catcher in the Rye* (1951).

Certain characteristics of De Daumier-Smith's reminiscence are symbolically suggested by the title, which refers to a period in the artistic development of the contemporary painter Pablo Picasso (1881-1973), whose "Blue Period" (1901-1904) was largely concerned with portraits of unhappy outcasts who were impoverished and lonely. Salinger draws a parallel with the unhappiness of his protagonist and his "blue" mood during the period of his late adolescence as chronicled in the story.

The narrator is also a student of Buddhism, a fact revealed on his first day in Montreal, when the Yoshotos claim to be Presbyterians. Thus, the mystical experience that causes De Daumier-Smith to see the surgical appliances in the store window transformed into brilliant, enamel-like flowers has been foreshadowed in the earlier text.

The cause of De Daumier-Smith's epiphany is the bond which the young artist feels with the nun, his student. The picture of "Christ being carried to the sepulchre" touches him (especially the woman signaling in the foreground to the viewer). He seeks a kindred spirit, and he acknowledges that Sister Irma is "greatly talented." He reaches out in his correspondence to place himself "entirely at [her] disposal." Sister Irma, or the presentiment of her presence, breaks the spell of the narrator's isolation and hypocrisy. Suddenly he sees himself as a Pierre Abelard, the romantic lover of Héloise, whose affair also ended in a famous correspondence and a tragic separation.

Later, De Daumier-Smith experiences at least partial enlightenment and true self-knowledge when the window of surgical appliances formerly presided over by a "dummy-deity" becomes a garden of light and color, no longer representative of emptiness in a mechanical, unfeeling world but rather of the power of empathy. Thus, finally the narrator realizes that "everybody is a nun" in his search for meaning and his capacity for understanding, even love. All petty distinctions are swept away, and even the untalented Bambi Kramer is forgiven as De Daumier-Smith attains Buddha-like acceptance and awareness.

Style and Technique

The method of narration is typical of Salinger's ironic tone. In another story, Salinger uses the phrase "the wise child." His stories are frequently concerned with intelligent, even brilliant, young people who point out some lesson to their elders, many of whom do not profit from the experience. De Daumier-Smith never reveals his legal name, but he reveals much else through his articulate comments, his mature vocabulary, and his sensitive observation of those around him.

De Daumier-Smith, the narrator, uses phrases such as "feeling almost unsupportably qualified" to describe himself at one point. Yet a few paragraphs later, he says that he used "all my spare time plus some that didn't quite belong to me," indicating a certain insecurity. Salinger's adolescent tends to "reiterate earlier lies" while reinforcing the dramatic irony of his situation as the plot develops. The reader is aware of the narrator's inadequacies as a result of the narrator's totally candid revelations about himself while presenting an opaque façade to the rest of the world—his "armor." The narrative is mainly chronological in its relation of the events of several months in 1939. Slight shifts or gaps in this sequence are indicated by double spaces between paragraphs.

The irony of the hero's situation is constantly underlined by the author with the use of words whose connotations are unmistakable and frequently amusing. A "highly unendowed-looking building" describes De Daumier-Smith's first view of his art academy. The "Harvard Senior" represents De Daumier-Smith's stepfather in his relation to the narrator, who is "a Cambridge Newsboy." Salinger also uses anticlimax ("Her eyes sparkled with depravity") for comic effect.

Thus, the tone of the story is lightly ironic and combines a self-deprecating narrative with the more serious aspects of character development and theme. As with many of Salinger's short stories and in spite of the considerable length of the narrative, the falling action is minimal and consists of a short epilogue of only two short paragraphs.

F. A. Couch, Jr.

DEFENDER OF THE FAITH

Author: Philip Roth (1933-   )
Type of plot: Social realism
Time of plot: Between May, 1945, and August, 1945
Locale: Camp Crowder, Missouri
First published: 1959

> *Principal characters:*
> SERGEANT NATHAN MARX, the top sergeant of a basic training
>   company at Camp Crowder, Missouri
> CAPTAIN PAUL BARRETT, the company commander
> PRIVATE SHELDON GROSSBART,
> PRIVATE LARRY FISHBEIN, and
> PRIVATE MICKEY HALPERN, trainees

The Story

Sergeant Nathan Marx, a veteran of combat in the European theater, is rotated back to the United States and assigned as top sergeant to a training company in Camp Crowder, Missouri. He soon becomes acquainted with a trainee, Sheldon Grossbart, who appeals to their common Jewish heritage as the rationale for granting him and the two Jewish fellow-draftees whom he dominates, Fishbein and Halpern, a succession of special favors. Grossbart cunningly uses their shared roots in the New York Jewish community to exploit Marx's humaneness, generosity, and sense of fairness. Their relationship is characterized by deviousness and self-serving opportunism on Grossbart's part, while Marx changes from open vulnerability to wariness to righteous indignation at Grossbart's increasingly outrageous conduct.

The first episode revealing their conflict occurs when Grossbart wants Marx's permission to attend Jewish services Friday night yet does not wish to give Gentile recruits the impression that he is ducking the customary "G.I. Party," or barracks cleaning. He insists, "this is a matter of *religion*, sir," deliberately using the salutation reserved for officers despite Marx's continuing reminder to address him as "Sergeant." At the synagogue Marx observes, from a back-row seat, Grossbart and Fishbein playfully pouring the contents of the sacramental wine to and from each other's cups, while their prayer books remain closed—until they notice his presence.

Army food becomes an issue for intrigue. Although Grossbart has a lusty appetite for it, he composes a letter for his father to sign and send to his congressman, complaining that his son is forced to eat nonkosher meals that Orthodox Judaism forbids. After Marx has been forced to explain Jewish tradition to his irate captain, Captain Barrett contrasts Grossbart's "goldbricking" to Marx's valor under fire: "Do you hear him [Marx] peeping about the food? Do you?" Formidably flexible, Grossbart writes another letter for his father's signature, addressed to the general who is the post commander, praising Marx as being "in part responsible for Sheldon's changing his mind about the dietary laws" and calling the sergeant "a credit to the U.S. Army and the Jewish people."

For a time, Grossbart eschews scrambling for special privileges. Then he confronts Marx with a request for a weekend pass to celebrate Passover with St. Louis relatives. At first Marx is firm: "No passes during basic, Grossbart." Grossbart, however, weeps and wears down Marx's defenses. After Marx has issued weekend passes not only to Grossbart but also to Fishbein and Halpern, he muses to himself, "Who was I to have been feeling so grudging, so tight-hearted? After all, I wasn't being asked to move the world." Marx soon discovers, however, that Grossbart and his friends never did attend the Passover dinner—they enjoyed a Chinese meal instead. Brazenly, Grossbart even presents Marx with an egg roll as a souvenir of the occasion.

The egg roll proves the last straw for Marx's tolerance. He now becomes Grossbart's enraged enemy. When he discovers that Grossbart is the only company recruit who will be assigned to a safe, stateside station at Fort Monmouth, New Jersey, while all the others are to be shipped to the Pacific combat zone, he smells connivance and goes into counteraction. This time, he pulls strings of his own, phoning the sergeant in charge of cutting orders to ask him for a favor: Marx tells him that a Jewish trainee in his company is burning to see action, having had a brother killed in Europe. Could Sergeant Wright therefore change one Monmouth order to the Pacific? Sergeant Wright can, and does.

Themes and Meanings

This is a complex, powerfully imagined tale portraying a conflict of loyalties and delineating the difficulty of being a decent and fair-minded person in a world beset with opposing priorities.

For Grossbart, Jewishness has no devotional or ritualistic substance. He is a cleverly conniving barracks lawyer who poses as a defender of the Jewish faith to manipulate Marx and other authority figures into granting him undeserved privileges. He articulates litanies of whining and wheedling, flattery and hypocrisy—all in a consuming desire for special treatment.

Marx's character is deeply layered: He wants to be a good person, a good soldier, and a good Jew—in that order. As a human being, he is at first vulnerable to Grossbart's performance as the victim in danger of having his rights crushed by the dehumanizing institution that the army often is. Yet as a soldier, he wants to treat his trainees equitably and humanely, balancing obedience to military regulations with empathy for the loneliness and confusion of young men uprooted from their families in wartime. As a Jew he has a particularly thorny dilemma: how to observe his tradition yet also fulfill his military duties; how to avoid the sentimental claims of Jewish solidarity when they contradict the ethical mandate for justice and equity; how to be strong without bullying; how to be compassionate without showing weakness.

Philip Roth concludes the story with a twist: Grossbart accepts his fate, to be treated no differently from his comrades, while Marx accepts his own fate after "resisting with all my will an impulse to turn and seek pardon for my vindictiveness." Thus, Roth stresses the existential nature of the protagonist's moral anguish: Marx finds training camp a far trickier moral terrain than the battlefield. He discovers that the best—for him, the only possible—way of defending the faith of Jews is to defend the faith of all recruits in the cause of a just community, to watch out not for one individual, but "for all of us."

Style and Technique

Roth's style is brisk, pointed, compact, and morally lucid. He masters with unobtrusive authority the sharply observed details of characteristic gestures, such as Grossbart sitting on the edge of Marx's desk the first time he approaches him, and then, on being ordered to stand on his feet, slipping up to the corner of the desk—"not quite sitting, but not quite standing, either." Then there is Fishbein, "his long yellow face a dying light bulb" while "his eyelids beat a tattoo." Captain Barrett is observed by Marx: " . . . his helmet liner squashed down so far on his head that I couldn't even see his eyes."

Roth's ear is even better than his eye. Grossbart and Marx duel in a vernacular charged with caustic, incisive urban idioms stripped to their starkest rhythms. "I owe nobody nothing," Grossbart shouts in their climactic scene. "I've got the right to watch out for myself."

Replies Marx, "For each other we have to learn to watch out, Sheldon."

Ironies pervade the story. The title phrase, "Defender of the Faith," mockingly alludes to a traditional obligation of English monarchs. More directly, it refers to the role of religious champion that Marx finds himself filling, no matter how unintentionally. Not only does Sergeant Marx defend the honor of his own heritage by rejecting Grossbart's advantage mongering, but also he can succeed in restoring the balance of the scales of justice only by using Grossbart's exploitive skills against him. In lying to Sergeant Wright regarding Grossbart's thirst for combat, Marx has to "pull a Grossbart," has to usurp Grossbart's identity as an unprincipled manipulator. For once, Roth indicates, a worthy end does justify unworthy means.

Gerhard Brand

THE DELICATE PREY

Author: Paul Bowles (1911-   )
Type of plot: Grotesque realism
Time of plot: Early twentieth century
Locale: Mauretania (North Africa)
First published: 1950

> *Principal characters:*
> Two FILALA TRIBESMEN, merchants and brothers
> DRISS, their young nephew
> A MOUNGARI TRIBESMAN
> ECH CHIBANI, a Filali

The Story

"The Delicate Prey" is the narrative of a journey through isolated places and hidden terrors. Three Filala tribesmen and leather merchants are about to move their business to a new town. Two are brothers—serious, older men. Driss, their nephew, is a young man interested in the pleasures of love.

To arrive at their destination, Tessalit, as soon as possible, the brothers choose a route through a remote and dangerous region. The area is prey to the marauding Reguibat tribe, known for its ferocity. An insignificant company of three men and their camels, so the brothers argue, offers no temptation to raiders seeking rich caravans. Still, they travel carefully, maintaining close watch at night.

Several days out, the travelers spot a lone figure moving toward them, matching his course with theirs. As the figure approaches, he hails them in friendship. The brothers are relieved to see that he is not dressed as a Reguibat, but observe him carefully for any irregularity. Driss is troubled by the man's small eyes that "give out nothing," but is dissuaded from his suspicion by his uncles' reaction. The man identifies himself as a Moungari, a respected tribe from a holy area. The stranger offers his skills as a hunter if allowed to join the group. Skeptical about finding game in these remote regions, the brothers accept him to increase their numbers in the dangerous environment.

One morning the Moungari goes off alone, on foot, to hunt gazelle among the hills. As distant shots are heard, first one brother, then the next, goes off to join the hunt. Driss is left alone, disappointed, to watch the camp. He dozes in the heat but is suddenly awakened. He feels an evil presence about him. Immediately he recognizes the danger he saw in the man's eyes and knows the fate of his uncles. Seeking safety in the open desert, he mounts his camel and sets off blindly. He lets himself be carried along, without purpose, for several hours before he stops and heads for camp. What if he is only foolish and his uncles are cooking the gazelle even now? He cannot bear the thought of the older men's mocking laughter.

As Driss approaches camp, a bullet whizzes by his head. A second catches him in the arm. Before he finds shelter among the rocks and grabs his fallen gun, the Moungari is upon him, pinning him down with a rifle. There is a new, peculiar intensity in the man's face that Driss knows only comes from hashish. The man quickly strips the boy, using a razor to cut away his robes, and binds his wrists and hands. Possessed by the excitement of the drug, the Moungari in one stroke severs Driss's sex.

Startled by a camel's grunt, the Moungari wheels about, nervous. He imagines the boy, who can see nothing in his pain, a witness to his fright. There is one last indignity he can inflict upon the boy, this time with leisurely pleasure. In the morning, he stifles the boy's moans by severing his head.

Once the body is concealed, the Moungari sets off for Tessalit, where he attempts to sell the Filala merchandise. Filala leather is unmistakable and sold by no other tribe. Ech Chibani, a local Filali, is suspicious, and persuades the French commandant to question the man. As the French leave, the Moungari remains sitting, unaware that he has been tried and sentenced.

Justice, however, is left to the Filala tribe. The tribesmen return, and, above his screams of innocence, they bind the Moungari. They wait calmly for night, drinking tea, before setting out into the desert. They place the Moungari, tightly trussed, into a deep pit and fill it in until only his bald head is visible. There the Moungari waits for day, for the inevitable heat and thirst, and finally for the visions; he will lose hold on reality and his sense of self, and die.

Themes and Meanings

In "The Delicate Prey," the harsh surroundings match the harsh realities of tribal jealousies and loyalties upon which Bowles bases his stories. The route the brothers take exists, as do each of the tribes with their hostilities toward one another. The loyalty of Ech Chibani to his tribesmen reflects an ancient and efficient mode of justice in which responsibility rests with the family, not with a state. The French do not interfere with traditions centuries old but let the Filala handle what is a family matter.

Another strong tradition is the fundamental sacredness of property. Each man must respect the property of others and the bond of trust crucial to survival in harsh environments. The uncles understand this and comment on the trust the Moungari shows in going off alone. In this case, that sacred trust is used perversely to trick the old men. The Moungari flaunts his villainy, however, and seals his fate by trying to sell property that belongs to others.

Bowles plays with complex relationships between the hunter and the prey. The gazelle is surely a delicate prey. By pursuing this imaginary game, however, the uncles are drawn into the trap prepared by the Moungari. More frightening is Driss's transformation into the delicate prey. Caught by his hunter, he is bound hand and foot. He is brutally dressed by the Moungari as any hunter might dress a carcass. Yet the hunter himself cannot escape becoming the prey as the Filala seek revenge. He, like Driss, is trussed and left to his fate in the desert. There is a precarious balance between the hunter and his prey, one that is easily disturbed.

Of all the characters in the story, Driss is the only one depicted in any detail. He is a young man who lives in his dreams and fails to trust his understanding of the world around him. He daydreams of love and the easy favors of the town beauties. As his uncles are being murdered, he is dreaming of the excitement of the hunt and the glory he is missing. He lets himself be readily convinced by his uncles' perceptions about the stranger even though his immediate reaction is distrust. Even when he acknowledges the danger and knows the truth, he lets himself again be persuaded by his imaginings of mocking laughter. For this reluctance to trust his intuition, Driss loses his life.

"The Delicate Prey" reflects Bowles's conviction that human civilization is fragile. Stripped of his superficial civility, man is a cruel animal capable of horrifying brutality. Hashish releases the Moungari's savage nature. No drug is needed for the rest of society. The veneer of modern civilization is thin, while the ancient traditions of blood revenge are strong and easily tapped. With a quick wink, the French commandant breaks that veneer and hands the Moungari over to an ancient justice, gruesome but swift.

Style and Technique

The story is marked by a muted, direct style that lets the action remain sharply in focus. There is little characterization, and the scenes are drawn with little description. There is a great economy of language as the author focuses on their events and their consequences without commentary. Bowles captures the exotic nature of his setting by using French and Arabic words: *hanoute, hammada, aoudad, mehari, mechoui, quartier reserve*. The author provides no explanations and lets the context of his words supply the meaning.

Bowles carefully weaves the motif of music throughout the work to create relationships between characters and events. Driss often plays a small flute on his watches; he prefers sad songs for the desert, regarding livelier tunes suitable only for the joys of town. He is destined never to hear brighter tunes again. The second uncle goes off to his death singing of "date palms and hidden smiles." As he waits alone at camp, Driss is too restless to play. As he approaches the camp after his flight, he hears singing, too indistinct to be recognized but immediately perceived as that of the Moungari. The last song is reserved for the Moungari. As he loses his mind in the punishing heat of the desert, the dust blows along the ground "into his mouth as he sang."

A smaller motif is that of tea. When the travelers first accept the stranger into their group, they make tea to seal their friendship. The Moungari, who violates this sign of trust and hospitality by his brutal actions, finds himself trapped by the Filala as he makes tea. As he lies trussed in a corner, the avenging tribesmen sit quietly and drink the tea which the Moungari has brewed.

Joan A. Robertson

DELTA AUTUMN

Author: William Faulkner (1897-1962)
Type of plot: Realism
Time of plot: November, 1940
Locale: Mississippi
First published: 1942

Principal characters:
ISAAC MCCASLIN, the central consciousness of the story
ROTH EDMONDS, Isaac's kinsman and owner of the plantation
Isaac relinquished
THE NEGRESS, Roth's lover and a distant relative

The Story

The story is set on the eve of the 1940 presidential election. As Isaac McCaslin and his fellow hunters drive the two hundred miles it takes to get to the wilderness, he reflects upon his sixty years of hunting and of how the land has been radically changed by human habitation. His life seems to draw inward as the wilderness itself draws inward in retreat from human progress.

The first half of the story is told almost exclusively from Isaac's point of view. He seems noble, selfless, and magnanimous—even in the face of the fact that his beloved wilderness has been virtually destroyed. The other hunters, especially Roth, are extremely cynical about the present. Roth, who is in a foul temper over an affair that is ending badly, taunts Isaac and tries to get him to say that better men hunted the land in the old days. Isaac, however, is serene in his faith in man, that man is only a little better than his circumstances usually allow him to be.

Isaac's values have, in fact, isolated him. While the hunters respect him for his bond with nature, he is as outmoded as the wilderness with which he seems to be coeval. This becomes apparent when he has trouble keeping up with the conversation in which one of the hunters, Legate, taunts Roth about the "doe," the woman he has been seeing during their hunting trips. Roth seems disgusted with the whole human race, not only with Legate's barbs, when he scorns Isaac's romantic view of the congress between men and women as close to God-like. "Then there are some Gods in this world I wouldn't want to touch, and with a damn long stick," he retorts.

The point of Roth's remarks is apparent in the second half of the story. The men have left for the first day's hunting. In the past few years, Isaac has not joined them immediately, and Roth, taking advantage of Isaac's position, asks him to give an envelope to a woman who may visit the camp. Isaac chides Roth for not having the courage to face the woman himself. When she arrives, Isaac is hard with her. In spite of his criticism of Roth, he is sure the woman has been given ample warning. Indeed, she admits Roth has been true to his "code."

As the woman begins to explain about her family, about her mother taking in washing, Isaac suddenly realizes that she is a "nigger." The harshness of the word, especially after his eloquent evocation of the wilderness and of the love between men and women, is shocking. He, in turn, is shocked to learn not only that the woman is a "Negress" but also that she is related to his family.

Suddenly a flood of details about the woman, details he has observed but not registered, make him realize that an unsuspecting Roth has loved a woman who is the descendant of a black woman by whom his grandfather had a son he would not acknowledge. Isaac compounds this family sin by advising the woman to go North, to marry a man of her race. In a frenzy of condemnation, Isaac thinks of "*this land which man has deswamped and denuded and derivered in two generations so that white men can own plantations and commute every night to Memphis and black men own plantations and ride in jim crow cars to Chicago to live in millionaires' mansions on Lakeshore Drive. . . .*" Isaac has preserved for himself a kind of purity in his reverence for the wilderness, and his isolation has kept him from the messiness of affairs such as Roth's, but his noble repudiation of plantation immorality has also led to his misunderstanding the modern world of which Roth, at least, is a part.

To the baby boy the woman has had by Roth, Isaac offers, as a weak reconciling gesture, a hunting horn, the symbol of all the good he has learned in his years in the wilderness. At the very end of the story, hearing that a deer has been killed, Isaac says to himself that it is the very doe, the principle of womanhood that he defended against Roth's bitterness but that he himself has defiled in his confrontation with the "Negress."

Themes and Meanings

The beautiful writing and themes of "Delta Autumn" remain intact when it is read alone, but the story's larger significance and resonance can be understood only by situating it within the context of *Go Down, Moses* (1942), the novel for which it was written. Like much of the novel, the story centers on the character of Isaac McCaslin, a veteran hunter who reveres the wilderness, deplores the civilization which is destroying it, and refuses to own or to run the plantation that his forebears helped to build with slavery.

Written on the verge of America's entry into World War II, "Delta Autumn" explores in the context of a hunting story a country that has gone through momentous changes in the twentieth century and is uncertain of the extent to which its founders' values remain relevant. Isaac and the hunters debate Roth's fierce attack on the degradation of the times. Dictators will prevail in a country where men sing "God Bless America in bars at midnight" and wear dime-store flags in their lapels, Roth predicts. Unemployment, welfare, and the centralization of government are all deplored and debated.

This complicated political world is juxtaposed against the grandeur and purity of the wilderness. Very appealing images of nature make human corruption even more intolerable. Yet the narrator make clear that to hold to a vanishing wilderness is to become caught in the rigidity which Isaac reveals at the end of the story.

In this respect, the "Negress" is a striking figure, for with her Northern pronunciation and educated manner she ought to scorn Roth's code and Isaac's antique ethics. Although she does criticize both men, she feels great tenderness for them—after all, they are her kin even if they do not know enough to accept her. She is steadfastly loyal to her love for Roth and will not deny her roots in the very shame that led her father, James Beauchamp, to leave the McCaslin-Edmonds plantation.

The "Negress" is the best evidence in the story that times indeed have changed, changed more than Isaac or Roth have realized. She is the only character in the story to reconcile herself to the past and the present, to Roth's "code" and to her own sense of family and of the love that a man and woman should have for each other. By failing to make the transition to the present, and to see no more than its corrupt aspects, Isaac has rejected his own family, a part of himself.

Style and Technique

The language of this story brilliantly captures the realities that divide the characters from one another. In long, nearly hypnotic sentences, the reader is carried by the flow of memory into the past while never losing sight of the present. A single sentence, for example, begins by describing a car and two trucks forming a caravan on a gravel road, "lurching and splashing and sliding among the ruts," and by its very rhythm shifts to the cadence, the "retrograde of his [Isaac's] remembering," so that the road, in his mind, gives over to "the ancient pathway of bear and deer. . . ." Such sentences, in other words, mimic the action of Isaac's consciousness, which constantly moves from present to past.

Clipped dialogue and short scenes among the hunters efficiently provide the context in which Isaac's reveries take place, and the final dialogue with the "Negress" shows the consequences of his absenting himself from worldly affairs. This kind of technique forces the reader to reevaluate Roth's harshness and Isaac's seemingly saintly behavior. Each man denies vital parts of himself and of reality. Roth has meant the hunting trip to be his last one, and Isaac has reneged on similar decisions in years past. That both men return to the hunting grounds in spite of knowing that the world of the hunters is now defunct is a sure sign of their inability to come up with a set of values that might bridge past and present.

Carl E. Rollyson, Jr.

THE DELUGE AT NORDERNEY

Author: Isak Dinesen (Baroness Karen Blixen-Finecke, 1885-1962)
Type of plot: Psychological fantasy
Time of plot: 1835
Locale: Norderney, a bath on the west coast of Holstein, a duchy of Denmark
First published: 1934

>
> *Principal characters:*
> CARDINAL HAMILCAR VON SEHESTEDT, a seventy-three-year-
> old divine
> KASPARSON, his valet or secretary
> MISS MALIN NAT-OG-DAG, a wealthy and aristocratic maiden
> lady close to sixty years of age
> COUNTESS CALYPSO VON PLATEN HALLERMUND, her sixteen-
> year-old companion
> JONATHAN MAERSK, a melancholic young man among the
> survivors at Norderney

The Story

The storyteller, looking back from the twentieth century, sets her tale before the backdrop of Romantically influenced early nineteenth century European culture. Fashionable society, in search of desolate scenery, moved its resorts to such areas as the wild seacoast of what was then a part of Denmark. In late summer of 1835, a terrible storm churned the sea, causing it to rise and break the dikes. Disastrous flooding ensued.

Cardinal Hamilcar von Sehestedt had been living for the summer in a small cottage near the bath at Norderney; there he was collecting his writings into a book on the Holy Ghost. Of an old and distinguished family, the cardinal was famous throughout Europe for his insight and compassion. He had traveled throughout the world and wielded great influence over all he met; he was credited with the power to work miracles. His only companion in the cottage that summer was Kasparson, his valet or secretary, a former actor who had known various adventures and who spoke several languages and read widely.

During the flood, the cardinal's cottage was destroyed. Kasparson was killed; the cardinal was wounded and wore a bloody bandage around his head during his rescue work. Despite his wound, the cardinal labored steadily all through the day of the flood to rescue survivors. Late in the day, he traveled to the bath to retrieve a group of visitors for whom there had been no room in the earlier boat. As the party returned with him to safety, they passed a castaway farm family unable to escape the rising water; because the boat would not hold the additional load, the group was forced to decide who would remain behind to wait for a returning rescue barge. The cardinal, affirming his safety in God's hands, announced that he would stay. Not to be outdone, the eccentric Miss Malin Nat-og-Dag determined to stay also; her companion, Countess Calypso von Platen Hallermund, would not leave without her. Young Jonathan Maersk roused himself to action and agreed to stay with them. The four survivors found refuge in the hayloft of a flooded farmhouse and settled in to wait for rescue or death.

The storyteller has set the stage, and the drama begins. Once closed inside the loft, the four establish the terms of their coexistence. The cardinal asks Miss Malin to act as hostess and treat the loft as her salon. The company dines on bread; the two older people drink from a keg of gin.

At this point, the storyteller offers an account of Miss Malin's life. She is and has long been a somewhat fanatic virgin. Earlier in life, she selected a prince to marry, but when he died before their wedding, she renounced the idea of marriage. At the age of fifty she came into a large fortune and then passed into a kind of madness, a condition in which she remains.

Following this narrative interlude, the action in the loft resumes as the cardinal proposes that each of those present reveal himself to the company by telling his story. Maersk goes first, calling his tale "The Story of Timon of Assens." His story concerns his learning that he is the illegitimate son of a nobleman. Upon learning of his birth, he became, unwittingly, a man of fashion; everything he did became further proof of his noble breeding.

As he concludes his tale, Miss Malin realizes that she must have him as a husband for Calypso. In pursuit of this end, she recounts the girl's story in a fantastic style more full of glamour and strangeness than Maersk's tale. Calypso was reared by her misogynistic uncle, the poet Count Seraphina. She decided to unsex herself in order to fit into the count's environment, but at the moment she prepared to do so, she came to her senses and escaped to the protection of her godmother, Miss Malin.

At the conclusion of her tale, Miss Malin has the cardinal marry Calypso and Maersk with a ritual suited to what will be a purely spiritual union. In their present state in the loft, a state which may end only in death, they have no need of procreation.

Following the ceremony, Miss Malin and the cardinal discuss matters theological and political. Miss Malin asks the cardinal if he believes in the fall of man; he answers that he believes instead that man serves a fallen divinity. Then, to illustrate that there exists something worse than eternal damnation, he offers to contribute to the evening's entertainment by telling a story which he calls "The Wine of the Tetrarch." The story recounts an encounter between the apostle Peter and a troubled stranger on the first Wednesday after Easter. The stranger, after identifying Peter as one of Jesus' disciples, tells the apostle a curious story of his recent participation in the theft of some valuable wine. Caught in the course of his crime, he was arrested, but now he is free. All wine now tastes bitter to him. He reveals himself to be Barabbas and claims that his name will be remembered.

After concluding his tale in the early hours before dawn, the cardinal reveals himself to be Kasparson; he struck and killed the cardinal early the previous morning. His revelation seems to negate the value of all he has said before, but Kasparson reestablishes himself as a figure of dignity, a creator of a great role; he has become the cardinal and appropriated a part of his spirit. Miss Malin sees in him a kindred soul and enters into a sort of "marriage" with him. She offers her lips to him; he kisses her. She lifts the hem of her dress and finds that the water has risen in the loft. They will not be rescued.

Themes and Meanings

"The Deluge at Norderney" contains a wide variety of Isak Dinesen's characteristic themes. Like the other stories in *Seven Gothic Tales* (1934), this tale deals with characters who create their worlds and their identities through telling stories. In this particular case, Dinesen places her characters in a setting which becomes quite literally a stage, a circle of light in the darkness. She positions the characters carefully and tracks their movements within the confined space as they take turns narrating their stories.

The cardinal, in proposing the tale-telling, furthers the stagecraft by introducing the mask image. In revealing themselves, the characters will "let fall the mask." As he quickly points out, however, masks may reveal more than they conceal; a clever woman at a masquerade, he says, will choose a mask which reveals some quality that her everyday life conceals. The stage is set for each character to be known by his or her mask.

In telling their stories, the characters show their understanding of the world and their place within it. Maersk shows the wit and nobility in his blood. Miss Malin, in narrating Calypso's story, proves that she possesses even greater wit and imagination than the young man. The cardinal's story is a revelation of his true identity and a statement of his understanding of the complexity of his role; he is Barabbas to the cardinal's Christ.

The presentation of their masks brings the cardinal and Miss Malin to a state of self-realization which prepares them to meet the death which comes with the rising water. The two young people, whose stories show them to be appropriately aware of their identities, sleep peacefully in the loft and will die in innocence. By their masks the characters have come to know one another as the reader has come to know each of them. With this resolution, the story concludes.

Style and Technique

Because "The Deluge at Norderney" unfolds by means of stories told by the characters, each tale must form a building block within the frame of the whole story. Each of the tales within the tale serves as a device, a sort of extended dialogue, which advances the action of the story. The intensity of the tales increases progressively, leading finally to the revelation following the most fantastic tale, "The Wine of the Tetrarch."

The beginning sentence of each tale follows a pause which heightens anticipation of the action to come. Then, with a flourish, the teller begins his tale with a statement which indicates a new development of the story's themes. Maersk begins: "If you had happened to live in Copenhagen, . . . you would have heard of me, for there I was, at a time, much talked about." His is a romantic tale full of barons, ladies, and poets. "Count Seraphina," Miss Malin begins, "meditated much upon celestial matters." What follows is a fabulously romantic tale containing a mad poet and a dim castle through which the innocent Calypso wanders. The cardinal's tale is different in tone but evokes the greatest mystery of all. He begins: "As, then, upon the first Wednesday after Easter. . . the Apostle Simon, called Peter, was walking down the streets of Jerusalem, . . . deeply absorbed in the thought of the resurrection." In his tale, the cardinal creates a parallel between the stolen and buried wine which Barabbas planned to dig up and drink and the mystical crucifixion and burial of Christ, upon whose resurrection Peter meditates.

Each of the tales treats in an increasingly fantastic form the theme of self-knowledge and understanding. As the mysteries deepen, the depth and quality of the tale-teller's understanding grow as well. Maersk realizes that aristocracy is a state of the spirit; Calypso has seen the relation of the physical and the spiritual in her womanhood; the cardinal has penetrated the mystery of the Holy Spirit, a truly great spirit moving among men in strange ways. Following the cardinal's revelation, Dinesen takes her developed themes and weaves them together in the tale's final pages to conclude her story of spiritual unmasking.

Beverly A. Findley

THE DEMON LOVER

Author: Elizabeth Bowen (1899-1973)
Type of plot: Psychological horror
Time of plot: 1941
Locale: London during the blitz
First published: 1941

Principal character:
KATHLEEN DROVER, a middle-aged wife and mother

The Story

A prosaic and dependable woman in her early forties, Kathleen Drover returns to her home in the Kensington area of London one afternoon to retrieve articles for herself and her family, who have taken refuge in the country from the blitz. As she enters the deserted street, a feeling of familiarity and strangeness overwhelms her. The German rockets have taken their toll on the street, on the square in which it is situated, on the house, and, the reader soon learns, on Kathleen herself.

She opens the door of the closed house and is immediately aware of the dead air that greets her. As she makes her way to her bedroom to retrieve the things she has come to fetch, the furniture and the marks on the floors and on the wall remind her of her life between two wars. She soon notices that the humid air outside has given way to rain.

Seeing a letter on the hall table, she is annoyed that it has not been forwarded to her by either the postal service or the caretaker. She notes that the letter has no stamps on it and wonders how it could have made its way there, since the caretaker has, ostensibly, been away for several weeks. She goes up the stairs, enters her former bedroom, and reads the letter, which bears that day's date. The brief message, signed K., reminds her of a promise that she made twenty-five years ago when she was engaged to a soldier who later died in World War I. The sender states that he is sure that, even though Kathleen has left London, she will keep the rendezvous. She is frightened not only by the message but also by the mysterious means by which it has found its way to her, by the fact that her every action may have been observed by an unknown person.

As she goes about gathering the items she has come to collect, she is haunted by her memories of the mysterious soldier whom she promised to marry twenty-five years before. She remembers the "unnatural promise" that he exacted from her. Her most vivid remembrance of him, however, is tactile—the feel of the brass button of his uniform against her hand—and she looks to see if the imprint of it is still on her palm. The twenty-five years that have passed since their last meeting dissolve like smoke in her moment of present awareness. She thinks that she cannot remember what her lover did to make her plight so sinister a troth, but as she recovers the emotion that occasioned the promise, she remembers. What she cannot remember is her lover's face.

She recalls that his death caused in her a "dislocation." She remembers that in the last week of his leave, she was not herself. She also remembers her parents' relief that their daughter would not marry the mysterious young man to whom she had engaged herself, and their belief that, after a suitable period of mourning, she would return to normal activity. Yet for years no suitors had presented themselves. Much later, when she was in her early thirties, to her parents' and her own surprise, she married William Drover and later bore him two children, the second being a difficult birth.

While making her preparations to leave the house, Kathleen examines and then dismisses the notion of supernatural intervention in her present life. She thinks, however, that she must concern herself with the appointed hour to which the note refers. Having heard the clock strike six, she assumes that she has sufficient time to complete her chores, walk to the taxi ramp at the bottom of the square, find a cab, return to the house for her parcels, and catch her train to the country. As she listens at the top of the staircase, she is disturbed by a draft of dead air that suggests to her that someone is leaving the basement by a door or window. She leaves the house, walks quickly to the cab rank, enters the taxi, and realizes that it has turned back toward the house without her having given directions. She scratches at the glass panel, looks into the driver's eyes for what seems an eternity, and screams as the car speeds into the deserted streets of the city.

Themes and Meanings

"The Demon Lover" can be read as a modern retelling of the folk legend and the ballads concerning the return of a lover from the dead to reclaim his earthly bride. As such, the story fulfills the finest demands of the tradition, for K. returns from the dead to exact from Kathleen the promise she made to him twenty-five years earlier. The taxi ride into an Unreal City at the story's end suggests that the lover has found his bride and is holding her to her bargain, to be his in death as in life. Yet this is perhaps not the most rewarding meaning of Elizabeth Bowen's story.

In a postscript to *The Demon Lover* (1945), a collection that contains "The Demon Lover" along with other stories that examine the effects of war on those that stay at home, Elizabeth Bowen addresses the central theme of the volume: "life, mechanized by the control of war-time . . . emotionally torn and impoverished by change. . . ." In "The Demon Lover" the intensity of an emotion lived in one period of war is revived twenty-five years later by the pressures of another war. The essential meaning of the story can then be interpreted as a nervous collapse brought on by war. Insofar as most novels and stories dealing with war concentrate on the conflict itself, Bowen's view of the effects on civilians of war's devastation is remarkable.

Style and Technique

"The Demon Lover," a third-person narrative, achieves its effects by means of the technique of juxtaposition. What appears at first to be a tale of the supernatural becomes in fact an account of a nervous breakdown. The imaginative paralleling of the ghost tale and the case history is achieved primarily through concentration on the details of setting. The boarded-up house, the reluctant lock, the dead air of the hallway, the mysterious letter for whose presence no rational explanation can be made, the mysterious lover from the past, the chiming bells emphasizing the passage of clock time as opposed to emotional time, the betrothed who seems to have no will of her own, and the persistent rain all combine to create a compelling and provocative ambience. Even the claw marks made on the floor by the absent piano assume an eerie significance.

The story also makes use of flashbacks to emphasize the notion that the past, though forgotten, exists in the mind to be recalled by the symbols and images of the present. The girl Kathleen promises in 1916 to marry a soldier who dies in the war. She suffers a psychic "dislocation," the seriousness of which she does not fully comprehend. No suitable young men present themselves for marriage for at least a decade, a comment on the decimation of a generation by the machine of war. Kathleen marries at the age of thirty-two and has two children. She is, furthermore, in her early forties, confronting another change in her life. She is like the cracked teacup mentioned in the story, from which time has evaporated, leaving a residue of memory. There are in Kathleen's psyche, symbolized by the house, "cracks in the structure," and there is nothing that she can do about them. The letter signed K., her own initial, may be a hallucination, a means of restoring the past to the present. Dependable, prosaic Kathleen Drover, her family's mainstay against time and change, succumbs to the pressures of World War II. The fear of death from the sky, the feeling of desuetude and decay brought to the city by the blitz, and the burdens of responsibility to herself as she was and as she is all combine to catalyze a nervous collapse that manifests itself as the return of a former lover from the dead.

The most compelling sequence in the story, Proustian in the immediacy with which it is rendered, is that in which Kathleen recovers the past as her younger self says good-bye to her doomed young lover in her family's garden. Past emotion overwhelms present inhibitions to fuse into a single overwhelming sensation: Kathleen reexperiences her promise and looks to her palm, feeling again the welt left by the button of her lover's uniform.

A. A. DeVitis

A DESCENT INTO THE MAELSTRÖM

Author: Edgar Allan Poe (1809-1849)
Type of plot: Adventure
Time of plot: Early nineteenth century
Locale: Northern Norway
First published: 1841

> *Principal characters:*
> THE NARRATOR, a tourist visiting Norway
> THE FISHERMAN, a Norwegian who has survived a maelström

The Story

In "A Descent into the Maelström," a Norwegian fisherman tells a tourist how he was caught during a storm in a maelström three years earlier and how he survived his ordeal. The tourist is the story's narrator, and he speaks as a reporter who has met an interesting character while traveling in Norway. The story opens with the description of their arrival at a fifteen-hundred-foot cliff on Helseggen mountain, from which the pair may observe the maelström to the south. Though the fisherman seems old and weak, he is rather comfortable on this narrow and windy cliff, where the narrator is unwilling to rise from a crawl in order to observe the sea below. The fisherman coaxes the narrator into looking over the edge; the narrator sees and hears the awesome phenomenon of the gigantic whirlpool that forms there at the changing of the tides.

The maelström is incredible, forming a vast hole, roaring and shrieking far more loudly than Niagara Falls, and shaking the mountain from which they watch. Having described the whirlpool, the narrator quotes from other accounts that find its alleged power to destroy ships and ocean life scarcely credible. For his part, the narrator believes the accounts to be conservative. He also discusses accounts of the causes of the maelström, the most likely of which attribute it to tidal currents. Yet his own observation makes the most fantastic account the most satisfying to his imagination. To experience the maelström even at a distance is to believe that it is a vast drain through which water passes, to rise again miles away. The narrator's observations and reading, both distant approaches to the maelström, are then enriched by the fisherman's account of his descent into the maelström.

The fisherman tells how he and his two brothers made a practice of fishing near the maelström because the risk of the venture was justified by the richness and the quality of the catch. One day, however, they were caught by a hurricane, which drowned one brother, rendered their ship helpless, and propelled it into the maelström.

Because the center of the storm passed over their ship as it was about to

enter the maelström, the whole scene was brightly lit by a full moon, allowing the fisherman to observe the maelström closely. The ship was drawn
toward the whirlpool and over its edge. The ship then rode around it as if it
were riding water down a drain, except that its forward speed varied, while
its speed of descent remained more or less constant. The fisherman concentrated on his unexpected psychological responses to being pulled in and to
the descent.

In his first despair, he found much of his terror dissipated. Instead, he
reflected on what a magnificent manifestation of God's power he was seeing
and on how wonderful an opportunity it was simply to see it. These attitudes
restored the self-possession that his remaining brother had lost permanently.
The fisherman relates that he was further calmed by the increasing calmness
and regularity of the ship's motion in what had seemed to be lawless violence
of motion. He felt a curiosity to explore this wonder of nature and began to
do so. Despite the brightness of the moon, he was unable to see to the very
bottom of the vortex because of a mist engendered there, but he did see "a
magnificent rainbow, like that narrow and tottering bridge which Musselmen
say is the only pathway between Time and Eternity." Gradually, his observations became cooler and more scientific. Eventually, he noticed that differently shaped objects descend at different speeds. This observation gave
him hope that he might survive if he could attach himself to a cylindrical
object.

Unable to convince his brother to join him, he lashed himself to a water
cask and leaped overboard. This strategy saved his life, while his brother
rode the ship down to destruction.

The fisherman says that when he was picked up by his friends and daily
companions, they failed to recognize him, for his hair had turned from raven
to white in those few hours, and his face, too, had changed beyond recognition. They did not believe his story of having survived the maelström, and he
does not expect the narrator to believe it either.

Themes and Meanings

"A Descent into the Maelström" appears on the surface to be little more
than a realistic tale of adventure, an eyewitness account of a distant natural
wonder for Edgar Allan Poe's American readers. Like several of his adventure tales, this one is constructed in such a way as to be indistinguishable
from similar nonfictional reports, which regularly appeared in popular journals of the day. Among the aspects of the story which tempt readers to see
more than adventure are the unusual description of the maelström, which
suggests that it may be a symbol, and certain patterns that are repeated in
other Poe tales.

The maelström as experienced by the fisherman is a whirling storm in the
water, which has above it a precisely corresponding whirling storm in the air.

At the eye of the storm is the brilliant full moon, which lights and glorifies the maelström, offering the fisherman a doubly unique revelation. Not only is he caught in the maelström, but he is also allowed to see it. The storm seems to allow him this unique vision as a gift. At the corresponding eye of the maelström is the mysterious veiling mist, illuminated by a rainbow which, to the fisherman, seems a bridge between time and eternity. The mist marks a literal entrance to eternity insofar as it marks the point at which a person must die, should he reach that point in the maelström. Yet, as the vision itself offers a revelation, it may also offer a way for the imagination to bridge time and eternity. This arrangement of storm and maelström indicates a fictional purpose beneath the surface of an apparently nonfictional text; it suggests that the scene may be symbolic, pointing to some meaning beyond itself.

The meaning to which it points is difficult to assert confidently. There are patterns of the story in Poe's works that are suggestive but do not lead easily to certainty. Stuart Levine, in *The Short Fiction of Edgar Allan Poe* (1976), has placed this tale with "The Pit and the Pendulum" because it exemplifies the theme of salvation through terror. The fisherman moves through stages of terror, despair, wonder, calm, curiosity, cool observation, discovery, action, and salvation. This pattern, or one like it, appears frequently in Poe's tales of adventure; it is several times placed in the context of a physical journey during which the protagonist approaches a barrier between time and eternity such as the irradiated mist at the bottom of the maelström. One possible meaning suggested by this pattern is that the recognition of the incomprehensible terror and wonder of the physical universe brings the human consciousness ultimately to a kind of heightened reason, in which fundamental truth may be discovered. What truth the fisherman discovers is also difficult to assert with confidence. It may be important to notice how his ease on the windy cliff contrasts with the narrator's terror at the opening of the story. Perhaps the fisherman has learned not to fear death and, as a result, has come to feel at home with the terrific wonders of the physical universe.

Style and Technique

The discussion of possible meanings has uncovered the main distinctive elements of Poe's technique in this tale. He creates what appears to be a nonfiction narrative yet places at its center a symmetrical setting of a hurricane over a maelström, which suggests symbolic meaning. The fisherman seems an ordinary man who has had an extraordinary adventure, but ultimately it appears that he may have been granted a kind of revelation, which has changed not only his appearance but also his attitude toward his life and his world.

Critics have taken note of the similarity between this tale and Samuel Taylor Coleridge's *The Rime of the Ancient Mariner* (1798). Each is a framed narrative, the seaman telling his tale to a landsman. In each, there is a similar pattern: The seaman is drawn into a wonder world in which despair leads to discovery, transformation, and a salvation which may be both physical and spiritual. Perhaps the main difference between Poe's tale and Coleridge's poem is that Poe presents a believable if extraordinary physical world in a journalistic, reportorial fashion. One result is that the meaning of Poe's tale seems to arise from experience of the world rather than from a fantasy designed to illustrate a moral truth.

Terry Heller

DÉSIRÉE'S BABY

Author: Kate Chopin (1851-1904)
Type of plot: Social realism
Time of plot: Sometime before the Civil War
Locale: Natchitoches Parish, Louisiana
First published: 1892

>*Principal characters:*
>DÉSIRÉE, the heroine, a beautiful young woman
>ARMAND AUBIGNY, her husband, a rich planter and
>   slaveholder
>MONSIEUR VALMONDÉ, Désirée's foster father
>MADAME VALMONDÉ, Désirée's foster mother

The Story

As the story opens, Madame Valmondé is on her way to visit Désirée and her new baby. As she makes the short trip to the nearby plantation, Madame Valmondé thinks back to the time when Désirée was herself an infant. Her husband had found the child lying asleep near a pillar at the entrance to the Valmondé plantation, probably having been left there by a party of Texans who had passed by that day. Childless themselves, the Valmondés adopted Désirée.

Désirée grows into a beautiful woman, and, when she is eighteen years old, Armand Aubigny falls in love with her. When he proposes, Monsieur Valmondé reminds Armand that her parentage and ancestry are unknown, but Armand dismisses all objections. After all, he can give her one of the finest names and lineages in Louisiana.

They soon marry, and at first their life together is happy. Armand, a harsh man toward his slaves, becomes more humane; following the birth of their first child, a son, Armand grows even kinder. Shortly thereafter, however, Armand becomes crueler than ever. He also stays away from home for long periods of time, and when he is at home he shows no affection for Désirée.

One afternoon, as Désirée sits listlessly in her room, she glances at her child lying on the bed. A quadroon slave is fanning the child, and suddenly she is struck by the similarity in their features. As soon as her husband arrives, she asks for an explanation. Armand replies that her suspicions are correct; the child is not white. If the child is not white, Armand continues, then neither is Désirée.

She refuses to believe Armand's accusation and writes to her foster mother to confirm her racial purity. Madame Valmondé responds by inviting Désirée and her baby to return home. She says nothing about Armand's accusation, though, thus tacitly confirming it.

After receiving this letter, Désirée asks her husband what he wants her to do. He wants her to go. She does indeed leave, but instead of returning to the Valmondés, she carries her baby into the swamp and disappears.

Several weeks later Armand builds a bonfire in the backyard to destroy all traces of Désirée and the child. Into the flames go the willow cradle, the baby's expensive layette, and Désirée's silk, satin, and velvet dresses. Finally he gathers up her letters; these, too, he consigns to the blaze. Now only one piece of paper remains in the desk. As Armand prepares to destroy it, he notices that the handwriting is not his wife's. Instead, he discovers that it is a note from his mother to his father. In it he reads, "I thank the good God for having so arranged our lives that our dear Armand will never know that his mother, who adores him, belongs to the race that is cursed with the brand of slavery." Too late, Armand learns the truth.

Themes and Meanings

Chopin clearly sympathizes with the plight of people of mixed blood and points out the evils of a slave system that at once creates and condemns miscegenation. Her chief concern, however, is not with the South's "peculiar institution," a topic she rarely treated in her fiction. Rather, she concerns herself with her characters' inner lives.

Certainly these lives confront external constraints. Désirée and Armand live in a world that values racial purity. To be black is to be condemned to a life of subservience; to be white is to inherit mastery. No matter how beautiful or how fair one may be, blood rules. Armand spends much time in the cottage of a slave named La Blanche, whose name suggests her skin color. Still, she is of mixed race, so she is a slave, and the quadroon boy who fans Désirée's baby is probably the son of Armand and La Blanche. The most such a woman can hope for is to be treated well by her master and to be his concubine, since she will never be his wife. Among Creoles, who pride themselves not only on their racial purity but also on their French heritage, the proper pedigree is especially important.

The characters' world is also one in which women, like blacks, are second-class citizens. Women have certain fixed roles—daughter, wife, mother. Désirée's world is small, moving between the neighboring plantations of her foster parents and her husband. She passes her days inside, while Armand is free to come and go as he pleases. Once her husband rejects her, Désirée must choose between disgrace and death; despite Madame Valmondé's offer of sanctuary, Désirée would remain an outcast.

Still, "Désirée's Baby" might have ended differently. The code of the outside world impinges on Armand but does not force him to act as he does. When he married Désirée he claimed indifference to her status as a foundling, but he is not, in fact, strong enough to reject the prejudices of the world. Indeed, he stands for those very attitudes that he seems to ignore: He defines himself by his pedigree and by his role as master of his slaves and his wife. Désirée is desirable only so long as she appears to be a valuable possession, like an antique chair. Once he believes that she is not "authentic," he loses interest, for he never regards her as a fellow human being with needs of her own. She is there, he believes, to satisfy him; when she no longer does so, he discards her.

In her poem "Because," Chopin writes, "Tis only man/ That does because he can/ And knowing good from ill,/ Chooses because he will." Armand has a choice: He can love Désirée for what she is (or thinks she is) as his father loved his black mother, or he can let his pride overrule that love. Chopin admires the character who defies convention, who is sufficiently strong to reject the false standards of his time and place. Armand's inability to surmount prejudice leads to the tragedy of the story.

Style and Technique

Kate Chopin has been described as a local colorist, and certainly most of her stories are set in a particular geographical area that she examines socially and physically. Unlike such local colorists as Sarah Orne Jewett and George Washington Cabel, though, Chopin did not write to preserve the past, nor did she focus on the conflict of past and present that characterizes the typical local-color story. Further, her work shows no nostalgia for a previous era. Only five of her stories lack a contemporary setting, and "Désirée's Baby" demonstrates no fondness for the antebellum period.

The carefully defined setting is, rather, a laboratory. What happens when one puts certain characters in a particular world? Like a scientist, Chopin observed their reactions and reported her results without obvious emotion. Significantly, she called this story "Désirée's Baby," not "Désirée," as though seeking to deflect sympathy from the central character. Also, the baby is the crucial ingredient in this experiment: Give Armand and Désirée a child of color and then watch how they behave.

They behave badly, each blaming the other. Neither knows the truth, but since Armand is the more powerful, Désirée is disgraced and banished. Chopin does not moralize; she merely reports. That clinical detachment makes the final lines all the more forceful, as the reader grasps the enormity of Armand's mistake.

Joseph Rosenblum

THE DEVIL AND DANIEL WEBSTER

Author: Stephen Vincent Benét (1898-1943)
Type of plot: Historical fable
Time of plot: Early nineteenth century
Locale: Cross Corners, New Hampshire, and Marshfield, Massachusetts
First published: 1937

Principal characters:
> DANIEL WEBSTER, the famous American lawyer, legislator,
> and orator
> JABEZ STONE, a New Hampshire farmer who makes a pact
> with the Devil
> "MR. SCRATCH," the name the Devil carries in the story

The Story

"The Devil and Daniel Webster" is narrated as a folktale told in the border country of Vermont, New Hampshire, and Massachusetts, regarding the famous American orator. Like so many folk legends, this one contains some exaggeration and several important lessons.

Jabez Stone is an unlucky New Hampshire farmer who, in a moment of frustration, sells his soul to the Devil. His farm prospers, but when the Devil returns near the end of the seven-year contract, Stone sees the soul of his neighbor Miser Stevens in the Devil's pocket, and his dread grows. Although the Devil grants him a three-year extension on his contract, the time weighs on Jabez Stone and, in desperation, he goes to see Daniel Webster, who was born near Stone's farm but who now lives and practices law in Marshfield, Massachusetts. Webster says that he has not argued such a "mortgage case" in some time, but he agrees to take it. The two return to New Hampshire to await the arrival of the Devil, who comes at midnight to claim his property.

The heart of the story is the debate between the Devil and Daniel Webster. At the beginning, it looks as if Daniel Webster has met his match. He argues that no American can be pressed into the service of a "foreign prince," but the Devil cleverly demonstrates that he has a long American history: "When the first wrong was done to the first Indian, I was there. When the first slaver put out for the Congo, I stood on her deck." Not to be outdone, Webster stands on the Constitution and demands a trial for his client, with an American judge and jury. Mr. Scratch agrees—and calls up a cast of pirates, cutthroats, and turncoats from the darker pages of American history, and the dreaded Judge Hawthorne, who presided at the Salem witch trials.

The trial that night does not go well for Webster, and his opposition nearly tricks him into getting angry and thereby falling into their power: "For it was him they'd come for, not only Jabez Stone." Thus, in his closing argument,

Daniel Webster starts off in a low voice "talking about the things that make a country a country, and a man a man." He talks about freedom and slavery and the early days of the republic.

> It wasn't a spread-eagle speech, but he made you see it. He admitted all the wrong that had ever been done. But he showed how, out of the wrong and the right, the suffering and the starvations, something new had come. And everybody had played a part in it, even the traitors.

His speech thus redeems, not only Jabez Stone and himself, but the jury of renegades as well.

> And his words came back at the end to New Hampshire ground, and the one spot of land that each man loves and clings to. He painted a picture of that, and to each one of that jury he spoke of things long forgotten. For his voice could search the heart, and that was his gift and his strength.

The jury finds for the defendant, and Daniel Webster wins his toughest case.

Yet Webster is not done. He forces Mr. Scratch to draw up a document promising never to bother Jabez Stone or his heirs, "nor any other New Hampshireman till doomsday!" The Devil tells Webster's fortune and predicts, correctly, that he will never become president (his secret ambition), that his two sons will die in the Civil War, but that the Union will be saved, thanks in part to Daniel Webster's speeches. Finally, Webster boots the Devil out the door.

> But they say that whenever the devil comes near Marshfield, even now, he gives it a wide berth. And he hasn't been seen in the state of New Hampshire from that day to this. I'm not talking about Massachusetts or Vermont.

Themes and Meanings

"The Devil and Daniel Webster" was one of three stories that Benét wrote in the late 1930's on the subject of the great orator, and it was a story that brought him, on its publication in *The Saturday Evening Post*, almost instant national acclaim. The story tapped America's love for folklore and legend, and, at a dark moment in the Depression when Americans were looking desperately for such handholds, it re-created the story of a genuine American hero. In the process of elevating Webster to a national honor, Benét also wrote a hymn celebrating America's past greatness and future possibility.

Like the legends of earlier American folk heroes (Daniel Boone, Davy Crockett, and so on), Benét's portrait of Webster is based on actual accomplishments, but embellished in a number of ways. Webster takes on Jabez Stone's case, even though he has "seventy-five other things to do and the Missouri Compromise to straighten out." All of his feats in the story are prodigious, in fact, but none so great as his eloquence. He is able in his speech to convince twelve of the most desperate villains ever assembled out of American history to free Stone from from the Devil's hold.

The story is praise not only for Daniel Webster, however, but also for his country, for the two are inextricably intertwined. Webster is, as Jabez Stone says of him, "the Union's stay and New Hampshire's pride!" Webster himself confesses, "I'd go to the Pit itself to save the Union." Webster's victory is won by describing the very qualities—love of country, love of the land, a belief in justice, and a faith in all men—that he himself so eloquently represents, and that America stands for.

Daniel Webster is also a "New Hampshireman," and part of the story's poignancy, and not a little of its humor, come from the delineation of Yankee character traits. Some of the poignancy is a pride of region, "For if two New Hampshiremen aren't a match for the devil," Webster boasts, "we might as well give the country back to the Indians." Another part is clearly satirical. Jabez Stone is indentured to the Devil only because, having said in anger that he would sell his soul, "being a New Hampshireman, he wouldn't take it back." Yankees reflect the qualities of their flinty soil, and Jabez Stone is no exception: "Hard and mean," as Daniel Webster admits in his summation, Stone is also pious, ill-educated, slow to brag, but quick to grab a profit. ("For any hades we want to raise in this state," Daniel Webster quips, "we can raise ourselves without assistance from strangers.") The humor of the last line of the story—on the difference between New Hampshire and its neighbors—is based on a regional New England pride and friendly rivalry.

The story is connected, thematically, to the Faust legend, which can be traced from works such as Christopher Marlowe's *The Tragedy of Dr. Faustus* (1592) in the sixteenth century and Johann Wolfgang von Goethe's *Faust* (1808, 1833) in the nineteenth to Thomas Mann's *Doktor Faustus* (1947; *Doctor Faustus*, 1948). In these and similar works, a man makes a pact with the Devil for some profit but suffers dire consequences for his act. In the American literary tradition, the story is also linked to treatments of the New England character, from Nathaniel Hawthorne's story "Young Goodman Brown" (1835), through Edith Wharton's novel *Ethan Frome* (1911) and Eugene O'Neill's play *Desire Under the Elms* (1924), to the contemporary fiction of John Cheever and John Updike.

Style and Technique

Most American folktales, from stories about Paul Bunyan and Pecos Bill through the Uncle Remus stories, depend for their effect on a successful merging of matter and manner: The subjects must sound like what they were. Like these earlier stories, "The Devil and Daniel Webster" manages to capture the very flavor of its Yankee subject. The anonymous narrator of the story is clearly a New Englander, and his voice carries a pride of region as well as its accent. Daniel Webster himself is capable of both sharpness and humor: "I never left a jug or a case half finished in my life." When, at the end of the story, he calls the Devil a "long-barreled, slab-sided, lantern-jawed, fortune-telling note shaver," Benét is capturing the language of the tall tale out of the oral tradition in American literature.

Benét chooses, however, *not* to try to recite Webster's speeches verbatim, but, instead, recounts them in his own modulated, poetic prose, and the effect is telling. (Most readers are not conscious, until it is pointed out, that the closing arguments in the trial are given, not by Webster, but by his fictional biographer, the narrator of "The Devil and Daniel Webster.") Benét's prose is capable not only of the broad Yankee humor and folk exaggeration of the story, but also of the poignant and patriotic sentiments of Webster's last speech:

> And he began with the simple things that everybody's known and felt—the freshness of a fine morning when you're young and the taste of food when you're hungry, and the new day that's every day when you're a child. He took them up and he turned them in his hands.

Much of the story's power comes from this prose.

David Peck

THE DEVIL AND TOM WALKER

Author: Washington Irving (1783-1859)
Type of plot: Regional romance
Time of plot: Eighteenth century
Locale: Massachusetts Colony
First published: 1824

> *Principal characters:*
> TOM WALKER, a pre-Revolutionary New Englander who sells
> his soul to the Devil
> TOM'S WIFE, a shrewish nag
> "OLD SCRATCH," the Devil

The Story

This tale, which was told to the narrator, Geoffrey Crayon, during a peaceful afternoon of fishing, begins with a local legend concerning treasure buried by the notorious pirate Captain Kidd in a swamp not far from Boston. Near this swamp, in 1727, lives a miserly fellow named Tom Walker and his wife, a woman as miserly as he. These two, so greedy that they even try to cheat each other, are constantly fighting, and Tom's face shows the physical marks of their arguments.

One day, cutting through the swamp, Tom comes across the remains of an old Indian fortification and discovers a skull with a tomahawk still buried in it. As Tom kicks at the skull, he hears a voice and looks up to see a black man, "neither negro nor Indian" seated on a stump. The man, wearing a red sash around his body, has a soot-stained face, which makes it appear as if he works in some fiery place. Tom soon recognizes the stranger as the Devil, Old Scratch. The Devil confirms the story of Kidd's buried treasure and offers it to Tom, but only on a certain condition, a condition which the story does not state but which is surely the possession of Tom's soul. Old Scratch proves his identity by leaving the imprint of his finger burned into Tom's forehead.

When Tom tells his wife of the encounter, she greedily urges him to accept the bargain, but to spite her he refuses. Unable to change Tom's mind, she decides to make her own pact with the Devil, keeping the profits for herself. After an initial inconclusive meeting with Old Scratch, Tom's wife sets out again for the Indian fort, this time taking with her all the household valuables she can carry. When she does not return for several days, Tom, uneasy for his valuables, goes to find her. After a long afternoon's search, he sees hanging in a tree a bundle tied in his wife's apron. Thinking that he has found the valuables, he opens the apron and discovers only a heart and a liver. Evidently, his wife died attempting to deal with Old Scratch as she had formerly dealt with Tom, for around the tree are tufts of black hair obviously pulled from the Devil's head. Although unhappy about the disappearance of his valuables, Tom is consoled by the loss of his wife.

Feeling grateful and with a growing desire to gain Captain Kidd's fortune, Tom seeks to renew his acquaintance with the Devil. Old Scratch does not appear for some time, however, and, when he does, he seems reluctant to discuss the treasure. Finally, though, he agrees to relinquish the treasure if it will be used in his service. He first suggests that Tom become a slave trader. Tom balks at sinking that low but agrees to go into business as a money-lender or usurer.

Tom moves to Boston and becomes successful, exacting hard terms and showing no mercy to those in his debt. Growing older, Tom regrets his bargain and searches to find a way out of the pact. He becomes zealous in church attendance, prays loudly and publicly, keeps an open Bible in his home, and always carries a small one with him. He does not, however, give up his harsh business practices.

One hot afternoon, dressed in a white linen cap and silk morning gown, Tom is about to foreclose a mortgage. When the poor victim begs for a delay, reminding Tom of the money he previously made from him, Tom replies, "The devil take me . . . if I have made a farthing!" Immediately, there are three knocks at the door, and standing in the street is Old Scratch and a black horse.

Having left the small Bible in his coat and having covered the large one with the mortgage, Tom is helpless to prevent the Devil from placing him on the horse, which gallops off down the streets of Boston. The next day, his house burns to the ground, and Tom never returns. It is said, however, that the swamp and Indian fort are haunted by a spirit on horseback wearing a white cap and morning gown. The story is so well-known, says the narrator, that it is the source of the New England saying, "The Devil and Tom Walker."

Themes and Meanings

Washington Irving is said to be the first to have used the phrase "the almighty dollar." This tale, found in part 4 (called "The Money Diggers") of *Tales of a Traveller*, comically presents the results of valuing the dollar above all else. Both Tom and his wife care more for possessions than they do for each other. She urges Tom to sell his soul, and he is more concerned for his household treasures than for her. The two live in conflict and misery because of greed and eventually die from greed, she by trying to bully the Devil into better terms and he by attempting to squeeze the last bit of profit from an unfortunate client.

The Faust theme, in which the soul is exchanged for knowledge and power, is reduced here to a story of money grubbing. The occupations which are viewed as of special service to the Devil—slave-trading and usury—are those which place monetary profit before humanity. (Irving also attacked the slave trade in his *A History of the Life and Voyages of Christopher Columbus*, 1828, and he had personal experience with the humiliation of debt and bankruptcy.)

Tom's turn to religion near the end of the tale is a combination of superstition and hypocrisy. Tom hopes to ward off the Devil through the outward trappings of Christianity, but the tale clearly satirizes those who make a public show of devotion while retaining meanness of spirit.

Style and Technique

As in other of his tales, Irving here combines a supernatural subject with a matter-of-fact narration. The reader is allowed to suspend disbelief partly through the framing of the tale, which is recounted by the fictional narrator Geoffrey Crayon, who has heard it from an old Cape Cod whaler, who claims to have memorized it from a manuscript written by a neighbor. Thus, the tale is several times removed from its source, with no one to vouch for its authenticity. The phrase "it is said" is used frequently, and once the reader is told that the facts "have become confounded by a variety of historians." Although the tale ends with a claim for its veracity ("The truth of it is not to be doubted"), readers can believe or not as they wish.

The serious and the comic are juxtaposed. While the selling of one's soul and the inhumane consequences of greed are significant, they become subjects for laughter through Irving's character portrayals and his use of ironic understatement. The characters are one-dimensional, stereotypical figures. Tom's unnamed wife is the typical nag of antifeminist literature. Tom himself is not described in detail and is given such stock traits as greed and hypocrisy. The reader need not be concerned for the fate of either character.

Irving has a keen eye for the ironies and contradictions of human behavior. When Tom becomes wealthy, he ostentatiously equips a grand carriage but has it pulled by starving horses. He builds a large house but leaves it unfurnished out of miserliness. He exacts the harshest business terms on those least able to pay. Throughout the tale, this irony exposes the vanity and meanness of those for whom material possessions become paramount.

Larry L. Stewart

THE DIAMOND AS BIG AS THE RITZ

Author: F. Scott Fitzgerald (1896-1940)
Type of plot: Satirical fantasy
Time of plot: c. 1920
Locale: Montana
First published: 1922

> *Principal characters:*
> JOHN T. UNGER, a student at "the most expensive and the
> most exclusive boys' preparatory school in the world"
> PERCY WASHINGTON, John's classmate and the son of the
> world's richest man
> BRADDOCK WASHINGTON, Percy's father
> KISMINE, Percy's sister and John's sweetheart

The Story

At St. Midas's School, John T. Unger befriends a new boy, Percy Washington, who invites him to spend the summer on the family estate in the Montana Rockies. Percy's boast that his father owns a diamond as big as the Ritz-Carlton Hotel seems preposterous, but upon arrival John learns that the Washingtons' château actually does sit atop a five-cubic-mile flawless diamond.

The next morning, Percy sketches the family history for his friend. In 1866, his grandfather Fitz-Norman, a "direct descendant" of George Washington and Lord Baltimore, left the defeated Confederacy accompanied by a group of faithful slaves to start a ranch in the West. The venture failed within a month. Then, while hunting for food, Fitz-Norman noticed a brilliant stone drop from a squirrel's mouth—a perfect diamond worth one hundred thousand dollars. Returning to the site with all of his male blacks the following day, Fitz-Norman soon filled his saddlebags with diamonds. When the sale of a few of these gems in New York City loosed a wave of wild rumors, he realized that he would have to operate clandestinely lest the government seize his diamond mine and establish a monopoly to avert financial panic. Accordingly, he poured his wares into two trunks and peddled them to the courts of Europe and Asia. Later, his son Braddock (Percy's father) sealed the mine and devoted himself to protecting the family's incalculable fortune—and its secret.

The more complex of the story's two strands unwinds from this effort at concealment. Fitz-Norman had corrupted the government surveyors and arranged for omission of the estate from official maps; Braddock, resorting to more elaborate measures, created an artificial magnetic field, tinkered with the surveyors' instruments, and altered the area's geographic features.

The advent of the airplane, however, has made discovery of the Washington domain inevitable. At the time of John Unger's visit, about two dozen aviators who have been brought down by Washington antiaircraft fire are being kept prisoner in a glass-lined pit; one of this group has recently escaped, however, and soon a squadron of American planes arrives and begins shelling the mountain in preparation for an invasion. Braddock, realizing that only divine intervention can preserve his family's treasure and privilege, tries to bribe God with a diamond so huge that it requires two slaves to lift it. When the bribe is apparently refused and the planes land on the château's lawn, Braddock detonates an explosion that reduces the entire mountain to dust.

Anchored in John's role as protagonist, the plot's other strand develops his romance with Percy's sister Kismine. It crosses the story's baseline at only two points: first, when, after falling in love with Kismine, John surmises that the Washingtons cannot risk allowing him to leave their El Dorado alive; and again in the ironic coda, when he learns that Kismine mistook the only rhinestones at the château for diamonds while hastily filling her pocket as they fled from the mountain's apocalyptic destruction. Yet, even though the relationship between the young lovers weaves no web of significant actions, Fitzgerald treats it as the central element; whatever the story's resolved meaning may be, its focus is certainly not on Braddock Washington's failure to escape retribution for his hubris; rather, it is on John's recognition that, for some unspecified reason, he has lost his illusions. (In the torrent of philosophizing that serves as conclusion, it is John who pronounces two of Fitzgerald's most quoted sentences: "Everybody's youth is a dream, a form of chemical madness" and "His was a great sin who first invented consciousness.")

Themes and Meanings

Published near the beginning of his career (Fitzgerald wrote it in either 1921 or, at the very latest, early January, 1922), "The Diamond as Big as the Ritz" shows a constellation of the motifs that would persist throughout the author's career. Despite the fantastic trappings, it tells a radically autobiographical tale. Fitzgerald situates Hades, the Ungers' hometown, on the Mississippi—like his own St. Paul—and devotes the story's initial pages to ridiculing its pretensions. (Even a Chicago beef-princess, the author sneers, would judge the most sophisticated social functions in Hades to be "perhaps a little tacky.") John Unger reflects the self-congratulatory boosterism of his provincial upbringing, and in this respect he is a target of satire. John also, however, evokes sympathy as a young man daunted by an unshakeable sense of his unworthiness among the aristocratic rich. The model is unmistakable. In a letter to John O'Hara in 1933, Fitzgerald described himself as having "a two cylinder inferiority complex. So if I were elected King of Scotland tomorrow after graduating from Eton, Magdelene the Guards, with an embryonic history which tied me to the Plantagenets, I would still be a *parvenue* [*sic*]. I spent my youth in alternately crawling in front of the kitchen maids and insulting the great."

Fitzgerald attributed his problem, in the same letter, to the tensions inherent in being "half black Irish and half old American stock with the usual exaggerated ancestral pretensions" (his paternal forebears included Francis Scott Key, after whom he was named). Precisely this personal conflict constitutes the story's subtext. As Midwestern burghers, the Ungers suggest his mother's side of the family: Grandfather McQuillan rose from poor immigrant to wealthy merchant through the wholesale grocery business in St. Paul. The Washingtons, whose breeding stands in conspicuous contrast to the Ungers' tackiness, clearly represent the Fitzgeralds (an association emphasized by the name Fitz-Norman), and in particular his father Edward, a gentleman with Southern grace characterized by his son as "one of the generation of the colonies and the revolution."

The biographical reference of St. Midas's is still more apparent. Like Basil Lee's search for acceptance in "The Freshest Boy," John Unger's need to adjust to living among social superiors harks back to Fitzgerald's painful entrance into the prep school world. Yet a simple identification of the mythical prep school on the outskirts of Boston as a vast exaggeration of the Newman School, the Catholic academy in New Jersey attended by the author, seems not to reach nearly far enough. The story's oneiric quality calls for psychological analysis, and from this perspective, the significance of St. Midas's relates to its position within the "dream's" structure: midway, in effect, between the Unger and Washington families. Essentially, "The Diamond as Big as the Ritz" traces a boy's transformation into a man. The pivotal moment in that process (which is set in motion by his departure from the "maternal fatuity" of Hades) is the encounter with his alter ego, Percy, at the school appropriately named for King Midas—in a manner of speaking, the "patron saint" of transmutation. As a result of the friendship with his "dream self," John virtually becomes a Washington, emerges as an heir of sorts to the "father" he has presumably wished dead in his fantasies, and confirms the meaning of his passage through adolescence by spending a symbolically nuptial night with Kismine.

That interpretation, however, strikes to the design written on the story's underside; what Fitzgerald presents at the surface seems to obey no corresponding intent. Indeed, he shifts direction so often that one infers that the fable is obedient to no conscious plan at all. Until well past the introductory sections, Fitzgerald makes a target of snobbery, fixing expectations that the plot will somehow produce a complementary moral. By the midpoint, however, the energy of this attack is spent, and snobbery does not affect the combination of events that brings the story to its climax. Nor, for that matter, does John Unger, who is relegated to the role of spectator while Braddock

Washington is being defeated by the United States government and rejected by God. Then, in the final section, Fitzgerald not only reestablishes John at the center but also assigns him a closing soliloquy about youth and illusion that has no discernible connection with either society's vanities or the destruction of the Washington empire.

Style and Technique

The thematic uncertainty of "The Diamond as Big as the Ritz" is reflected in the story's style as well. Having identified no urgent, shaping idea for what is presumptively an allegory, Fitzgerald allows himself to be seduced into conceits that develop no coherent metaphoric pattern. For example: John rides the last miles of his journey to the Washingtons' celestial estate in a huge automobile made of precious metals; the train has taken him only as far as the village of Fish, populated by twelve "sombre and inexplicable souls who sucked a lean milk from the almost literally bare rock upon which a mysterious populatory force had begotten them." "Fish" points to "ichthus," the emblem of Jesus the Saviour, the village's dozen inhabitants patently represent the apostles. The meaning seems clear: The magnitude of the Washingtons' opulence sets them beyond the pale of Christian teaching. Yet why invent an extravagant metaphor to introduce an idea that will quickly become self-evident upon John's arrival at the château? Why, having gone to such lengths, subsequently neglect to elaborate the implications of an existence without moral stricture or to link that philosophical issue to any of the several other themes, including the one grandly paraded in the ending? In this instance, as in others, Fitzgerald apparently became infatuated with his own cleverness: Once he had created the image of the twelve men of Fish nursing at the ungenerous breast of St. Peter's church, he could not surrender it, even though it engages no broader purpose.

A similar self-indulgence is manifest in the story's sophomoric humor. The many puns on "Hades" show no wit. For example, Mr. Unger, on saying farewell to his son, assures him that "we'll keep the home fires burning"—and their coy naughtiness is wearing. Still more annoying is the smirky sexual innuendo that stretches from start to finish. Exactly what information the author is pretending to convey in describing Mrs. Unger as famous for "political addresses" delivered "from hot-box to hot-bed" is unclear, but no one can mistake the covert message. The names Fitzgerald produces are in the same vein. The repeated use of the middle initial stresses that John T. Unger is susceptible to being read "John Tonguer." Kismine is plainly "kiss mine," and the imperative in her sister's name, Jasmine, is only slightly less obvious ("jazz," before it came to mean the kind of music played in black brothels, meant "to copulate"). Most egregious of all, Fitzgerald names the personal servant who assists John at his bath Gygsum—one of several variants of "jism," slang for semen.

Finally, however, "The Diamond as Big as the Ritz" is larger than the sum of its deeply flawed parts. Though immature and crudely executed, it displays a profligate talent, a poetic genius that has not yet learned to respect itself or to value the importance of discipline. In conceiving a symbol of wealth so stupendous as to be beyond valuation, Fitzgerald was not imaging a yearning for luxury or power; rather, the diamond reifies the impossible dream of escape from all humiliating restraint. If, at this stage of his development, the expression of that idea is amateurishly clumsy, one nevertheless responds to the energy the idea is generating as it presses outward from the core of the writer's mind. Two years later, Fitzgerald would complete his masterpiece, *The Great Gatsby*. In James Gatz's transformation into Jay Gatsby, the "Platonic conception of himself," one sees the refinement of John Unger's fantasy.

Frank Gado

THE DIAMOND LENS

Author: Fitz-James O'Brien (1828-1862)
Type of plot: Fantasy parable
Time of plot: Mid-nineteenth century
Locale: New York City
First published: 1858

> *Principal characters:*
> MR. LINLEY, the narrator and protagonist, a man obsessed
>   with the microscopic world
> JULES SIMON, the possessor of a rare diamond, for which he is
>   murdered by Linley
> MADAME VULPES, a spirit medium
> ANIMULA, a beautiful inhabitant of the microscopic world,
>   with whom Linley falls in love

The Story

"The Diamond Lens," a scientific fantasy, was very popular in the mid-nineteenth century. This work situates author Fitz-James O'Brien somewhere between Edgar Allan Poe and Ambrose Bierce in the development of such imaginative quasi-scientific fantasies, although O'Brien is not as profound in his use of genre as either of those writers. O'Brien wrote a clever and interesting story about moving beyond the realm of external reality into a world of absolute beauty and mad obsession, a theme that certainly places him in the Poe-Bierce tradition, but "A Diamond Lens" never goes beyond the surface gloss of the slick magazine writing of the time.

The plot focuses on the obsessive fascination that the narrator, Linley, has had with microscopic investigations from the time he was ten years old. Beneath the microscope, he sees a world akin to *The Arabian Nights' Entertainments* in which the dull veil of ordinary existence that hangs across the world seems to roll away and to lay bare a land of enchantments; like many of the narrators in the stories of Poe, he feels elevated above all other men, seeing the world in a more profound way. Yet, as is also typical of Poe characters, it is not a scientific thirst that drives the protagonist, but rather the pure enjoyment of a poet lost in the enchanted gardens and fantastic foliage of a world of imaginative wonders. The world he seeks is the world of aesthetic, not material, reality.

When the narrator grows up, he has little real interest in anything but his microscopic investigations, Since he has a considerable amount of money, as is often the case in such stories, he sets up a laboratory in New York City and begins to teach himself to become an expert microscopist. Throughout his studies and experiments, however, he feels frustrated by the limitations of his instruments. He imagines depths beyond that which his microscopes can reveal, and he dreams of discovering a perfect lens that will allow him to see what no man has ever seen. After months spent in a futile search for such a lens, quite coincidentally, as again is often the case in such fantasies, a young neighbor drops by and tells him of his visit to Madame Vulpes, a spirit medium who has related to him secrets that only magic could provide. The young man is a Jew, which supplies the stereotype of mysterious occult connections, as well as the stereotype of a peddler with mysterious objects in his possession. Hoping that Madame Vulpes will direct him to the secret of the powerful lens that he desires, the narrator goes to visit her.

In pursuit of his quest, Linley wishes to speak to Leeuwenhoek, the great father of microscopics, who tells him that he must find a diamond of 140 carats and subject it to electromagnetic currents to rearrange its atoms to make a universal and perfect lens. The greatest ironic coincidence in this story which depends on such coincidences is that Jules Simon, the Jewish neighbor, indeed has such a diamond. When the narrator discovers this, he gets Simon drunk, tricks him into revealing where the diamond is, and then kills him to get it, afterward calmly concealing his crime by making it look like a suicide—all of which is typical of a Poe story.

The last section of "A Diamond Lens" introduces the final element of the story and changes it from a fable about the quasi-scientific overreacher to a Romantic parable about the aesthetic ideal. When the narrator finishes constructing the lens, he puts a drop of water under it and discovers a realm of indescribable beauty filled with an atmosphere of magical luminousness. He knows that he has penetrated below the realm of protozoa to a world of supernatural radiance—a forestlike expanse, without a living thing—a beautiful chromatic desert. Then, most fantastic of all, he sees something moving, a female form, a divine revelation of perfect beauty that makes him think of aesthetic realms beyond actual reality. Given the conventions of such fantasies, it is inevitable that Linley fall in love with her, even though he knows that the planet Neptune is not more distant from him than she.

He names this microscopic vision of beauty "Animula" and longs for her with a passion reserved for that which is totally unobtainable; his whole life becomes absorbed by her. Trying to shake off his obsession, he goes to a theatrical presentation by a dancer reputed to be the most beautiful and most graceful woman in the world. Yet he can see only how gross and discordant are her movements, how thick are her ankles, how heavy and muscular are her limbs. When he returns to Animula, she seems to be growing ill, and he frantically tries to discover what ails her, mourning as she withers away. Finally, he discovers (in the typical ironic revelation of the Poe/Bierce fantasy) that the water drop in which Animula lives has evaporated; knowing that it is too late to save her, he watches her shrivel up and blacken. The story ends, in typical Poe fashion, with madness.

Themes and Meanings

The basic theme of "The Diamond Lens" begins to reveal itself only in the last quarter of the story, when the protagonist discovers the beautiful creature in the drop of water under the microscope. It is a typical Romantic theme, predominant in the early part of the nineteenth century and sustained in the century's closing decades by the influence of Poe's work on the Aesthetes. "The Diamond Lens" focuses on the difference between the realm of actual, perceptible physical reality and that realm of a more profound reality which is a projection of the human imagination. The issue is the fineness of the perceiving eye, based on the assumption that there is a realm of reality beneath or beyond that of the everyday physical world which partakes of the spiritual and is thus the truest.

The theme is made most clear in the contrast between the figure of Animula and that of an actual female. There is no way that any actual female can compete with the almost spiritual nature of Animula, spiritual because she is so little body. The theme is an aesthetic one, in which it is clear that the most human aspiration is to transcend the physical, for the physical is an indication of the grossness of the body itself. The great Romantic ideal is that one responds to a spiritual transcendence of body. The more that body is distanced from the sense of physicality and thus mortality, the more beautiful it is taken to be.

O'Brien inherits this Romantic ideal from Poe's Platonic retreat from body. The problem of this particular story, however, is that it depends too much on the simple trick ending of the evaporation of the drop of water in which the beautiful creature resides. This event has nothing to do with the theme of the beauty of the spiritual; it is simply a convenient way to indicate the impossibility of the narrator's love for absolute beauty. "A Diamond Lens," although it has some of the characteristics of a Romantic fable, is really primarily a trick story appealing to the mid-nineteenth century fascination with trick endings and with scientific fantasies.

Style and Technique

The style of "The Diamond Lens" primarily depends on O'Brien's manipulation of the point of view of a narrator who is so obsessed with his own desire and quasi-scientific aims that the entire world of the story centers on his obsession. The technique is a common one with such Romantic writers of the early nineteenth century as E. T. A. Hoffmann, Ludwig Tieck, and Poe. The language of the story suggests a narrator who is less an actual person than he is a convention of point of view itself—a stereotypical representation of the ultimate Romantic dream, here trivialized by a clever craftsman of the short story who knows how to capitalize on a typical short-story theme but who does not manage to elevate that theme and technique beyond popular slick fiction. It was precisely such stories as O'Brien's that gave the short-story genre during the late nineteenth century the unsavory reputation of being little more than a vehicle for facile technique. What marks the difference between O'Brien's story and the most powerful stories of Poe and Bierce is that O'Brien never achieves either the profound sense of the Romantic ideal of these writers or their keen sense of the particular characteristics of the short-story form.

Charles E. May

THE DIARY OF A MADMAN

Author: Nikolai Gogol (1809-1852)
Type of plot: Diary
Time of plot: The 1830's
Locale: St. Petersburg, Russia
First published: "Zapiski sumasshedshego," 1835 (English translation, 1945)

> *Principal characters:*
> THE NARRATOR, an unhappy clerk who is part of the vast
>   government bureaucracy of mid-nineteenth century
>   Russia
> HIS BOSS, who is also referred to as "The Chief of the
>   Division"
> SOPHIE, the chief's daughter
> MADGIE and FIDELE, two dogs who can speak and exchange
>   letters, the madman claims

The Story

"The Diary of a Madman," told in the first person, purports to be a diary kept by a forty-two-year-old clerk who has a meaningless job in the vast governmental bureaucracy of mid-nineteenth century Russia. His best prospects for advancement are far behind him, and his duties consist of routine tasks such as sharpening his employer's quills or copying information from one departmental form to another. He is unmarried, bored, and treated without kindness or courtesy. "They don't listen to me, they don't hear me, they don't see me," he realizes late in the story. "I cannot bear this suffering."

The daily entries in his journal reveal a man slowly going mad as he comes to understand his own insignificance. The narrator is scorned by his landlady, reprimanded by his boss, and accosted by strangers in the street. The diary shows how he manufactures explanations for these indignities. "There are so many crooks, so many Poles," so many civil servants "who sit on top of one another like dogs." He is quick to blame others for his shabby life. "I see through his indignation. He is envious," he says of one foe who has belittled him. "Perhaps he's noticed the marks of favor bestowed on me. A lot I care what he says of me." Such entries show the clerk using the conventional and commonplace rationalizations to which many people resort to explain away their failures and to evade their own contributions to their unhappiness. "High officers, they get all the best things in this world. You discover a crumb of happiness, you reach out for it and then along comes a high official and snatches it away."

Increasingly, these mild misperceptions cease to be effective. When reality metes out to the clerk more than his commonplace ideas can explain, he

starts inventing more fantastic rationalizations, which seem to remove him
further from reality. Adding to the pressures are his rare glimpses of Sophie,
his boss's daughter. He indulges in obsessive thoughts of love and devotion
toward her which are far out of proportion to her occasional and demeaning
comments to him. "Holy Fathers, the way she was dressed! Her dress was
white, and fluffy, like a swan, and when she looked at me, I swear, it was like
the sun." His comments about Sophie reveal a mind gradually losing touch
with reality. "Perhaps I am really a general or a count and only seem to be a
clerk. . . . There are plenty of instances in history when somebody quite
ordinary. . . turns out to be a public figure." As the madman loses himself in
this kind of wishful thinking, his personality begins to fragment. One part of
him actually starts believing that he occupies a high place on the social ladder. Another part, the part which seems to need feedback from the "real"
world, is reduced to a series of occasional hallucinatory experiences which
tell him the truths he otherwise could not hear. He thinks that he overhears
Sophie's dog, Madgie, talking with another dog. He thinks that he intercepts
some of the letters which the two dogs are secretly writing to each other; one
reveals that "Sophie can hardly control her laughter when she sees him,"
while another suggests that Sophie is about to be married.

As the journal entries start to show the fragmentation of the pathetic
clerk's mind, the sane part of him concocts "mad" explanations and the mad
part of him which reveals "sane" truths grow further apart. In the gap, yet a
third personality begins to emerge. "This is a day of great jubilation. Spain
has a new king. They've found him. I am the king." As a way of healing the
disparity between who he is and who he wants to be, the madman comes to
believe that he is the uncrowned king of a Western European country. At
work, he takes to signing his forms as "Ferdinand VIII." At the post office,
he inquires about the arrival of his royal retinue. To his landlady, he shows
off his new royal robes, patched together from pieces of his overcoat. Three-
quarters of the way through the story, the clerk has clearly turned into the
madman. His pathological behavior finds little understanding from those
who know him, and he is committed to an asylum for the insane.

This attempted cure simply multiplies the madman's disjointed personalities. As the king of Spain, he interprets what happens to him as an international conspiracy to keep him from his throne. He even sees the shaved heads
of the lunatics in the asylum and thinks that they are Dominican or Capuchin
monks. When his old personality returns and he again knows himself as a
clerk, he experiences being beaten with sticks, a common "treatment" for
the mentally ill in a nineteenth century European asylum. The beatings bring
out an even more childish personality fragment. He cries, "Mother, save your
wretched son! Let your tears fall on his sick head. See how they torture
him!" The story ends with him once again retreating into his "King of Spain"
fantasy, that being the psychological mode which seems to bring him the

most comfort. The ending leaves the disconcerting suggestion that sometimes it is better to be mad and happy than it is to be sane but miserable.

Themes and Meanings

"The Diary of a Madman" is one of Nikolai Gogol's most troubling and complex stories. It works on several different levels at once. On a psychological level, it is a surprisingly accurate account of the onset of a mental pathology, rendered decades before psychosis was carefully studied by European scientists. The story depicts a man growing increasingly psychotic. He misinterprets the information from his surroundings and gives himself an unrealistic, though more tolerable, sense of who he his. These reinterpretations increasingly remove him from the real world, and those around him begin to see him as a threat. They move to institutionalize him, this prescription for a cure accelerating the speed of his journey into insanity.

On a sociological level, though, this story is not so much about insanity as it is about the kind of society which causes it. The madman's job, his acquaintances, and the characters he meets in the streets are so configured that his madness is in itself a "sane" response or adaptation to the social pressures around him. In this sense, the story is a realistic portrayal of a social system which drives at least one of its members crazy. Nineteenth century Russia's emphasis on status, appearance, and bureaucratic rules, Gogol claims, creates an environment which encourages people to be more concerned with their roles than with their real selves: Their egos seem to have less value than the social positions those egos occupy.

Gogol here explores the effects of such a system, hinting that values such as these may tempt many into attending to the wrong things. His remains a portrait of madness, but a madness brought on by a society which in itself is more than a little mad.

Style and Technique

Many of Gogol's stories have such a contemporary ring to them that it is easy to forget that they were written a century and a half ago about a culture which had neither the industrial nor the urban attributes which are supposed to account for some of the characteristic themes and styles of modern fiction. Like many of his stories, Gogol's "The Diary of a Madman" studies how individual selves become alienated from the societies which are supposed to support them. This twentieth century motif is developed with an equally modernistic approach to narrative style. In this story, Gogol explores alienation by studying its effects on an individual consciousness. Readers are eased into the conflict by being allowed to experience directly the narrator's twisted thoughts. Like many moderns, Gogol avoids the comforts of a realistic plot and a detached, objective narration. Instead, he plunges his readers into a worldview where the fantasies, projections, and hallucinations of the narrator are treated as if they were as "real" as the setting, the commentary of other characters, or the incidents of the plot.

Gogol, however, is a bit gentler on his readers than many moderns. He eases them into the fantastic and implausible patterns of perception characteristic of his narrator by starting them off with a relatively "sane" speaker who is keeping an apparently "sane" diary. Since Gogol's interest is in showing how sanity can dissolve under societal pressures, his trick is to begin gradually with a more traditional and familiar narrative style and only gradually to introduce the oversensitized, psychotic quirks of his madman. Thus, when the narrator first claims to have overheard the two dogs, Madgie and Fidele, talking, Gogol returns his readers to a saner ground: "As a matter of fact, the world has seen many similar occurrences before." The narrator alludes to the English fish who broke water and "uttered a couple of words" and to the two cows whose stories recently received newspaper coverage for going "into a store and asking for a pound of tea." These early entries in the diary show a normal or familiar reasoning process trying to explain abnormal and unfamiliar data.

Page by page, though, the reader is encouraged to follow the disintegration of the narrator's personality by deciphering progressively more alien words and ideas. Thus, the dating of the journal entries starts familiarly: "December 8" or "November 13." They then progress oddly to: "Year 2000, April 43" or "No date. A day without date." They end with the nonsense of "25th date" or "da 34 te Mnth. Yr. yraurbeF 349." Similarly, the narrator's experiences seem to begin at the familiar "I see no advantage in working in our department. No side benefits whatever"; they progress to the confusing "But today something suddenly became clear to me when I recalled the conversation between the two dogs I'd overheard on Nevsky Avenue"; finally, they end at what seems to be full-blown psychosis: "I hear the twanging of a guitar string through the fog; on one side, the sea, and on the other, Italy." With such progressions Gogol hopes to give his readers a firsthand glimpse of a mind going mad. For early in the nineteenth century, this was an unusually innovative narrative structure.

Philip Woodard

THE DIFFERENCE

Author: Ellen Glasgow (1873-1945)
Type of plot: Domestic realism
Time of plot: c. 1920
Locale: A large eastern seaboard city
First published: 1923

>   *Principal characters:*
>   MARGARET FLEMING, a forty-four-year-old housewife
>   GEORGE FLEMING, her forty-five-year-old husband, a
>   businessman and real-estate developer, to whom she has
>   been married for twenty years
>   ROSE MORRISON, an artist in her early twenties, George's
>   recent lover
>   DOROTHY CHAMBERS, a housewife, Margaret's best friend
>   from girlhood

The Story

On a Saturday afternoon, Margaret Fleming gazes out at the autumn rains stripping leaves from the trees, as she has every fall for the past twenty years, but with quite different feelings. Before she saw them as symbols of loss; now she sees them sweeping away all her illusions. On the hearth of the library study, her husband George's room, lies the fallen letter which has caused this change. It has announced the death of her marriage. Gazing at herself in the mirror, she wonders how he, one year older, could begin a new love, for her an act of desecration. Hearing his step, she retrieves the letter, hiding it in the front of her dress.

They exchange trivial conversation. Looking at him, vital and healthy as always, she is surprised to discover signs of slackness about his mouth that she had not noticed before. She wonders why these appeared only after he loved another, and suspects she does not really know him even after twenty years. Yet until now she had believed her marriage nearly perfect. He admires her colorful flower arrangements; she remembers that she has always been pale, and muses upon how her surface life can look unchanged while she has been struck to the roots of her being. Does Rose Morrison, George's young lover, have the color she lacks?

Before he leaves for business, he asks if she will correct the galleys of a history of law he has been writing. She realizes he could not have done it without her; she has been necessary to his serious life. She agrees, as always. He also asks her to do some routine domestic tasks for him. She wonders whether Rose has done any of these things.

She paces, hearing the rain and falling leaves, and resolves never to give

him up. The butler announces Dorothy Chambers, her oldest friend and
principal support, yet Margaret is reluctant to see her, discovering that suffering leads to deception and fearing that Dorothy will detect the difference
in her.

Dorothy asks Margaret's help in a charity drive, then mentions that two of
their separated acquaintances have reconciled. Margaret is shocked out of
her numbness; she cannot understand how the woman agreed, since he had
claimed to love the other woman. Dorothy cynically dismisses the quality of
man's love and states that the woman enjoys the act of forgiveness because of
her "spiritual vanity." To her, Margaret, though lovely, knows nothing of life.
When Margaret retorts that Dorothy knows little of love, the latter asks
whether she means man's love or woman's—for women love ideally, men
only sensually. When Margaret still cannot understand why a man would
want to live with a woman he has said he does not love, Dorothy points out
that marriage involves more than love; it also involves convenience. Margaret
bursts out that the woman then ought to give up the man; Dorothy asks her
whether she would in a similar situation.

Margaret hesitates, then declares that she would. In making that decision,
she experiences a peace beyond pain, grief, and bitterness. Dorothy tells her
that she is a fool; George would be a comfort and a source of security even if
love were over. Then she leaves.

Margaret takes a moment to plan her actions, then carries out the routine
duties George had requested. Then, disdaining to take the car provided by
George, she sets out to ride the trolley to the suburban address given in the
letter—a villa George has acquired in an unfashionable suburb. Out in the
rain, she is overwhelmed with melancholy, feeling utterly deserted; in the
streetcar, immersed in isolation, she finds Dorothy's phrase "spiritual vanity"
echoing in her ears. Details from the entire twenty-year marriage drift
through her mind like dead leaves.

From the suburban station she walks to the villa through piles of sodden
leaves that look like graves. The villa itself is nondescript, neglected. A maid
answers the bell, informing Margaret that her mistress is out; when Margaret
announces that she will wait, she is led to a recently occupied living room.
Then Rose enters. Margaret is at first dazzled by her beauty, then sees it only
as the flame of burning leaves.

Behind Rose's youth and beauty Margaret senses the assurance of habitual self-gratification. Rose says that she is glad Margaret came, that it hurt
her to write the letter, but that she believes in always telling the truth. She
says that George does not know she wrote; she wanted to spare him, as, of
course, Margaret does. Margaret believes she has spent her life sparing him.

Rose offers Margaret a cup of tea or a cigarette, speculating on what Victorian women like Margaret did for solace without cigarettes. Margaret
declines, now seeing in Rose all the crude rapacity of youth and also the

insolence of an artist. Rose acknowledges this: She has a studio in Greenwich Village but paints in the summers at Ogonquit, where she met George. She knew George was married, but also that Margaret did not understand him, as she does. Rejecting Margaret's claim of shared experiences, she asserts that only an artist could understand him. When Margaret asks whether George claimed to be misunderstood, Rose becomes nearly indignant, stating that George would rather suffer silently than make her unhappy. As proof of George's love, Rose offers to show his letters. Then she states that if she were in Margaret's position, she would gladly give him up out of love.

Margaret recoils from this, finding Rose, like youth in general, eager to benefit from the sacrifices of others and realizing that all of her sacrifices have preserved George's youth at her expense. Yet she has been trained in sacrifice, and she feels convinced that George must love Rose; otherwise he would not have brought her this much grief. She resolves to concede; as she leaves, Rose assures her that she and George share a superior understanding.

Margaret returns, convinced that George truly loves Rose, that his dilemma must have been devastating, that she has failed to understand him, and that she must sacrifice herself for him. Her love compels her not to stand in his way.

When they meet, she tells him that she has seen Rose Morrison, expecting him to be overcome by remorse. Instead he is blank, merely asking what she knows of Rose. In the face of this apparent denial, she discloses bit by bit her discoveries of that afternoon, ending with the confession that she does not want to stand in his way. Finally he exclaims, "What does it have to do with you?" and denies that he has ever loved Rose. He admits that Rose loves him, after her fashion, but for him it has been only a tawdry affair and he has no intention of leaving Margaret. He rehearses the history of their liaison, begun the previous summer when Margaret was ill, calling it simply a "recreation."

Margaret feels totally compromised, even sensing for a moment that she and Rose were bonded more closely in this experience of female disillusionment than she and George could ever be. She finds herself incapable of responding to George's pleas, mutely caught up in a sense of loss of more than love, for she has ceased to believe in life. As he embraces her, her glance strays through the window to the falling leaves outside.

Themes and Meanings

The story is intricately plotted, with three climaxes and reversals, all carefully controlled by the focus on Margaret's consciousness. The first phase centers on her discovery of betrayal and infidelity, on the contrast between her placid assumption of routine domestic duties and George's varied outside interests. She is devastated that a twenty-year marriage should expire in an afternoon, but he blandly carries on with business as usual. Her first instinct is to fight for what is hers. This movement comes to a climax in the visit of Dorothy Chambers with her cynical views of the different ways of men and women in love and her suggestion that marriage involves both more and less than love. Margaret rejects that counsel and decides to confront Rose; the implication is that she continues to feel that marriage depends on mutual love.

The second phase involves her exchange with Rose. Here the conflict is partly older woman and experience against younger woman and the intensity of youth, partly domestic housewife against independent career woman. Yet more is engaged than that. Both women speak of love as a common, identifiable experience and feeling, almost a supreme law to which both must conform. Margaret realizes that if George loves Rose—and Rose is confident that he does—in the way the women speak of love, then Margaret must give him up. Only for that supreme reason could he have hurt her so much. She resolves to concede.

The third and final phase is her conference with George. Here, once again, things turn out not as she expected. Far from confirming Rose's account of their relationship, George denies its substance, asserting that it was no more significant than a game of golf. Margaret cannot understand this; he seems to be giving words such as "love" a totally different meaning, and this allows him to treat women as adversaries. This attitude desecrates all of them. Small wonder that she now feels life has no meaning; she has discovered that the kind of love which means so much to women is unappreciated by men. This final climax is shattering, because the only alternative it leaves is the cynical opportunism of Dorothy Chambers.

Style and Technique

The major stylistic device used by Glasgow is the symbolism of autumn rain and falling leaves, which take on different nuances throughout the story. They appear prominently at both beginning and end, enclosing the action in an allusive arch of tone and feeling.

At the outset, the leaves are tied into the annual cycle of year: Their falling signifies the necessity of passing, of the old giving way to the new. Thus autumn reminds Margaret that she too is aging, but she accepts it as the price of her memories and values. This time; however, the fall seems final: Her hopes of continuing happiness have been destroyed.

The image of the leaves recurs at critical points throughout. Margaret's beauty is passing like the leaves; her spirit has been stricken like the leaves and is driven by the storm. She is pale of complexion, colorless like the fallen leaves; Rose has the blazing glow of youth. Margaret remembers her engagement in a rose garden; now the petals and leaves of that garden are nothing but withered ashes. Her universe is dying down.

The flame of love in Rose's eyes is likened to the blaze of color in burning leaves. Yet her neglected villa is surrounded with heaps of rotting leaves, like grave mounds; George derides her dream that he and Rose had reached a "secret garden of romance" in which he became the "perfect lover." Both women's hopes and fantasies are stricken like leaves before George's selfish brutality. In the end, they have only the leaves.

James L. Livingston

DI GRASSO
A Tale of Odessa

Author: Isaac Babel (1894-1941)
Type of plot: Impressionistic realism
Time of plot: 1908
Locale: Odessa
First published: 1937 (English translation, 1955)

> *Principal characters:*
> THE NARRATOR, the interpreter of the story, presented as the
> same person as the author
> THE NARRATOR as a boy of fourteen, the protagonist of an
> autobiographical recollection
> NICK SCHWARZ, a dealer in theater tickets (a scalper), for
> whom the boy works in his spare time
> DI GRASSO, a Sicilian actor, the hero of a play performed by
> an Italian troupe
> MADAM SCHWARZ, the obese wife of Nick

The Story

Because this brief work is a sophisticated commentary on the nature of art as well as "just a story," it is all the more interesting for the reader to know that it is the last work Babel published in his lifetime, before he fell victim to Stalinist justice. Although the exact circumstances of Babel's arrest in 1939 are not known, it is believed that he was charged with espionage, a patently contrived accusation; he was executed in 1941. The Jewish author, whose collections of stories were often reprinted during his lifetime, was "rehabilitated" after the death of Stalin—and again his stories were reprinted.

"Di Grasso" ostensibly focuses its attention on the Jewish theatrical world of prewar Odessa (about 1908), where one learns that the narrator as a boy of fourteen has recently "come under the sway" of the "tricky" ticket scalper Nick Schwarz and his "enormous silky handle bars." Without looking further into the relationship between the boy and the older man who is his "boss," the narrator instead describes (entertainingly) almost the entire action of a very bad play being newly performed by a traveling troupe of Italian actors. In this play, a "city slicker" named Giovanni temporarily lures the daughter of a rich peasant away from her betrothed—a poor shepherd played by the Sicilian actor Di Grasso. Di Grasso pleads with the girl to pray to the Virgin Mary—a huge, garish, wooden statue of whom is onstage—but to no avail. In the last act, when Giovanni has become insufferably arrogant, Di Grasso suddenly soars across the stage, plunges downward onto Giovanni, bites through his throat, and sucks out the gushing blood—as the curtain falls.

Recognizing a hit when he sees one, Schwarz rushes to the box office, where he will wait all night, first in line to buy at dawn as many tickets as he can afford, for resale. The narrator shortly remarks that everyone in Theater Lane has been made happy by the new hit—except himself.

Now an entirely new story line develops. It seems that the lad has taken his father's watch without permission and pawned it to Schwarz—who eventually grows very fond of the big gold turnip. Even after the boy pays off the pledge, Schwarz refuses to give back the watch. The boy is in continual despair, imagining his father's wrath. He suggests that Schwarz and his father have the same character.

Then one night Schwarz and his wife, along with the boy, attend the final performance of the Italian troupe, with Di Grasso playing the shepherd "who is swung aloft by an incomprehensible power." Schwarz's wife, a fat and sentimental woman with "fishlike eyes," is overwhelmed by Di Grasso's great leap of love. She laments her own loveless life and berates her husband as they walk home from the theater with the boy trailing behind. The boy sobs openly, thinking of his father and the watch. Madam Schwarz hears the sobs and angrily forces her husband to return the watch, which he does, but not without giving the lad a vicious pinch.

The Schwarzes walk on, reach the corner, and disappear. The boy is left alone to experience ultimate happiness; he sees the world at night "frozen in silence and ineffably beautiful."

Themes and Meanings

At an elementary level of meaning, this story reveals the hidden relationships that may exist between apparently unconnected things and events. The Italian play, with its fantastic Sicilian actor, acts powerfully on the unloved wife of the swindler Nick Schwarz—and the boy and his watch are saved.

The story becomes more interesting when the reader sees that it is precisely the power of art that is significant, rather than merely "a play." Finally, it is not art in general that is at issue, but art of great passion. Here, bad art is "transformed" by a passionate actor. Commenting on Di Grasso's acting, the narrator insists that the Sicilian, "with every word and gesture," confirms that there is "more justice in outbursts of noble passion than in all the joyless rules that run the world."

Such an explicit statement, not all that common in Babel, must be taken seriously. One wonders if "joyless rules" might refer to the Soviet Union of the bleak 1930's, and if Nick Schwarz, with his handlebar mustaches, is not intended to be seen as a pitiless Stalin figure. In any case, however, such political overtones are not the central focus of the work.

Passion in life, as in art, is a recurring motif in Babel's writings. Often it is accompanied by violence, as in the present work—which depicts not only the murderous leap of Di Grasso but also the descent of the curtain "full of menace" and the "vicious pinch" exacted by Schwarz. If life is lived fully and passionately, some violence is inevitable.

As art influences or works itself into life (here moving Schwarz's wife to take pity on the boy), so may life be transformed into art. Thus the boy, dizzy with happiness, sees the ordinary world of the city transformed into ineffable beauty. Here reality, art, and transcendent beauty merge in a remarkable vision. The boy's epiphany has the character of a future writer's first glimpse of the world beyond everyday reality (or of the way reality really is if one looks at it right).

Style and Technique

One of the most interesting aspects of "Di Grasso" is the author's tone. What exactly is Babel's attitude toward his subject?

Throughout the story, the narrator seems affectionately and playfully condescending toward the characters he describes. For example, the reader learns that the Italian actors are bad not from any direct statement by the author (or by Schwarz, who cannot necessarily be trusted when he says "This stuff stinks"), but from such observations as "the shepherd twisted his head this way and that like a startled bird," or, he kept "dashing off somewhere, his pants flapping." In general, Babel uses what the Russion Formalist critic Viktor Shklovsky called "defamiliarization" (*ostranenie*) to induce one to see the play as a profane work, though in a humorous light. That one is suddenly asked to see the terrible actor Di Grasso as a genuinely passionate hero is a welcome surprise, even if one realizes also that this perception is rather more symbolic than real. (The way that Babel describes the play is much like the way Leo Tolstoy describes grand opera in *War and Peace*.)

Babel employs colorful and exotic imagery to depict not only the Italian actors, but also the Jews of the bustling seaport of Odessa. Giovanni onstage seems to have been transported to his native land: "Beneath the Sicilian sun the pleats in his waistcoat gleamed." After reporting the success of the play and making his homage to passion, the narrator notes that a "pink and dusty sultriness was injected into Theater Lane." The imagery hints at a sexual passion shortly made explicit in the description of "moneyed Jews with beards parted down the middle" coming to "tap discreetly on the doors of fat women with raven hair and little mustaches, Di Grasso's actresses."

Babel makes the reader understand that this is the profane world—but he declines to judge it and probably even likes it, as he doubtless likes and respects, though condescendingly, a certain wooden stage prop used by the Italian troupe—"a poverty-stricken but brightly painted image of the Holy Virgin." Babel seems to imply even early in the story that this icon is the profane counterpart to some higher and sacred possibility. Only at the close of "Di Grasso," however, does the narrator fully abandon his condescending tone.

When the boy has his transcendent vision, it is described in a wholly serious tone reflecting the author's recognition of its authenticity. All the elements of the story come together at this point, and one sees the transformed buildings "soaring up into the heights, the gas-lit foliage of the boulevard, Pushkin's bronze head touched by the dim gleam of the moon" as a powerful showing forth of the true relationship between art and reality.

Donald M. Fiene

DISORDER AND EARLY SORROW

Author: Thomas Mann (1875-1955)
Type of plot: Domestic irony
Time of plot: c. 1922
Locale: Munich
First published: "Unordnung und frühes Leid," 1926 (English translation, 1929)

> *Principal characters:*
> DR. CORNELIUS, the protagonist, forty-seven years old, a history professor
> FRAU CORNELIUS, his wife
> INGRID,
> BERT,
> ELLIE, and
> SNAPPER, their children
> MAX HERGESELL, a friend of Ingrid and Bert

The Story

At midday dinner (turnip green croquettes and a trifle made of a dessert powder that tastes like soap), all the Cornelius family members are introduced, their personalities quickly sketched, and their relations with one another indicated. Told entirely from the point of view of the professor, the story begins as his two older children, Ingrid and Bert, remind him that they are giving a party that evening. Ingrid assures her father that he will not be disturbed. Somewhat disconcerted by the slight disruption of his orderly routine, the professor nevertheless is determined to be affable in his formal, old-fashioned way. It is clear from the beginning of the story that Dr. Cornelius is dismayed and bewildered by the discrepancies between his values and those of his older children, and by their slang, their practical jokes, their frivolous ambitions, their casual manners. It is also clear, however, that there is affection and good humor between them as well, though tolerance seems to come much more easily to the young people than to their parents.

The case is different with regard to the two younger children, five-year-old Ellie (her father's favorite) and Snapper (four years old and more comfortable with his gentle mother). The professor is able to set aside his natural dignity while he plays with Ellie and Snapper. Today the games are cut short by preparations for the party, so Dr. Cornelius retires to his study, the little ones return to the nursery, and the others go off on various errands. Later, while the professor is resting, the guests begin to arrive.

Slightly nervous and self-conscious, the professor goes down to the dining room and is introduced to several young people, including Max Hergesell, who is charming, courteous, and humorous. Ellie and Snapper join the festivities, and Dr. Cornelius, having conversed with several of the guests, returns to his study to work, but with his attention distracted by the dancing and singing in the room next door. In due time he goes out for his nightly walk, first pausing for some conversation. He observes with a pang how Ellie persists in trying to get Max's attention while he is dancing with a fat young woman.

As he walks, preoccupied with his professional concerns, Dr. Cornelius also thinks about the need to be just toward the younger generation, especially in these chaotic and desolate times. Upon his return home, he is called to the nursery, where he finds Snapper asleep but Ellie in tears, sobbing and wailing, suffering because she does not understand her sorrow as her father, with pity and distress, does. It is for Max that Ellie is weeping, and when he appears to say goodnight, Ellie is transfigured with a joy she also does not understand. The father is grateful to the young man for his kindness, but he also feels embarrassed and hostile. After Max leaves and Ellie falls asleep, Dr. Cornelius sits by her bed thinking tenderly of his angelic daughter and of the games they will play again as Max, he thankfully supposes, will fade into a shadow with no more power to grieve and bewilder her.

Themes and Meanings

The title of the story suggests the primary issues with which Thomas Mann is concerned. From the opening sentence, with its dismal account of the family's frugal meal, Mann presents a detailed picture of postwar Germany as reflected in the experiences of the Cornelius family. The inflation, the shortages and privations, the general lawlessness and laxity—all are indicated in details about the servants and the guests, in conversations among the family members, and especially in the professor's musings. Frau Cornelius must interrupt her preparations for the party to cycle hurriedly into town to buy provisions with money which may lose all value at any moment. The refreshments are extremely simple, many of the guests are not in evening clothes, the dancing is strange and unattractive, the music too loud.

The professor realizes that he is out of place in this postwar world, and he feels hostile toward the present. Thus, he is troubled by his devotion to his little daughter, suspecting that his great love for her is somehow connected with his love for the past and also connected in some way to death.

The second part of the title is related to Ellie's uncontrollable and bewildered sorrow, her childish yearning for the kind young man who danced with her. In her unrestrained anguish, Ellie also appears to partake of the general "disorder" of the times.

Style and Technique

The principal characteristic of Mann's style in this story is irony. The story about the professor's dedication to the past and his conflicting emotions about the younger generation's ways is told in the present tense; in addition to giving the narrative dramatic immediacy, the use of the present tense highlights the underlying theme. Mann's distinctive use of telling details is particularly evident here; even minor characters such as the good-for-nothing young manservant and the blue-faced nurse spring to life in a few sentences. The professorial protagonist is characteristically thoughtful, serious, courteous, and restrained; his feelings are merely suggested or briefly mentioned, while his thoughts are expressed clearly and forcefully. Thus, Mann avoids bitterness, contempt, or sentimentality. In the end, the effect of this restrained and controlled style is deeply moving.

Natalie Harper

THE DISPLACED PERSON

Author: Flannery O'Connor (1925-1964)
Type of plot: Psychological realism
Time of plot: After World War II
Locale: The rural Southern United States
First published: 1954

> *Principal characters:*
> MRS. MCINTYRE, the owner of a farm
> MR. and MRS. SHORTLEY, white farm workers
> MR. GUIZAC, a Polish emigrant who comes to work on Mrs.
>   McIntyre's farm
> FATHER FLYNN, a local priest

The Story

The title of this story suggests that is is about one displaced person. In fact, the tale is about several people who are displaced. In one character's words, "Displaced Persons . . . means they ain't where they were born at and there's nowhere for them to go—like if you was run out of here and wouldn't nobody have you." To explore this idea of displacement, Flannery O'Connor divides her story into three parts, emphasizing Mrs. Shortley, then Mrs. McIntyre, and finally the displaced person, or D.P., who connects all the other D.P.'s, Mr. Guizac.

In the first part, the idea of displacement is introduced through the character of Guizac, a Polish emigré who comes to Mrs. McIntyre's farm with his family after escaping from his native country. Mrs. Shortley, a farm worker with her husband on Mrs. McIntyre's farm, views Guizac as a foreigner who does not belong. His name is strange—she pronounces it "Gobblehook"— and he speaks a strange language. Because of her limited vision, she sees Guizac not only as a stereotype but also as a threat, for he endangers both the predictability of their lives and the security of their jobs. Guizac is, after all, far more efficient and skilled than her husband, Chancey. When she overhears Mrs. McIntyre telling the priest that she will be giving the Shortley's notice that they are to be replaced—displaced—by the Guizacs, Mrs. Shortley decides to pack up her family and depart before Mrs. McIntyre has the chance to fire them. Leaving the farm, Mrs. Shortley has her second dramatic inner vision (the first was immediately before she overheard Mrs. McIntyre's conversation). This final, mysterious, personal vision destroys Mrs. Shortley and leaves her family dumbfounded: "They didn't know that she had had a great experience or ever been displaced in the world from all that belonged to her."

The second part of the story focuses on Mrs. McIntyre's vision, which, unlike the ultimately enlarging vision of Mrs. Shortley, is a gradually restricting view of Guizac. When Guizac first arrives and demonstrates his farming skills and efficiency, Mrs. McIntyre is delighted, believing that Guizac is her "salvation." His redemptive qualities, however, escape her notice when he arranges for one of the black farm workers to pay for the transportation of Guizac's cousin to the United States. In return for transportation, the cousin would be married to the farm worker. When Mrs. McIntyre learns of this arrangement, her anger overtakes her earlier delight, and she repeats, with new emphasis, her earlier adage: "The devil you know is better than the devil you don't know." She knows the white farm workers; she knows the black farm workers; she does not know know the ultimate implications of life with the Polish farm worker. Mrs. McIntyre decides that he is "extra," that he does not fit in, that he "upsets the balance." Estranging herself from the Polish D.P., she becomes increasingly displaced, separating herself from her place and her help. She becomes desperate and cooperates in a desperate action.

This action occurs in the third part of the story, after Mr. Shortley returns to the farm and systematically speaks out about Guizac's foreignness. He announces his dislike for foreigners because, in the war, he saw what they were like. As he recalls, "none of them were like us," and, in fact, one man who threw a hand-grenade at him "had had little round eye-glasses exactly like Mr. Guizac's." Although Mrs. McIntyre recognizes the problem with that logic, since Guizac is a Pole and not a German, the general unwillingness to accept the foreigner persists. Mrs. McIntyre, Mr. Shortley, and the blacks— all fearful that they will be displaced by the D.P.—are united by their desire to rid themselves of this "devil" whom they do not know.

In the final scene of the story, Guizac is killed by a runaway tractor. The death appears to be caused by the machine, but O'Connor suggests another cause: Perhaps Mrs. McIntyre, Mr. Shortley, and the black farm workers caused the death, since they did nothing to stop the machine. Since all of their eyes had "come together in one look that froze them in collusion forever," perhaps the displaced survivors really destroyed the displaced victim.

Themes and Meanings

All the characters in this story are displaced and are displacing someone else. Guizac is literally a D.P., but the other characters are also displaced, alienated from one another and from the place where they were born. As Mrs. McIntyre puts it, "Times are changing. . . . Do you know what's happening to this world? It's swelling up. It's getting so full of people that only the smart thrifty energetic ones are going to survive." Gone is the simple world of simple values; replacing it is the complex world of modern war, technology, and the victims of both.

At the end of the story, even "the smart thrifty energetic ones" do not survive, for Mr. Shortley leaves without notice for a new position, the young black farm worker departs, and the old black helper cannot work without company. Mrs. McIntyre becomes bedridden, visited only by the priest who comes not only to teach her the Church's doctrines but also to feed the peacock, the ultimate reminder of mystery in the midst of ordinariness.

Style and Technique

Since O'Connor is interested in the way in which people see, she uses various strategies and images related to the idea of vision. In the opening scene, Mrs. Shortley is blind to the beauty of nature and the peacock and notes the arrival of strangers through her narrow, bigoted vision. This tunnel vision is replaced by another kind of seeing, one so monumental as to be overwhelming, leading her to prophesy and then to succumb to her own prophecy of destruction.

Mrs. McIntyre's vision is pragmatic, not prophetic, for she sees the universe in practical, useful terms. When she comes to see that the Pole is an unfathomable mystery, she decides that he is the devil she does not know, and she is compelled to rid herself of that unknown quantity.

Contrasting with Mrs. McIntyre's pragmatic vision is Father Flynn's spiritual gaze. He sees everything and everyone as a reflection of the divine: The peacock, for example, is not a beautiful creature on the farm; it is a symbol of Christ and a reminder of the Transfiguration. Mrs. McIntyre on her deathbed is not a woman seeking human comfort; she is a potential convert to the Church. In O'Connor's fiction, what one sees is not always what one gets, but what one sees is indeed what one is.

Marjorie Smelstor

A DISTANT EPISODE

Author: Paul Bowles (1911-   )
Type of plot: Psychological realism
Time of plot: The late 1930's
Locale: North Africa
First published: 1947

> *Principal characters:*
> THE PROFESSOR, the linguist who becomes the victim of the
>   Reguibat
> THE BUS DRIVER, who transports the Professor to Ain
>   Tadouirt
> THE WAITER, who guides the Professor
> THE REGUIBAT, the desert nomads

The Story

The story begins with a description of the Professor (no proper name is given) being transported by bus to Ain Tadouirt, a town in eastern Morocco. The Professor had spent three days in the town ten years previously, during which time he had established a friendship with a café keeper named Hassan Ramani. The driver asks the Professor if he is a geologist, and the Professor tells him that he is a linguist "making a survey of variations on Moghrebi" dialects. The Moghrebi are a people who live in a region in Africa north of the Sahara.

When the Professor arrives in the town, he visits the café and is told by the waiter that his friend Hassan Ramani is now "deceased." This same waiter—whose tone of voice is insolent and whose face takes on a look of anger when the Professor inquires about getting camel-udder boxes—agrees, for a price, to take the Professor to the place from which he can "get camel-udder boxes if there are any."

When they arrive at the place, the waiter-guide tells the Professor that he must proceed ahead alone. The Professor pays him fifty francs and dismisses him. Then, after experiencing mingled feelings of fear of what dangers might lie ahead for him on the desolate road and relief that the guide did not play a trick on him, he starts down the path, which leads into what looks like a quarry. As soon as he reaches the bottom, he is attacked by a wild dog, and, while the dog is unrelentingly tearing at him, he experiences the sensation of something "cold and metallic . . . pushed brutally against his spine." It is at this point that an echo of a phrase or maxim that the Professor has heard in many shops and marketplaces in town reverberates in his mind: "The Reguiba is a cloud across the face of the sun . . . when the Reguiba appears the righteous man turns away." Who else could these attackers be but the

Reguibat, who go about their brutal business quickly, kicking aside the dog and then, with the same vigor, the Professor, all over his body? Semiconscious, the Professor can hear the low, guttural voices of his attackers as they go about emptying his pockets, fiercely pulling and twisting his tongue, doubling him up and dumping him into a sack before slinging him alongside a camel. Later, he is taken out of the sack and is girdled with tin bands around his torso, arms, legs, and face until he is "entirely within a suit of armor." To celebrate the occasion, one of the Reguibat plays his flute and is accompanied by the general merriment of the others.

The Reguibat keep the Professor for one year and consider him their valuable possession. It is a year during which the Professor entertains the Reguibat by performing a senseless hopping routine, making jangling noises with his tin-banded body, doing handsprings, growling, and making obscene gestures "which never failed to elicit delighted shrieks from the women."

Finally, the Professor is taken to a town and sold to one of the villagers, but he suddenly enters "into consciousness again" and will not perform for his new owner. The man, who paid a handsome price for him, becomes infuriated, thinking he has been cheated by the Reguibat. He seeks out and finds one of the Reguibat still abed with one of the village girls and gets his revenge swiftly by nearly decapitating him. Meanwhile, the Professor, left unattended in his new owner's house, begins bellowing as loud as he can, crying out to escape from his captivity. He bangs against the door and when it finally bursts open, he rushes out into the street "bellowing and shaking his arms in the air to make as loud a jangling as possible." People only look at him with curiosity. A French soldier, after observing the Professor's strange behavior, says to himself, "Hey! A holy maniac," and then takes a "potshot at him for good luck" while the figure of the Professor, cavorting beyond the village gate, grows smaller and smaller in the shadow of the "oncoming evening darkness."

Themes and Meanings

"A Distant Episode" reflects a tragic circumstance that goes beyond mere ironic reversal. The obvious, uncomplicated irony in the story is that the Professor, the educated, "civilized" observer, goes among the Moroccans to survey the variations of their dialects and, while he is at it, to pick up a camel-udder box or two; instead, the Professor-Linguist—whose tongue and whole being are brutally violated by the Reguibat—becomes the victim of a cruel twist of circumstances which turn him into the observed species.

After reading this story, a tale of terror alongside which the stories of Edgar Allan Poe and Flannery O'Connor pale in comparison, one is compelled to ask, why must one whose only real flaw seems to be poor judgment suffer such cruel consequences? Although no explicit explanation is offered, Bowles implies that the Professor is guilty of a certain unconscious arrogance, a presumptuousness that is dangerous in a harshly absurd world.

Evidently, the Professor thinks that because he is an educated man and a linguist by profession, he has the right to practice his profession anywhere. This merely wrongheaded thinking results in consequences outrageously humiliating and cruel. Yet who ever said that life was fair? Or that justice measures out equally? Or that going to the grocery store to buy a quart of milk merely because it is a routine business is going to guarantee one a safe return home?

Bowles does not give the Professor a proper name because he represents Everyman; he is an Everyman who does not realize that the contingencies of life combined with one's conscious actions will not be denied their due. For every planned conscious intention one conceives, good or bad, there is a Reguiba lurking in the darkness nearby, waiting to become a part of it and metamorphose its victim into doing its will, which indeed will be done if the right combination of circumstances fall into the intruder's favor. Civilization, personified in the Professor, is simply no match for mindless, free-roaming evil, personified in the Reguibat, who move only in the darkness of night and like night itself are collectively " a cloud across the face of the sun."

The desolate landscape where this "distant episode" takes place is an appropriate setting for such a drama. Yet Bowles's North African locale can be seen in its larger metaphorical sense as the centerpiece setting for similar, if less cruel, episodes which take place daily all over the world, episodes which go mostly unnoticed. Who knows when, because of one's little misjudgments, the "Reguibat" may not turn up in the desert of one's own life?

Style and Technique

How leisurely and urbane the tone of the language is in the opening paragraph of "A Distant Episode." Long, slowly measured sentences, with modifiers practically banging into one another, abound:

> Now facing the flaming sky in the west, and now facing the sharp mountains, the car followed the dusty trail down the canyons into air which began to smell of other things besides the endless ozone of the heights: orange blossoms, pepper, sun-baked excrement, burning olive oil, rotten fruit. He closed his eyes happily and lived for an instant in a purely olfactory world.

Sun-baked excrement and all, reflected in the opening paragraph is the anticipation of romance or adventure, certainly not a sense of imminent danger. The opening paragraph sets the ironic tone of "A Distant Episode," and the unrelenting, crushing weight of it is felt fully by the time the reader gets to the end of the story.

There is a sharp contrast to this leisurely rhythm when, near the end of the story, the Professor begins to feel "the slow sharpening of his consciousness"; the vital action patterns of the sentences give thrust to his sudden, urgent need to find release from his condition: "He felt . . . he attacked . . . he climbed . . . he began to gallop. . . ." When nobody pays attention to him except the French soldier "who takes a potshot at him for good luck," one sees the fading image of what was once a civilized man, a cavorting figure growing smaller and smaller, framed in a funereal "great silence out there beyond the gate."

P. Angelo

THE DISTRICT DOCTOR

Author: Ivan Turgenev (1818-1883)
Type of plot: Vignette
Time of plot: The 1840's
Locale: Rural Russia
First published: "Uezdnyi lekar'," 1848 (English translation, 1855)

> *Principal characters:*
> TRIFON IVANYCH, a lower-middle-class, semieducated, but
>   conscientious country doctor
> ALEXANDRA ANDREYEVNA, a beautiful young woman
>   unsuccessfully treated by Trifon Ivanych

The Story

Here, as in all the stories in *Zapiski okhotnika* (1852; *A Sportsman's Sketches*, 1855), Ivan Turgenev (or his transparently disguised alter ego, the gentleman sportsman on a hunting trip) encounters the protagonist, the "district doctor," in a natural, casual fashion. The weather is bad, the sportsman falls ill, and his only choice of a doctor turns out to be a modest local man, Trifon Ivanych. Grateful for any distraction, the patient listens to the doctor unburden himself of a haunting incident. Turgenev subtly persuades the reader to identify with the fretfully ailing sportsman and to await the unfolding of the doctor's tale with impatience.

Yet the doctor, who tells the story in his own words, has difficulty in sticking to his subject. His apologies, self-deprecations, and fussy details not only increase the suspense but also draw the portrait of an earnest but limited fellow, very uncomfortable with the subject matter that he is trying to convey.

One night, in his younger days, the doctor was summoned to an emergency: A young woman is critically ill with fever. The horses and carriage sent for him are pitiful, the roads are impassable, and the house is a long way off. The doctor feels wretched, both at these conditions and at the meager remuneration that undoubtedly awaits him.

At last, in the middle of this terrible night, the doctor arrives. He finds himself deeply moved. The dying girl, Alexandra Andreyevna, is very beautiful; the widowed mother is in despair; the two other sisters are touchingly concerned. They are cultivated people, but very poor: This doctor is their only hope for saving her.

The doctor's life thus veers from its course: He is unable to leave the girl's side. He forgets all of his other patients, virtually stops fretting about fees, and moves into her house to devote himself to curing her.

Long before it is over, the doctor knows that her case is hopeless, yet he cannot bear to leave. His feelings are a mixture of professional duty, pity, and fascination. There is a mystery locked inside this dying young woman. On the first night, she began to say, "I will tell you, why I don't want to die," but she has not yet come out with her explanation.

The reader endures increasing suspense, in parallel with the doctor's growing despair, as Alexandra only gets worse the harder he tries to cure her. One night, when she realizes that she is probably never going to get well, she confesses to the doctor: "If I can know for certain that I must die . . . then I will tell you all—all!" What is the terrible secret that has been tormenting her? "Do you hear, I love you!" she lets out at last.

The doctor copes with this most ineptly. Alexandra grasps at him with physical passion, and he almost screams aloud. As an act of mercy, he pretends a proposal of marriage, not very convincingly.

Then a note of bitter comedy enters. Having known him only as "doctor" until now, Alexandra wishes to learn the first name of her beloved. Highly cultivated and high-class as she is (at least in his eyes), she finds his resoundingly plebeian name (which even in Russian sounds funny) hard to take: Trifon Ivanych. The "unpleasant" laugh and the French phrase with which this poor but extremely proud young woman reacts to his ridiculous name are not lost on Trifon.

Nor is the falseness of her position, as his pretended "fiancée," lost on Alexandra. By the next morning, she has seriously deteriorated. The final three days include an excruciating charade of asking for her mother's blessing on their union. The girl herself dies unconvinced.

After years of pondering this strange event in his life, the doctor has come to his own understanding of it: "Say what you will, it's hard to die at twenty without having known love; this was what was torturing her; this was why, in despair, she caught at me—do you understand now?"

Having gotten the morbid story off his chest, and now perfectly calm again, the doctor modestly refers to his subsequent marriage to a merchant's daughter: "seven hundred for a dowry" coming out in the same breath.

Themes and Meanings

In this very early story, Turgenev introduces some well-worn romantic themes: the motif of three sisters, the confession of love as a terrible secret, and the image of Death itself seemingly in love with Beauty. Amid this romantic material, Turgenev sardonically plunks Trifon, the apologetic, snuff-taking, ruble-counting sawbones who shies away from "exalted emotions" (as he understands Alexandra's passion).

Turgenev stays well in the background of this story, in his guise as a sympathetic listener, giving scarcely a clue as to his own interpretation of the events. He does make clear, however, that Trifon is a very limited fellow and a highly imperfect witness. The reader must fill in and make corrections for Trifon, and this gives rise to many possible interpretations. For example, the fate of the extremely proud girl, who has to be at the point of death before she can bring herself to confess her feelings for the too modest doctor, would seem to be the story's chief irony. If one corrects for Trifon's extreme humility and class-consciousness, however, it may well be Trifon who is the victim of an irony of fate. Perhaps Alexandra's appreciation of his devotion to her had awakened a genuine love in her, which was totally lost on him.

The twin themes of the unendurable burden of unspoken love, and the equally excruciating consequences of confessing it, later attain a rich development in all of Turgenev's mature major works. The type of the morbidly proud woman, while generally associated mainly with the works of Fyodor Dostoevski, is here seen to be a part of Turgenev's world as well, even at a very early stage.

Style and Technique

In "The District Doctor," Turgenev experimented with a narrative technique that was still new in Russian literature at that time and that later (notably in the hands of Nikolai Leskov) became known as *skaz*. In *skaz*, a humble, semi-educated (or even illiterate) narrator relates an incident from his own life, in his own words, with much unconscious irony as well as unconscious self-portraiture.

Though the doctor appears to ramble, Turgenev crafts every word of the doctor's self-revelations carefully. Apart from contributing to the plot, every phrase that the doctor uses gives another clue as to his own background, virtues, blind spots, and life-style.

The advantages of the *skaz* technique are its naturalness and the feeling that it gives of real life as lived by real, ordinary people. It thus helps to forestall any tendency toward disbelief on the part of the reader, especially in a tale dealing with inherently sensational subject matter. It provides a particularly fine foil to romantic themes, infusing them with new realism.

D. G. Nakeeb

DR. HEIDEGGER'S EXPERIMENT

Author: Nathaniel Hawthorne (1804-1864)
Type of plot: Satiric analogue
Time of plot: Early nineteenth century at the latest
Locale: A doctor's study, perhaps in New England
First published: 1837

> *Principal characters:*
> DR. HEIDEGGER, an elderly doctor
> MR. MEDBOURNE, an avaricious merchant, now poor
> COLONEL KILLIGREW, a debauched seeker of pleasures
> MR. GASCOIGNE, an unscrupulous politician
> CLARA WYCHERLY, a former beauty, now a widow in seclusion
> because of scandal

The Story

Dr. Heidegger invites to his study four elderly friends to engage in an experiment. Three are men: Mr. Medbourne, Colonel Killigrew, and Mr. Gascoigne; the fourth is a woman, the Widow Clara Wycherly.

The study is a dusty, old-fashioned room replete with a skeleton in the closet, a bust of Hippocrates, books and bookcases, and a portrait of Sylvia Ward, who died fifty-five years before the night of the experiment on the eve of marriage to the doctor after swallowing one of his prescriptions.

The doctor shows his guests a faded rose which she gave him those many years before, and places it in a vase containing liquid from the waters of the region in Florida where the Fountain of Youth is located, sent to him by a friend.

The rose revives and the doctor pours some of the liquid from the vase into four champagne glasses for his friends. They drink and shed their years, showing signs of intoxication. Dr. Heidegger suggests to them that they allow their experience in life to guide them in virtue and wisdom when they gain a second chance at youth. As they drink, their inhibitions vanish. Colonel Killigrew takes interest in the widow's charms and flatters her; Mr. Gascoigne waxes eloquent in periods of a sort dear to politicians; Mr. Medbourne projects a plan to supply the East Indies with ice by means of whales harnessed to icebergs.

Dr. Heidegger does not take part in the rejuvenating experiment; he witnesses their antics with gravity. Young again, they laugh at their quaint clothes, showing contempt for the traits of old age which they have shed. Finally, the widow asks the doctor to dance with her, but he pleads old age and rheumatism. The three other guests seek to join her in dance, and in the ensuing riot, the table with the vase of the Water of Youth and rose overturns. The liquid reaches a dying butterfly, reviving it so that it flies to rest on Dr. Heidegger's white hair. The rose fades; the guests show their age again. The doctor states that he is glad not to have partaken of the liquid; he has learned that this unnatural return to youth was no occasion for satisfaction. His guests, however, undaunted, determine to sally forth in search of the Fountain of Youth in order to drink from it three times a day.

Themes and Meanings

The title, "Dr. Heidegger's Experiment," gives clues to the story's meaning. A doctor is a man of science, and the story describes an experiment, from which some sort of lesson might be derived. In conjunction with the word "experiment," the title suggests medicine, chemistry, physiology, or physics.

The name Heidegger is Swiss, meaning someone from the fortress Heidegg in the canton of Zurich. The doctor bears the same surname as that of a Swiss contemporary of the composer Handel, John James Heidegger (1659?-1749), manager of the opera house and master of the revels under England's King George II. The other characters also have surnames of distinguished figures from roughly the same era of English history. Most famous is a playwright known for the immorality of his works, William Wycherley (1640?-1716), who left a widow, a woman much younger than he, named Elizabeth. Others include two dramatists, father and son, Thomas Killigrew (1612-1683) and Thomas Killigrew the younger (1657-1719) and another dramatist, Sir William Killigrew (1606-1695); a master of the revels named Charles Killigrew (1655-1725); a poet, George Gascoigne (c. 1539-1577); an alleged conspirator, Sir Thomas Gascoigne (1593?-1686); and an actor and dramatist, Matthew Medbourne (died 1679), translator of Molière. The name of the long-dead lover of the doctor, Sylvia Ward, may suggest that of the quack doctor Joshua Ward (1685-1761), famous for "Ward's remedy," a "drop and pill" intended as a cure-all, which may have killed as many as it cured. Dr. Heidegger's fiancée, appropriately, swallowed one of her lover's prescriptions with fatal results. It was indeed a "Ward's remedy" in this case. It seems more than possible that Hawthorne modeled his characters on these people for their dissoluteness and effect of recalling a bygone age. Most, too, lived well into old age.

The doctor does not partake of the potion himself, but the elderly group undergoes a temporary rejuvenation. They all represent some vice or weakness and, despite the lessons experience should have taught them, remain true to their flawed characters during their return to youth.

For the doctor, who does not strive to combat the effects of Father Time in his own life, the experiment proves that people of shallow, vicious character do not benefit from the passing of the years, but persist in pursuing illusory pleasures.

The guests may be considered as allegorical, the widow representing scandalous coquetry; Mr. Medbourne exemplifying mercantile avarice; the colonel embodying self-indulgent lechery; Mr. Gascoigne epitomizing political corruption. They continue in accordance with their natures throughout the story, paying no attention to Dr. Heidegger's advice to behave with mature wisdom. The precious elixir spills and they lose their fleeting youth but not the desire to seek the unattainable. Hawthorne amusingly teaches a moral lesson and satirizes human shortcomings.

The transient nature of youth and beauty are symbolized by Sylvia's rose, and by the butterfly, which revives in the spilled fluid.

Style and Technique

This moral fable is made palatable by Hawthorne's command. If Dr. Heidegger were a paragon of virtue, the lesson might be less beguiling, but his skill as a doctor is insufficient to prevent the spirits of his deceased patients from staring at him whenever he directs his gaze at the fabulous mirror. The mirror suggests the power of illusion, a motif of the tale, as does the untitled book of magic. Hawthorne (or the narrator) has sport by suggesting that some of the doctor's reputation as an eccentric is attributable to the writer's "own veracious self" in the role of "fiction monger."

Hawthorne makes use of the trappings of gothic romance (the cobwebs, dust, bookcases, skeleton in the closet, and fabled mirror) with skill. One startling event, characteristic of the genre, still not outmoded in the author's time, is that when the chambermaid lifts the book of magic in her dusting, the skeleton rattles in the closet and several faces (presumably of the doctor's deceased patients) peep out from the mirror, while the bronze bust of Hippocrates frowns, uttering the command to forbear.

A whimsical humor can be felt in the story. For example, the narrator hints that the doctor and guests "were sometimes thought to be a little beside themselves—as is not infrequently the case with old people when worried either by present troubles or woeful recollections." Here is displayed a mock gravity. Humorous also is Dr. Heidegger's revelation of the location of the Fountain of Youth, undiscovered by the Spanish conquistador, Ponce de Leon. As the doctor says, "The famous Fountain of Youth, if I am rightly informed, is situated in the southern part of the Floridian peninsula, not far from Lake Macaco." The guests, when they set out in their quest for the elixir, will not be much helped by the reference to Lake Macaco; the name itself, applied to a type of lemur, is humorous. In addition, adjectives used to describe the guests, such as "venerable," "respected," and "respectable," gain humor from their inappropriateness, given the questionable nature of the guests' character and behavior.

Hawthorne is mindful of readers filled with skepticism when confronted by a miracle. He holds out alternative explanations for the phenomena depicted. For example, the youthful actions of the three men are attributed to intoxicating elements in the water from the Fountain of Youth, "unless, indeed, their exhilaration of spirits were merely a lightsome dizziness caused by the sudden removal of the weight of years."

Edgar C. Knowlton, Jr.

THE DOCTOR'S SON

Author: John O'Hara (1905-1970)
Type of plot: Social realism
Time of plot: 1918
Locale: Lantenengo County, Pennsylvania
First published: 1935

> *Principal characters:*
> JAMES (JIMMY) MALLOY, the narrator and protagonist, a
>   fifteen-year-old boy
> DOCTOR MIKE MALLOY, his father
> "DOCTOR" MYERS, a medical student
> EDITH EVANS, Jimmy's girl
> ADELE EVANS, her mother
> DAVID EVANS, Edith's father

The Story

"The Doctor's Son," a long story in four parts, concerns James (Jimmy) Malloy, a boy who is confronted with the fact that one may be physically grown yet not grown up. Jimmy, the doctor's son of the title, narrates this story about his loss of illusions against the backdrop of the influenza epidemic of 1918. During the epidemic, Doctor Mike Malloy works himself into exhaustion, and "Doctor" Myers, a medical student, is called in to work Malloy's patients until he has recovered. Jimmy, though only fifteen, is commissioned to drive Doctor Myers around the county to see all of the flu victims. Their first stop, at the request of Doctor Malloy, is the Evans home in Colieryville, where Jimmy looks forward to seeing Edith Evans, a girl several years his senior. Because the Malloys and Evanses are friends, Jimmy and Doctor Myers are invited for lunch by David Evans, Edith's father. At lunch (which Mr. Evans cannot attend because of business commitments), Doctor Myers is attracted to Adele Evans, though Jimmy notices something unusual only in the glances passed between Edith and her mother.

As they travel to see patients in single-family dwellings and gathered in bars to await the doctor, Jimmy is impressed by the compassion and skill with which Doctor Myers works. He has an unnerving experience, however, when they visit a miner's house in which the husband has died, and one of the children dies while they are there. Although Jimmy is a doctor's son and has been exposed to death, he has always been prepared for it, "if only by the sound of the ambulance bell. This was different." It is his first realization that death can come unexpectedly, and he is shaken by it.

The third part of the story, the shortest of the four, opens with the story's only extended digression, as Jimmy discusses various people who are taking advantage of the flu epidemic to profit in one way or another, whether financially or sexually. This digression foreshadows the affair between Doctor Myers and Adele Evans, which follows when Mrs. Evans asks Doctor Myers to come by on the pretense of examining the maid; Jimmy and Edith are unsuccessful in preventing liaison.

Soon after this, Mr. Evans interrupts an examination Doctor Myers is performing in a bar and demands to speak to him about his wife. Mr. Evans knows nothing of the affair; he is simply concerned from Doctor Myers' visits that his wife may be sick. The relieved Doctor Myers assures him that she is fine, and agrees to reexamine her after finishing with his patient. While he waits, Mr. Evans shares a bottle of whiskey which is being handed around, even though Doctor Myers advises him not to (it has been identified earlier as a means of passing the flu virus).

At the Evanses' house, a call from Doctor Malloy recalls Doctor Myers and Jimmy. Doctor Malloy feels fit enough to resume his practice, and Doctor Myers returns to medical school (asking Jimmy to "say goodbye to the Evanses" for him). Jimmy and his father resume seeing patients around the clock, but the strain of the two working together so closely begins to tell, and Doctor Malloy decides to drive himself on his next rounds after they have a physical confrontation. The following day, Jimmy discovers that Mr. Evans has died of the flu. He buys flowers for Edith, but she refuses to see him, and he soon finds another girl, revealing that Edith really meant little more to him than Mrs. Evans did to Doctor Myers.

Themes and Meanings

The primary focus of "The Doctor's Son" is on Jimmy's initiation into adult behavior and his disillusionment upon realizing that many of his accepted beliefs are false. Perhaps the most important of Jimmy's realizations is that his father is fallible, despite the fact that he is a doctor. Doctor Malloy has taught Jimmy to show respect for a doctor as he would, for example, show respect for a priest, and this leads Jimmy to believe that doctors occupy a privileged place in society. The debasement of the medical profession that he observes during the story, however, is followed by a loss of respect for his father.

The flu epidemic is the catalyst for Jimmy's education. First, his father's debilitation, surprising to Jimmy in itself, brings Doctor Myers to town. Myers is a capable doctor, despite his lack of training, but his affair with Mrs. Evans causes Jimmy to lose respect for him, and Doctor Myers is not an isolated case; other doctors are also taking advantage of the situation to make sexual conquests or extra money. By the time Doctor Malloy is back on his feet, Jimmy first reveals his disillusionment with the medical profession by omitting a doctor's title in conversation with his father, an oversight which his father immediately corrects. The final, physical confrontation between the two is almost anticlimactic, as Jimmy has already accepted the fact that his father can make mistakes, and he is no longer afraid to stand up to him.

Style and Technique

As the title implies, the story centers on the relationship between Doctor Malloy and Jimmy. The two serve as doubles; both have multifaceted and unpredictable natures, emphasized by the variety of names by which they are known (for example, "Mike Malloy," "the dad," "Daddy," and "Poppa" are a few of the names used for Doctor Malloy; "James," "Jim," and "Jimmy" are all used for his son). After his introduction, Doctor Malloy is unseen for most of the story, yet O'Hara succeeds in keeping him continually in view by having Jimmy compare his father to Doctor Myers, and by having Jimmy and other characters reminisce about him in his absence.

John O'Hara was well-known for his exacting attention to dialogue and dialect (he believed that if fictional characters did not "talk right," they would not become "real people" for the reader), and "The Doctor's Son" is an excellent example of his use of dialogue to illuminate character. Each of the characters (and there are many, from several different racial and socioeconomic backgrounds) has a distinctive way of speaking; at the same time, although they have individual idiosyncrasies, they often use dialect which links them to larger groups. The natural conversation both gives insight into the characters involved and enhances the sense of reality found in "The Doctor's Son."

Greg T. Garrett

THE DONAGH
Or, The Horse-Stealers

Author: William Carleton (1794-1869)
Type of plot: Allegory, social realism
Time of plot: Early nineteenth century
Locale: Rural Ireland
First published: 1830

>   *Principal characters:*
>   ANTHONY MEEHAN, a thief with an invincibly evil and cruel
>   character
>   ANNE, his young daughter, who is still uncorrupted by her
>   father's actions
>   DENIS MEEHAN, his brother and accomplice

The Story

The action of the story takes place in an isolated Irish village where the community is closely knit, where the people are bound together by shared suspicions and fears, and where absolute evil is recognizable and verifiable. The story tells of a test of innocence which the whole community undergoes in an effort to identify a gang of horse thieves. The reader knows that the thieves are a gang led by Anthony Meehan, but the tension of the story is created by the suspense of waiting to see if Anthony will succumb to the test.

Anthony Meehan is introduced as an absolutely evil character: violent, secretive, hateful, fearless, and relentlessly hard-hearted even to his own brother. There is a general assumption in the community at Carnmore that he has sold his soul to the Devil, and the narrator frequently refers to him as "diabolical" and "Satanic." His characterization and the setting are calculated to intensify this almost supernatural quality of evil, and his only relief from this role is when he loves his young daughter, Anne.

Denis Meehan has been his brother's reluctant accomplice and is vulnerable to the superstition to which Anthony is immune. One night before they set off to steal a valuable horse, Denis reveals that he is afraid because he has found a bad omen in the ashes of the fireplace. When Anthony begins to imagine Denis as "a Judas," he intimidates Denis with threats of violence against Denis' family, and only Anne's appeals for peace calm down her father. Anthony mocks those who are afraid—"What's the stuff about the other world but priestcraft and lies?"—and doubts Denis' loyalty; "only I bate the courage in, and the fear out of him," he says, Denis would not have stayed so long.

Some days later, the gang reassembles to prepare for the public test of innocence. Anyone who stays away is presumed to be guilty. Some of the thieves relieve their conscience by evasive tricks or theological distinctions between the magistrate's Bible and the priest's mass book, but Anthony insists that fears about perjuring themselves are mere superstition. He argues that "religion's all a sham" and "the world's all chance"; God cannot exist if He allows evil to triumph and innocence to be punished. Fearlessly, he urges them to be courageous and free of guilt and to recognize that Providence allows all kinds of injustice in nature compared to which their actions are insignificant.

On the following morning, the community is assembled, and there is quiet gossip about the test. The usual oath on the Bible is required of those who are under suspicion. One thief is caught using the thumb-kissing trick, and Denis reluctantly perjures himself under the threatening eye of Anthony. The older brother swears with an air of mockery toward the whole proceedings. At this moment, the priest holds up a box covered with a black cloth, the Donagh, and announces that all must retake the oath on this ancient shrine. The Donagh has been used in extreme cases before, and the common belief is that perjury on this religious object brings on the offender "awful punishment . . . sudden death, madness, paralysis, self-destruction, or the murder of someone dear to them." The priest challenges the guilty to step back and those who want to prove their innocence to come forward. Almost all step back, and soon the two Meehan brothers stand alone, as the tension builds to a climax.

They advance together, but Denis has already made up his mind that he will not swear on the Donagh. Anthony takes the oath and steps aside for Denis, but the younger brother faints. The crowd assumes that he has been struck dead. When he comes to, he calls out, "Save me from that man," and it appears that he is going to turn witness against the gang. Anthony produces a pistol and prepares to shoot him, but Anne rushes forward; the bullet intended for Denis hits her. Her blood bursts onto Anthony as he desperately tries to ask her forgiveness, but all she has time to do is ask his forgiveness for plotting to deceive her father. Grief-stricken, he collapses and dies.

The community sees in these events the confirmation of its belief in the great power of the Donagh, and for many years swearing on it continues to be used as a test of innocence of even greater reliability than swearing on the Bible.

Themes and Meanings

The primary motivation of Carleton's narrator is to illustrate a thesis: Irish peasants are inescapably governed by a superstitious fear which is intertwined with their religious faith but which is so attached to a religious object that the superstition appears pagan. The story has an almost sociological scheme. It tells of the evil one who is punished by what appears to be divine retribution, which is what the villagers expect to happen, and it also shows an evildoer repenting under the fear of that divine retribution. When Anthony Meehan shoots his daughter at the climax of the story, the narrator comments: "Shudderings, tremblings, crossings, and ejaculations marked their conduct and feeling; for though the incident in itself was simply a fatal and uncommon one, yet they considered it supernatural and miraculous." Such a comment is designed to sum up what the narrator has demonstrated about the villagers and also to distance him from those credulous people. The rational explanation of coincidence rather that the superstitious one of divine intervention is favored by the narrator.

Yet, the narrator's status as commentator is only one element of his role in creating the world of the village, and the power of the story comes from the fact that, like Carleton's contemporaries Edgar Allan Poe and Nathaniel Hawthorne, the writer is more fascinated and involved with the evil character and the atmosphere surrounding that character than his rational self would admit. At first, Anthony Meehan is an almost allegorical figure representing absolute evil in a medieval morality play. His "dark brow" and "Satanic expression" are clichés, and the purely innocent daughter with natural love for her father also belongs in an allegorical conception. Who sees Anthony in this manner? It appears that the narrator is more in sympathy with the villagers' way of thinking and feeling than he realizes. To depict a character in this fashion is to conceive of him outside realistic psychology, as an elemental principle of evil. The setting and descriptive details draw on the villagers' ways of feeling to heighten their sense of life as a drama in which human actions have supernatural origins or consequences.

The narrator deepens the psychological conception of Anthony in the relationship of the brothers. This adds a sense of an abnormal personality, a perversion of natural affection which is not simply "savage" but is truly chilling. The man who had seemed to be possessed of diabolical powers is shown to gain his power over people and his skill as a thief from a cynical and rational cast of mind. He hates the people of the community because their superstition weakens their will, and his satisfaction in life is to dominate by physical abuse or by psychological intimidation. Anthony Meehan is definitely a monster, but an intelligible one; he is not a village Faust, only a criminal gangleader.

The narrator's sympathies seem to be divided between this psychological portrait of Anthony and the view of the villagers, which is governed by their urge to mythologize and allegorize. The double title of the story reflects Carleton's awareness of this double manner of seeing. While he may want to expose the superstitious reverence for the Donagh and the depth of fear that it provokes, his feelings are drawn into the telling of the story so that his detachment fades, and the insulated and special reality of that community becomes more prominent than his thesis.

Style and Technique

This story was written before the modern short story became a form of conscious literary artistry; here, proverbial advice to trust the tale rather than the teller is appropriate. Carleton's purpose early in his writing career was to present the Catholic peasant population in a satiric light. Yet by the time that he wrote *Traits and Stories of the Irish Peasantry* (1830, 1833), his sociological and evangelical purposes had been subverted by his talent for re-creating a fictional world that was deeply rooted in his inherited ways of hearing and feeling. The traditional fiction of peasant life tended to romanticize or caricature, and Carleton's fiction has traces of these tendencies, but whatever the outer intention or theme, the heart of this writer's style is in the re-creation of an integrated community. It is in the dialogue, above all, that his intimate knowledge of the feeling and language of the peasants is made concrete. This is a closed world, less definable in historical or psychological terms than in ways of thinking which are timelessly associated with a mythic drama of Good and Evil and with powers that are beyond human comprehension. These universal concerns become real because of Carleton's intimately communicated feeling for the life of the peasants.

Denis Sampson

THE DREAM OF A RIDICULOUS MAN

Author: Fyodor Dostoevski (1821-1881)
Type of plot: Fable
Time of plot: The 1870's
Locale: St. Petersburg
First published: "Son smeshnogo cheloveka," 1877 (English translation, 1916)

>   *Principal characters:*
>   THE RIDICULOUS MAN, the unnamed protagonist

The Story

The ridiculous man introduces himself as he is seen by his friends and neighbors, a madman who was formerly considered to be merely ridiculous. He states, however, that he does not mind being the object of laughter and does not dislike those who ridicule him; on the contrary, he pities them. He alone possesses the Truth; he wishes that others would believe him. After this introduction, the narrator goes back in time to describe why he was always considered ridiculous, how a dream changed his life, and why he is now considered a madman by his peers.

The narrator relates that he has always been considered ridiculous, that he himself knows that he has always been ridiculous, but that pride has kept him from admitting this fact to anyone else. As he gets older, this feeling of ridiculousness is balanced somewhat by a growing realization that nothing matters; life is meaningless. One evening, this latter feeling oppresses the narrator, and he decides to commit suicide that very night by shooting himself with a revolver which he has bought for that specific purpose. On his way home to commit the act, he is intercepted by an eight-year-old girl who is sobbing and seeking help for her mother. The narrator dismisses the girl, but he returns home deeply impressed by the poverty and fear which she exhibited. He places the revolver on the table before him, but, as he sits and stares at the gun, his mind wanders back to the girl. He reflects upon the fact that he can still feel pity for another person and that there are people who are, or who might be, dependent upon him. This startling conclusion leads him to think about life again, and he decides to put off his suicide until he can resolve the questions in his mind. As he continues to think, he falls asleep in his chair and begins the dream which will change his life and his attitude toward the world about him.

The narrator imagines his own suicide, the ensuing confusion when his body is discovered by the landlady and neighbors, and then the placing of his coffin into the grave. After an unspecified time, a strange being opens the coffin, picks the narrator up, and begins flying through space. The ridiculous man realizes that he was wrong; death does not mean the end of existence, but the beginning of some new type of life. That conclusion is confirmed when the strange being deposits him on another planet, which he recognizes as a duplication of Earth. The setting is beautiful; left alone by the strange being, the narrator inspects the trees and birds of his new home. The inhabitants of the area find him and welcome him with open arms. He, in turn, is impressed with their sincere friendliness, their beauty, and the joy which they project. He then realizes that these people have never done evil and reside in a paradise with an almost perfect society. They seem to know of the suffering on Earth of the ridiculous man and they attempt to cheer him up by loving him. He, on the other hand, is touched by the fact that he is finally being accepted by a group of people as their equal.

As the story progresses, the narrator describes his new neighbors and the society in which they live. There is no science or technology, yet these people have a mature understanding of life which makes science and technology irrelevant. Science seeks to explain the meaning of life and to explore the frontiers of knowledge, but these people already knew the meaning of life, were perfectly contented, and, therefore, saw no need to develop scientific knowledge. The ridiculous man is impressed by the bond between the people and the other manifestations of nature, such as trees and animals. When the people speak to the trees, the narrator senses that some understanding is taking place. The people live in perfect harmony with the beasts, neither fearing the other. People work only to procure what they need, not to accumulate possessions for the sake of accumulation or for appearances.

After this glowing report of the society which he discovered on this planet, the ridiculous man then discloses that he corrupted all these happy people and that their nearly perfect civilization degenerated into a society very similar to the one he had left on Earth. He cannot remember exactly how it happened, after all, this is only a dream, but it did occur and he was responsible for it. The citizens of this lost paradise began to tell lies, gave themselves over to lust instead of the selfless love they had practiced, and allowed jealousy to be introduced into relationships. In time, jealousy led to violence, and the first person was killed as a result. The people were horrified; they formed protective associations, but these groups turned hostile and eventually engaged in violence against one another. The animals, sensing the discord and experiencing the cruelty of people, withdrew to the mountains and forests; hostility ensued between the humans and the beasts. The various groupings of people began to develop their own languages and became even more hostile to one another. To prevent crime, a system of justice, including the guillotine, was invented. The people sought to develop science and technology in order to bring civilization into their unruly lives; once having known the meaning of life and having possessed sufficient knowledge to lead a full life, they were compelled to attempt the slow and painful re-creation of a livable society.

Surveying the destruction of this society, the ridiculous man implored the people to crucify him; perhaps then they would return to their old ways. Having only dim memories of a better society, however, they viewed the narrator as a saintly fool preaching an impossible morality. He was informed that he would be incarcerated in a mental institution if he continued to proclaim the virtues of an ideal society. At the point of despair, the ridiculous man suddenly awakened from his dream, finding himself in his room with the revolver on the table before him.

The dream changed the life of the ridiculous man, as he explains; he now believes that people can be happy and construct a much better society. Evil is not natural; the present human condition is merely a fall from that state to which human beings can aspire. It is this newfound belief that allows the narrator to carry on with his life and to view people with affection and love. He puts aside all ideas of suicide and begins to preach the Truth which he has seen in his dream. People still believe that he is ridiculous, but he loves them anyway.

Themes and Meanings

Fyodor Dostoevski is much better known for his lengthy novels than for his short stories. This short story contains many of the themes which Dostoevski used in his novels, but in a much-reduced form. The author, a devout Russian Orthodox Christian, was intrigued by the human condition and sought answers for human imperfection in traditional Christian thought, although he often imparted to it an original insight or twist.

In this particular story, Dostoevski deals with a paradox familiar to all Christian philosophers: How does one reconcile the desire for social change and the quest for perfection with the human condition of imperfection as a result of the Fall in the Garden of Eden? This central theme is placed within a secondary theme also familiar to all readers of Dostoevski's novels, the inability of the rationalist to supply all of life's answers. The central character in this story lives by theories and has no real communication with his fellow human beings. When he cannot find the answers to life and concludes, therefore, that life is meaningless, he decides to commit suicide.

The dream shows the ridiculous man where he has gone wrong: in his dependence upon the intellect rather than the heart. In order to live meaningfully, one must live as people did before the Fall, instinctively and with love. How does one do this? The vision of the perfect society and the desire to re-create it give him the wherewithal to choose life over death, for although perfection is unattainable in this life, the quest for it makes life bearable.

Style and Technique

Like many Russian writers, Dostoevski wished to express his views on life in a form which would catch the attention of the general public and be an attractive means of furthering discussion of serious questions. Literature reached a much wider public than did theoretical journals of philosophy, and Dostoevski employed fiction in the hope that he would have an effect outside the academic community. In the process, he wrote works of literature which are considered masterpieces even by those who disagree with the author or do not even understand what point he was attempting to make. In this story, the author uses a dream to make his point, a device which he also used in other works. This particular dream recounts the biblical tale of the Fall in slightly different terms, a story which would be very familiar to the average Russian reader of the nineteenth century. By the use of this dream as parable, Dostoevski takes a very difficult point of Christian philosophy and simplifies it so that almost anyone can understand the point he is attempting to make.

Philip Maloney

DREAMERS IN A DEAD LANGUAGE

Author: Grace Paley (1922-   )
Type of plot: Satiric comedy
Time of plot: The late 1950's
Locale: Coney Island, New York
First published: 1977

> *Principal characters:*
> FAITH DARWIN, a single parent, recently divorced
> ANTHONY (Tonto) and
> RICHARD, her sons
> PHILIP MAZZANO, one of her boyfriends
> MR. and MRS. DARWIN, Faith's parents

The Story

From a conversation between Faith Darwin and one of her three boy-friends, Philip, the reader learns of a poem written by Faith's father ("one of the resident poets of the Children of Judea, Home for the Golden Ages"), lamenting the loss of his wife but expressing the desire "to go sailing in spring among realities." It also alludes to "a young girl who waits in a special time and place/ to love me." This reference becomes a topic of debate between Faith and Philip.

Philip likes "old people" (for example, his former wife's dad) and hopes to talk to Faith's father, which he does at the end. He is a worldly businessman who bewails his being forced into "low practicality" by "the thoughtless begetting of children, and the vengeance of alimony." Faith chides him for ascribing malice to Anita Franklin, her old friend and Philip's former wife. She warns Philip not to disillusion her parents about Anita, whom Philip "dumped." In passing, Faith confesses her romantic disposition, preferring John Keats's and Percy Bysshe Shelley's fantasies to John Milton's moralizing.

Visiting her parents in a retirement home, Faith is scolded by her father for criticizing her former husband in front of the children. Her son Richard wonders whether the home is a hospital. "Worry and tenderness" characterize Faith's attitude. When she was a child, she was "a constant entertainment" to her parents—her father tells her children. Mrs. Darwin enjoys Richard's sense of humor; Faith's other son, Tonto, however, reveals the truth about his mother's gloomy moods. While the father takes the boys on a tour, Faith visits her mother, "the saint," who is ministering to the bedridden Mrs. Hegel-Shtein. The latter launches into a litany of complaints centered on the responsibility of keeping "a sick old man alive." Faith responds with "What you mean is—life has made you sick," to which Mrs. Hegel-Shtein assents. Mrs. Darwin thinks that that is a "lopsided idea," revealing her concern for Faith's mental health following the collapse of her marriage.

After showing Faith and the children around the roof garden, Mr. Darwin returns, praising Faith's former husband, Ricardo: "such an interesting young man." Eventually he confesses that he wants to leave the place (and his wife) because he feels that he is not old; he resents his wife's fancying the home a Grand Hotel. Faith flees from her father's scolding, and her father compares Faith to her mother's "crazy sister Silvia," who "died in front of the television set." The story ends with a memorable scene: Faith playing with her children in the "old Brighton Beach of her childhood," the boys burying her in the sand but "giving her lots of room for wiggling and whacking."

Themes and Meanings

Writing usually "from distress," Paley seeks to recover from the "history of everyday life" those nuances of humor and pathos that relieve the sardonic tone of her characterization and counterpoint the moral disintegration of modern society.

Here the breakdown of Faith's marriage symbolizes the ordeal of a time when idealism (suggested by the mention of Theodor Herzl and her father's poem, appropriately named by Philip "Dreamer in a Dead Language") is challenged by a materialistic, egocentric world. Faith tells her father, "I'm just like you, an idealist" who wants "only the best, only perfection." She justifies sleeping with three men by her search for "perfection." Ironically, her father claims that he and Faith's mother never formally got married because they were "idealists." For all of his daydreaming, the father is shocked by Faith's entertaining three divorced men, and he blames her for being "more mixed up than before."

Mr. Darwin's stubborn, patriarchal ways are revealed in his excessive sympathy for Ricardo, Faith's former husband, for being young. He considers Faith "demented" in her treatment of her former husband, he considers his wife and Mrs. Hegel-Shtein to be psychosomatic cases. When he condemns Heligman (another resident of the home), whose view of life allows for the process of healing and fulfillment after crisis—time unfolding its spontaneous cure—Faith blurts out: "I can't stand your being here." Although attached to her father's poetic genius, the daughter cannot stand his domineering and supercilious attitude. His joke—"Honesty, my grandson, is *one* of the best policies"—and his defense of his unconventional liaison with Faith's mother as a proof of "idealism" demonstrate the destabilizing contradiction in the lives of the older generation. In this sense, the "modesty of the old" noted by Philip in the first line of the story seems the opposite of their intolerant but vulnerable self-righteousness.

Faith's mother, while sensitive to her daughter's plight and proud of her own compassion, also bears down on her: "You went to college. Keep your hands clean," and so forth. She reinforces the authoritarian bent of the father: "Tell her, Sid, she has to be more sensible. She's a mother. She doesn't have the choice."

Contradicting that advice, Faith's whole emotional and ethical behavior toward her parents, former husband, lovers, and children argues for an intelligent understanding of the present generation's predicament, their anxious quest for a new morality affirming tough but sensitive realism, collective determination, and hope for a better future (suggested by the romantic aura of the title, Anthony's sand castles, Herzl's Utopianism, and allusions to Keats and Shelley). Her son Richard's alert intelligence and caring thoughtfulness incarnate two qualities that coalesce in Faith's conflicted sensibility. The closing exchange between Richard and Faith encapsulates the thematic issues posed by the dynamics within the family and between generations: "Why is everything my responsibility, every goddamn thing?" Faith asks. "Had she been born 10, 15 years later, she might have done so, screamed and screamed. Instead, tears made their usual protective lenses for the safe observation of misery." Faith asks to be challenged and convinced by the younger generation, but she also claims the right to impose her painfully won maturity on her children.

When Faith insists that the younger girl addressed in her father's poem is her mother, the reader perceives her refusal to accept an impersonal and alienating reality different from her wishes. She seems caught in the dilemma of suppressing her true feelings and compromising her integrity. She craves affection, she is afraid of jeopardizing Philip's friendship, but she castigates him anyway: "She didn't want to hit him. Instead her eyes filled with tears." Faith's tear-filled eyes, the dominant image that the text interposes at the end between an unfeeling world pervaded by Darwinian competitiveness (note Faith's surname) and a dreaming soul, evoke the crisis of the modern individual: As the old Jew in Mr. Darwin's anecdote discovers, no more space exists for those whom life and worldly changes have victimized. The hospital or home symbolizes the intermediate space between the innocent questioning of children and the cynical or sexist males who idealize women only to abandon them.

Aware of the injustice of the world and encroaching physical debility, Mr. Darwin has his moment of insight when he "felt the freedom of committed love" as his daughter demonstrates her affection. His desperation exemplifies the difficulty of personal commitment: "If it were possible, the way I feel suddenly toward life, I would divorce your mother." Like individuals in a marriage, freedom and responsibility coexist in dialectical tension.

Style and Technique

Paley's lively seriocomic style has been frequently praised for its blending of sardonic wit and spare description, which somehow intimates the gap that she experiences "between knowing and telling."

The three settings noted earlier—Faith's apartment, the retirement home, and the beach of her childhood—divide the narrative into the spheres of the intimate relationship between lovers, the argumentative tension between parents and daughter, and the playful communication between mother and children. In all of them, the prose scarcely focuses on physical appearance (except telling details such as the boil on Faith's wrist). Snapshot impressions punctuate the dialogue. Saturated with diseased or pain-afflicted bodies, the text is largely made up of disembodied voices (no quotation marks are used, and words are rarely attributed to their speakers) whose diverse tones— mocking, derisive, ambiguous, frank, vulgar, urbane, sentimental—more than compensate for the sparseness of "realistic" details to convey the abundant zest or élan of her characters in confronting the cruel indifference and betrayals of life.

The narrative is chiefly composed of dialogue interspersed with brief summaries. The rapid and sometimes discontinuous exchanges between the characters suffice to disclose their temperaments and motivations. When the father says about Faith's delinquent husband, "Young. Young is just not old. What's to argue, What you know, *you* know. What I know, *I* know," one can detect the authoritative register in the tone. Her mother's solicitude is displayed also with suggestive economy.

To establish the consumerist milieu of industrial society, Paley puts these words into Philip's mouth as he ridicules Faith's husband, whose "dancing" around her father seems to irk him: "Who's that jerk know? Four old maids in advertising, three Seventh Avenue models, two fairies in TV, one literary dyke. . . ." His anecdote about Ezra Kalmback, like the vignettes and jokes of Faith's father, exemplifies the divided selves of the marginalized and alienated (especially ethnic immigrant groups, Jews, women, blacks, and others), a condition which may culminate in the sixth-floor ward of incurables where physically sound young people are "tied with shawls into wheelchairs."

When the unforgettable Madame Elena Nazdarova, editor of the prize-winning journal *A Bessere Zeit*, sees "Mr. Darwin, breathless, chasing Faith," and calls, "Ai, Darwin . . . no love poems this month? How can I go to press?" one can perceive in this event the old father-dreamer pursuing youth, faith, passion, this time no longer hobbled by spurious idealism or self-doubt. Paley's austerity and idiomatic tactfulness succeed in controlling the welter of violent emotions unleashed here. Intractable and recalcitrant impulses and psychic drives are contained by the sheer gusto of urbane wit, folkloric and aphoristic gestures, and compassionate knowingness.

E. San Juan, Jr.

A DRIVE IN THE COUNTRY

Author: Graham Greene (1904-   )
Type of plot: Psychological realism
Time of plot: The 1930's
Locale: London and the countryside immediately beyond
First published: 1947

>   *Principal characters:*
>   THE PROTAGONIST, an unnamed girl who is about to elope with
>   Fred
>   FRED, an unemployed and desperate young man determined
>   on a suicide pact
>   THE YOUNG MAN, a stranger who gives the girl a lift back to her
>   father's house in Golding's Park

The Story

The narrative begins with a young woman's observations of her father's careful ritual of preparing his household for the night. He is the head clerk at Bergson's Export Agency, and she feels a mild contempt for him as a worker, for his pride of ownership, and for the devotion to convention that he exhibits in his daily life and in the fulfillment of his church obligations. In contrast, the young woman thinks of Fred, her young man, and "his air of unbalanced exultation."

Once the doors and windows are locked, and the household put to sleep in the jerry-built house that her father will own outright in fifteen years, the young woman leaves for her rendezvous. She hears again, in her imagination, her father's statement about having improved the property, and she remembers the apple tree that has produced one more tasteless apple each year since it was planted.

She meets Fred, ready, she thinks, for anything. Fred has borrowed a car, he says, and she settles into her dream of reckless adventure. They drive outside the city, past a roadhouse, and, to please her, Fred goes deeper into the countryside. She is aware of his restiveness, his mood of desperation, as he drinks from his bottle. She is also aware of the assertion of his will over hers. As they drive deeper into the country, the protagonist, excited as always by Fred's need to live on the dangerous edge of things, by his seeming nonchalance in his inability to find a job in the economically depressed 1930's, by his failure to gratify either himself or his family, listens to his proposal: that they kill themselves as a means of escaping a world that has rejected them. The young woman, who thought that she understood the limits of Fred's "craziness," is frightened by the gun he carries and the certainty of his choice. She comes to a realization that what attracts Fred to suicide is not so much an escape from the tedium of a deprived existence as the thrill of the action itself. She understands Fred's need to gamble with life and death—the attraction of the uncertainty that lies beyond. Since neither of them believes in God, he says to convince her, they have a chance, "and it's company, going like that." For the first time, she questions Fred's protestations of love for her, and the nature of hers for him.

She attempts to reason him out of his decision, finally admitting to herself that his "craziness" has gone beyond her ability to comprehend or contain it. She realizes, "He had always wanted this: the dark field, the weapon in his pocket; but she less honestly had wanted a little of both worlds: irresponsibility and a safe love, danger and a secure heart."

The young woman leaves Fred, and the last word that she hears him speak is "damnation" as he stumbles over a root. The sound of the word fills her with horror. She makes her way to the roadhouse as it begins to rain and asks a stranger for a lift to London. The young man who offers to take her to Golding's Park, suffering from much the same social and economic malaise that Fred has experienced, offers to drive her to Maidenhead instead, but she refuses. "Hell of a life," he says. She makes her way to the jerry-built villa, and once inside, she locks the door firmly against the rain and the escape that Fred offered her. She recognizes now, as she did not at the story's beginning, the bravery of her father's refusal to give in to the dark.

Themes and Meanings

A third-person narrative, "A Drive in the Country" achieves its somber effects through a psychologically acute presentation of the young woman's dawning awareness of the value of life, and the uncertain consequences of death. In the course of the narrative, Graham Greene convincingly presents a character who changes from an attitude of come-what-may to one of stoic vulnerability. The turning point of the story is reached when she refuses Fred's offer of a love-death and accepts instead everyday life in an economically depressed society. Talk of unemployment and Bolshies (as she makes her way back to London) contributes to the reader's awareness of time and place and establishes the dominant theme of social inequality.

Greene is known primarily as a writer who employs Roman Catholic notions in his novels and stories. "A Drive in the Country" can, although it need not, be read as a commentary on the sham suicide pact into which Pinkie Brown attempts to trick the girl Rose in *Brighton Rock* (1938). In that novel, Pinkie and Rose are Roman Catholics, and the love-death bears on their understanding of the moral ramifications of the sin of despair. The bird whose gigantic wings beat against the windscreen of the car that carries Rose and Pinkie to Peacehaven and, as Rose believes, to their deaths, can consequently be read as a divine prompting that tempts Pinkie to good as Satan has tempted him to evil. There are in "A Drive in the Country" no statements that are overtly religious in intention, except the one in which Fred notes that neither he nor the girl believes in God. Yet the wood, suggestive of Dante's dark wood of error; the fact that the girl makes a choice for life over death; the use of the word "damnation"; and the references to suicide as a desperate gamble suggest a moral interpretation that is difficult to dismiss.

Style and Technique

To direct his reader to a proper appreciation of the social and moral themes suggested by the narrative, Greene makes subtle use of imagery and symbolism that suggest reconciliation and renewal within a starved landscape. As the girl leaves her father's house for her rendezvous with Fred, the narrator directs the reader's attention to the "crazy paved path" that takes her past the half-finished development in which she lives with her family. She is aware of the "wounded" fields that remain "grimly alive in the form of thin grass and heaps of clay and dandelions," and of the small garages that suggest graves in a cemetery. As she and Fred make their way deeper into the country, the notion of the journey into the self becomes apparent. The girl is suddenly made aware of the fact that a choice that she has not fully considered is being thrust on her, and she is forced to choose between the annihilation that Fred offers and the bleak life of London that she has hitherto considered lacking in value. Her choice, regardless of whether she is fully aware of the sights about her, is confirmed by the references to the continuing life of nature in the dark of night, to the bird that beats against the car that Fred has stolen for the drive into the country, to rabbits and owls, to oaks and elms, and to the clover that covers the earth where they stop the car. The symbols of house and apple tree, as well as the many references to a meager nature, offer the reader the best means of appreciating both the social and the moral meanings of the story.

A. A. DeVitis

THE DROVER'S WIFE

Author: Henry Lawson (1867-1922)
Type of plot: Domestic realism
Time of plot: c. 1890
Locale: The Australian Outback
First published: 1894

> *Principal characters:*
> THE DROVER'S WIFE, who is referred to as "she"
> TOMMY, her elder son
> ALLIGATOR, a big, black, yellow-eyed dog-of-all-breeds

The Story

Like many stories by Henry Lawson (and like those of Anton Chekhov and Katherine Mansfield), "The Drover's Wife" has remarkably little action: The plot, such as it is, suggests the absence of action that characterizes life in the Outback (the dry, sparsely settled, and inhospitable areas distant from the few major urban settlements of Australia) during the long intervals between recurrent natural disasters, such as floods, bushfires, and droughts. This indicates a technical aspect that Lawson mastered in his short stories: the construction of a coherent fiction on the flimsiest of plots. One of his aims was always to use a slight plot.

In its simplest form, the plot is limited to the discovery of a five-foot black snake in the woodheap, watching it go under the house, and waiting through the night for its reemergence so that it can be killed. The variety and violence of life in the Outback are indicated by the omniscient narrator's allusions to memorable episodes that have punctuated the drover's wife's life, which is frequently marked by her solitude from adult companionship. (She has not heard from her husband for six months as the story begins.)

She has two boys and two girls ("mere babies") and a dog, Alligator, for company; she has two cows, a horse, and a few sheep as possessions; her husband is often away driving sheep and cattle, and has been away for periods of up to eighteen months. During one of his absences she contracted fever in childbirth and was assisted by Black Mary (an aboriginal midwife); one child died when she was alone, and she had to carry the corpse nineteen miles for assistance.

Times were not always so desperate. When she was married, her drover husband took her to the city, where they stayed in the best hotel. Soon after, however, they had to sell their buggy; her husband, who started as a drover and rose to become a squatter (a small-scale cattle raiser on government-owned land), met the inevitable "hard times" of the Outback and returned to droving, with its isolation, low pay, low status, and long absences from home.

The wife's only connection with the few pleasures of her life is *Young Ladies' Journal*—a bitter irony under her circumstances.

Yet her life in the bush (another name for the Outback) has not been wholly uneventful: A nephew died from snakebite; she battled a bushfire; she coped with a flood, even to the extent of digging trenches in a vain attempt to avoid a dam break; she shot a mad bullock; she treated pleuro-pneumonia in the cattle (though her best two cows succumbed); she has had to control crows and magpies; and she has always had to be "the man" in getting rid of sundowners, bushmen, and "swaggies" (itinerants). Clearly, the snake poses a threat to her children, but she has successfully handled crises of far greater significance in her years in the Outback.

Still, for all her impressive practicality, she has been tricked: Only the day before, an Aborigine bargained to collect a pile of wood in exchange for a small amount of tobacco; she praised him for doing a good job and then, when the snake was first seen, discovered that the "blackfellow" (the term then used for Aborigines) had built a hollow woodpile. She was hurt and cried, but she has "a keen, very keen, sense of the ridiculous, and some time or other she will amuse bushmen with the story. She had been amused before like that. . . . Then she had to laugh."

Themes and Meanings

Lawson's stories are almost all authentic illustrations of the several hardships and few small pleasures of proletarian domestic life—especially in the country. "The Drover's Wife," which appeared in his very first book, is of major significance because it so clearly and impressively states one of his pervasive themes, that the lives of people in the Outback are molded by the environment so that they, too, become hardened, desiccated, silent, and of necessity even predatory. Yet in spite of all this, the occasional blossoms of the bush have their equivalents in the tender, soft, beautiful, yet temporary moments of life of the drovers and squatters.

The opening paragraphs of the story indicate Lawson's approach to his theme; the lean, starved, drab minimalism of life in the bush is conveyed by the description of the drover's house: "The two-roomed house is built of round timber, slabs, and stringy-bark, and floored with split slabs. A big bark kitchen standing at one end is larger than the house itself, veranda included." The individuals who live there are also gaunt and hardy, for the children are described as "ragged, dried-up-looking"; and the mother, who has a "worn-out breast," is described as a "gaunt, sun-browned bushwoman."

Further, this identification of people and place is brought out in the second paragraph, where one finds one of Lawson's best descriptions of the bush itself with all of its negative connotations: "no horizon, for the country is flat. No ranges in the distance. The bush consists of stunted, rotten native apple-trees. There is no undergrowth, nothing to relieve the eye save the darker green of a few she-oaks which are sighing above the narrow, almost waterless creek. Nineteen miles to the nearest sign of civilization—a shanty [shack] on the main road." This is the bush at its grimmest, yet in many ways it is the real Australia, for only one-tenth of the continent is arable, fertile land: The "sunburnt country" is the typical land, the land of Australian literary and cultural mythology. In great measure this was the achievement of Henry Lawson. He knew the country at first hand, his stories pictured it in all its drab, horrendous realism, and his popularity assured acceptance of the image that he presented. Some readers and critics have taken a somewhat different approach: One considers stories such as "The Drover's Wife" to be social satire redeemed by a strong sense of nationalism, and there is some merit in this appreciation.

Essentially, this story is a study of human adaptation to adversity and environment that shows the strength of individuals isolated from the main currents of civilization. In a way, too, it is a strong statement for the cause of feminism, and reminds the reader, perhaps, of the California rancher's wife in John Steinbeck's "The Chrysanthemums." Yet the emphasis is less on the delineation of character than on the description of the oppressive nature of the eternal round of disasters and trials that bedevil people in situations that resemble that of the drover's wife.

Style and Technique

Clearly, a story that has slight action, such as waiting for a snake to reappear, must have some compensatory elements (especially in the absence of any direct characterization) to account for its popularity and fame. In part these are stylistic, in part technical. First, Lawson makes Tommy, the drover's young son, a representative of his father, a foil for the drover's wife. Though still a child, he sees the emptiness of his mother's life and the hollowness of the family existence, so that the story ends when he says, "Mother, I won't never go drovin'; blarst me if I do!" and she hugs and kisses him "while the sickly daylight breaks over the bush."

Even the use of "Mother" is significant. Instead of the more usual "Mum" or "Ma" in country children's speech, there is the more polite, tender "Mother," which suggests a child's desire to be separated from the harshness of the bush. (His "normal" language is revealed in the double negative and "blarst.") This epiphany occurs, significantly, at dawn. The daylight, though, is "sickly," with all that this connotes.

Alligator, the dog, is developed as a character in the story. (His name is another irony in a waterless environment.) When the snake is first encountered by Tommy, Alligator "takes small notice" of Tommy's stick and "proceeds to undermine the building." He is an equal, a colleague, and "they cannot afford to lose him." He felt, readers are told, "the original curse in common with mankind" and approaches the snake as if it were a representative of the intruder in Eden in this least Edenic of places.

The structure of the story is of some interest. It opens near sunset as a storm approaches. At midnight the drover's wife reminisces about her life; at about 1:00 A.M. and 2:00 A.M. she remembers past difficulties on the land; and near daylight Alligator catches and shakes the snake, which then has its back broken and head smashed and is thrown on the fire. In the nightlong vigil, Tommy and Aligator are her company and comfort; all three share a vital interdependence. Animals, like people, are friends and foes.

After the initial reported conversation between the drover's wife and the children, there is no dialogue until Tommy's announcement at the close of the story that he will not become a drover; this is more than an accidental taciturnity—it further emphasizes the isolation of the Outback and of the drover's wife, even within her own family.

A. L. McLeod

THE DRUNKARD

Author: Frank O'Connor (Michael Francis O'Donovan, 1903-1966)
Type of plot: Social realism
Time of plot: The first quarter of the twentieth century
Locale: Cork, Ireland
First published: 1948

> *Principal characters:*
> MICK DELANEY, a laboring man, whose weakness is drink, the
> father of the narrator of the story
> LARRY DELANEY, the adult narrator and the little boy in the
> story
> MRS. DELANEY, Larry's mother, a hardworking, anxious
> woman

The Story

A first-person narrative by the adult Larry Delaney, "The Drunkard" opens with his recollection of a critical episode in his childhood. The crisis began with the death of his father's friend and confidant, Mr. Dooley. Larry's father, Mick Delaney, took Mr. Dooley's death very hard, not only because Mr. Dooley was about the same age as he but also because he lost in Mr. Dooley his best source of inside information, of "the news behind the news." To express the depth of his mourning, Mick Delaney decides to attend the funeral, a decision which causes Larry and his mother great anxiety. Mick Delaney will be tempted at the public house afterward; as Larry recalls, "Drink . . . was Father's great weakness." Consequently, Larry's mother sends Larry along to act as a "brake" upon his father. With humor and poignancy, the narrative records the boy's feeling of utter ineffectualness, as his father pulls him into a public house, where the boy expects, one more time, to stand helplessly by, watching his father get drunk. His father bribes him with a lemonade while ordering beer for himself. Thereafter oblivious to the child, he turns away from the bar to expatiate upon the merits of the funeral. In the meanwhile, Larry, bored and still thirsty, samples and then finishes his father's drink. In turn, Larry becomes drunk, noisy, and sick. Larry's father, assisted by a barroom friend, is obliged to bring his sick, drunken child home in broad daylight, before the astonished eyes of all his neighbors, while Larry, in his drunken state, mimics the belligerent behavior that he has observed in his father's past drinking bouts. Mrs. Delaney returns home in a rage, prompted by her neighbors to conclude that her husband and his crony have plied the child with drink for their amusement; her husband, feeling increasingly sorry for himself, tries unsuccessfully to explain. The next day, when Mick Delaney quietly goes off to work, the mother's mood changes, and she praises and pampers Larry for having proved indeed to be his father's "guardian angel."

Themes and Meanings

Characteristic of Frank O'Connor, the story combines humor and seriousness, a mixture which the author referred to as "crab apple jelly." The narrative provokes laughter and sadness as it explores the moving plight of a child who is apparently following in his father's drunken footsteps. The equivocal title points to the dual meaning: Is the reader to focus on the humorousness of the inadvertent drunkard, Larry, or on the irresponsibility of the more habitual drunkard, Mick, who pays for his drinking bouts by pawning everything in the house down to the kitchen clock? As the grown Larry ruefully remembers, "I could never get over the lonesomeness of the kitchen without a clock."

The particular satisfaction of the story is not only in the reversal of expectations that it creates but also in the poetic justice which it delivers to the father. Victim and victimizer exchange roles: The potential victim Larry becomes victimizer of his father, who is passive witness and helpless victim to his son's drunkenness. The potential victimizer Mick sees how he himself looks, acts, and speaks when he is drunk, as his son Larry proves to be a most unflattering mirror. The reader's awareness that Mick has been the model for Larry's drunken behavior underlies the hilariousness of Larry's mood shifts from grandiosity to belligerence to melancholy self-pity, in which final state he proclaims his heroic martyrdom by singing "The Boys of Wexford."

While the story records a small triumph for Larry and his mother, it avoids sentimentality by reminding the reader of all the other times when they stood by helplessly, watching the drunkard's progress of Mick Delaney. Larry recalls his father saying, after the incident, "Never again, never again, not if I lived to be a thousand!" In response to this statement, the older Larry comments, "To this day I don't know whether he was forswearing me or the drink." He thereby points out that, after this particular episode, his father repudiated neither him nor the drink. Thus, the story ends happily, but not "happily ever after."

Style and Technique

Neither a rigorous naturalist such as Émile Zola nor an avant-garde experimentalist such as James Joyce, O'Connor strived for a style that captured what he called the "glowing center of action." In a voice that is candid, straightforward, terse, and colloquial, he puts before his audience the central facts and the telling details; he points to a theme that is clear, simple, and universal. Unwilling to call attention to itself, O'Connor's style seems almost transparent, yet the simple phrases can turn suddenly to eloquence, as in

Larry's description of his father, "He had long months of abstinence behind him and an eternity of pleasure before," or the words can turn to salt, as when Larry notes his father's "pleasant awareness that however much he would miss poor Mr. Dooley in the long summer evenings, it was he and not poor Mr. Dooley who would do the missing."

One outstanding feature of O'Connor as a storyteller is his ability to recapture the feel of childhood. He does not comment on what a child feels; he records it. Again and again he notes the child's earnestness, literalness, and befuddlement in trying to make sense of what adults say. When Larry vomits, his father says, encouragingly, "You'll be grand when you get that up." Yet Larry notes, "Begor, I was not grand! Grand was the last thing I was." When another man similarly states, "You'll be all right in a minute," the boy bewilderedly comments, "I never met two men who knew less the effects of drink."

Perhaps the most remarkable characteristic of O'Connor's style is his ability to capture the lilt, the peculiarities, the quaintness, and the occasional luminousness of Irish speech. It penetrates his descriptions: "He was first up in the morning and brought the mother a cup of tea in bed." It colors the speech of his characters: "I wouldn't give it to say to them"; "Whisht, woman, whisht, whisht!" Throughout, it heightens and particularizes the world that the narrator sees: "Ever since, when somebody has given me some bit of information off the record I have found myself on the point of asking: 'Was it Mr. Dooley told you that?'"

Like the traditional Irish storytellers whom he admired, O'Connor, as an artist, was always a real man speaking to real men and women. In each of his stories, which echo the vitality and the roughness of life itself, he seems merely to be pausing, for the brief pleasure of a tale's telling, from life's more urgent and mundane labors.

Carola M. Kaplan

DRY SEPTEMBER

Author: William Faulkner (1897-1962)
Type of plot: Psychological realism
Time of plot: The late 1920's or early 1930's
Locale: A small Southern town
First published: 1931

> *Principal characters:*
> MISS MINNIE COOPER, an aging white spinster who accuses
> Will Mayes of having attacked her
> WILL MAYES, a black man
> HAWKSHAW, a reasonable barber who argues against violence
> JOHN MCLENDON, the leader of the murderers of Will Mayes

The Story

Faulkner organizes the plot of "Dry September" around a single incident: the murder of an innocent black man. An aging and sexually frustrated white spinster starts the rumor that the black man has attacked her. A group of men, led by a former war hero, murder him before they substantiate his guilt.

After two months without rain, the small Southern town of Jefferson has an explosive atmosphere. A rumor spreads through Jefferson that the black man, Will Mayes, has "attacked, insulted, frightened" Miss Minnie Cooper. No one knows exactly what has occurred, but the rumor of an attack by a black man on a white woman spreads "like a fire in dry grass."

The first section of "Dry September" takes place in the town barbershop on Saturday evening. Whether Will Mayes has actually molested Miss Minnie Cooper does not seem important to most of the men in the barbershop. Since a white woman has accused a black man of attacking her, the accusation alone requires that these men demonstrate their white superiority. Hawkshaw, the barber, stubbornly refuses to believe that Will Mayes has attacked Miss Cooper. His rational demand for facts provokes the hostility of the other men.

The smoldering tension flares into violence when John McLendon crashes through the screen door. McLendon leads the party of men who set out to murder Will Mayes. When one member of the group gathered in the barber shop questions what really happened, McLendon whirls on the speaker and asks: "Happen? What the hell difference does it make? Are you going to let the black sons get away with it until one really does it?" Enraged by the heat as well as the rumor, the heavyset McLendon wants to kill. The honor of an aging white spinster gives him an excuse.

The second part of the story describes Miss Minnie Cooper. Her life seems as stale as the "vitiated air" in the barbershop. Despite a short period of youthful popularity, she did not marry. Her gaunt aunt, a "thin, sallow, unflagging" woman, runs the house, and her invalid mother stays in her room. Miss Minnie's only romantic experience was with a widower in the town bank. The town "relegated" her "into adultery" twelve years ago, and eight years ago the cashier went to a Memphis bank. The narrator comments that Miss Minnie's "bright dresses, her idle and empty days, had a quality of furious unreality." Intensified by the heat, Miss Minnie's sexual frustration explodes, as does McLendon's brutality. Both vent their personal frustration upon Will Mayes.

Part 3 of the story returns to the account of Will Mayes's murder. The rumor which spreads like a fire in dry grass has destroyed the humanity of the men who plan to teach the "black sons" a lesson. Hawkshaw accompanies McLendon and the others, hoping that he can reason with them and prevent the murder of Will Mayes. When he realizes that he can only watch, not stop them, Hawkshaw begins to retch and asks McLendon to let him out of the car, but the car does not slow down. Will Mayes repeats the barber's name twice. Unwilling to witness the actual murder, Hawkshaw jumps out of the speeding car. The barber hides in the weeds and watches the cars return without Will Mayes. Hawkshaw limps back to town.

Parts 4 and 5 conclude the story by showing the murder's effect upon Miss Minnie, the townspeople, and McLendon. As Miss Minnie dresses to go to the picture show, her flesh feels "like fever." Her friends call for her early, and their eyes, too, glitter with a bright feverishness. Miss Minnie enjoys the walk to the cinema, strolling "slower and slower, as children eat ice cream," because "even the young men lounging in the doorway tipped their hats and followed with their eyes the motion of her hips and legs when she passed."

The picture show, which is described as a "miniature fairyland," recalls the "desert rat" in the barbershop and the "furious unreality" of Miss Minnie's bright dresses and her "idle and empty days." Miss Minnie begins to laugh as she watches the young couples enter the theater: "bodies awkward, divinely young, while beyond them the silver dream accumulated, inevitably on and on." Miss Minnie started the rumor to make herself part of a life which is only a "silver dream" to her, but she cannot stop her empty, feverish laughter as she watches the "young men and girls . . . scented and sibilant in the half dark." Her friends take her home and put ice on her temples. As they freshen the ice pack, they smooth her hair, "examining it for gray; 'poor girl!'" They enjoy Miss Minnie's frustrated laughter—their eyes "darkly aglitter, secret and passionate."

The narrator does not tell the reader that Miss Minnie created the rumor herself, but the reactions of both the men in the barbershop and her friends indicate that she did. They whisper to one another: "Do you suppose anything really happened?" When Miss Minnie realizes that her dry, frustrated life will continue, she becomes hysterical.

In the story's concluding part, McLendon arrives home at midnight. His house is described as "trim and fresh as a birdcage and almost as small, with its clean, green-and-white paint." He half strikes, half flings his wife across a chair because she has waited up for him. His "birdcage" home and small Southern town provide no outlets for the violence in his nature. He strikes his wife, as he killed Will Mayes, to relieve his personal frustration.

Themes and Meanings

Faulkner extends the meaning of "Dry September" beyond an account of racial violence in the South by including Hawkshaw, who wants to "get the sheriff and do this thing right." Hawkshaw, "a thin, sand-colored man with a mild face," is contrasted with the heavy and powerful McLendon, who "had commanded troops at the front in France and had been decorated for valor." To emphasize the contrast between Hawkshaw and McLendon, the narrator states: "They looked like men of different races."

Faulkner ironically suggests that though Hawkshaw and McLendon both have white skin, they do not belong to the same race. Hawkshaw considers Will Mayes a human being who deserves justice. To McLendon, he is a Negro, an object upon which he can safely unleash his brutality. Society approved McLendon's violence during the war, and in Jefferson, his violence against a black man is still sanctioned.

Style and Technique

The images contained in the first sentence of "Dry September" establish the story's scheme of imagery: "Through the bloody September twilight, aftermath of sixty-two rainless days, it had gone like a fire in dry grass—the rumor, the story, whatever it was." The equally important image of a "bloody September twilight" foreshadows the violence which will erupt.

Faulkner intensifies the horror of the murder by using images which evoke a sense of impending violence and death. As the barber hurries up the street after McLendon and the others, the streetlights glare "in rigid and violent suspension in the lifeless air." The "bloody September twilight" has passed into evening: "The day had died in a pall of dust; above the darkened square, shrouded by the spent dust, the sky was as clear as the inside of a brass bell." As the car moves along the road, its motion is like that of "an extinct furnace blast: cooler, but utterly dead." The imagery and diction of violence and death intensify the impact of the story. Later, as the "brass bell" begins to toll the death of Will Mayes, "the wan hemorrhage of the moon" increases.

The violence of the "bloody September twilight" has burned itself out; only the red dust remains. Hawkshaw could not prevent the murder of an innocent black man, but he lives and can limp home. The "eternal dust" absorbs the "glare and the sound" of McLendon and the others. Hawkshaw's race of humane and rational men may fail to control the violence and inhumanity of McLendon's race, but the dust of the land and of all men absorbs them: "They went on; the dust swallowed them; the glare and the sound died away. The dust of them hung for a while, but soon the eternal dust absorbed it again." Faulkner suspends one violent moment in a Southern town, but the eternal cycle of life and death, of timeless motion, can absorb even the moments of violence.

Jeanie R. Brink

THE DUEL

Author: Anton Chekhov (1860-1904)
Type of plot: Psychological realism
Time of plot: The 1880's
Locale: The Caucasus
First published: "Duel," 1891 (English translation, 1916)

Principal characters:
IVAN ANDREITCH "VANYA" LAEVSKY, the protagonist, a young
government clerk
NADYEZHDA FYODOROVNA, his married mistress
ALEXANDR DAVIDITCH SAMOYLENKO, a good-natured army
doctor, friend of Laevsky
"KOLYA" VON KOREN, a zoologist who hates Laevsky
ILYA MIHALITCH KIRILIN, the police captain, lover of
Nadyezhda Fyodorovna

The Story

"The Duel" is often classified as a short novel because of its length and
because of the complexity of its structure. In most Chekhov short stories,
there is one scene in which the protagonist comes to realize a truth about life
or a revelation about himself. "The Duel," on the other hand, has several
important revelatory scenes before the duel and a final scene three months
after the climactic duel, wherein there is a final turn of character.

The first five sections of "The Duel" explore the emotional and mental
states of two lovers, Ivan Andreitch Laevsky and Nadyezhda Fyodorovna,
who have fled to the Caucasus in search of happiness and now are living
together without benefit of matrimony, to the scandal of local society. Now
realizing how different daily life is from romantic dreams, how different life
as a farmer would be from visions of love in a vineyard, Laevsky is convinced
that he no longer loves Nadyezhda Fyodorovna. Only the lack of money prevents him from deserting her. As he tells his friend Alexandr Daviditch
Samoylenko, the fact that Nadyezhda's husband has died, leaving her free to
marry, makes Laevsky's plight more pressing. He does not want to marry a
woman he does not love, and Samoylenko's attempts to shame Laevsky for
irresponsibility have no effect on him. To the zoologist Von Koren, Laevsky's
attitude is shocking, typical of the hedonists of the 1880's.

Nadyezhda's dreams of love in a seaside cottage have been as much
unrealized as those of her lover. Rather than breaking her heart, his recent
cold behavior has relieved her sense of guilt, for she has not only grown
unenthusiastic about life on a farm; she has also run up debts without
Laevsky's knowledge and has taken Ilya Mihalitch Kirilin, the police captain,
as a lover. Although she is now bored with Kirilin, Nadyezhda has some dif-

ficulty in justifying her infidelity.

At a picnic, while Laevsky contemplates flight from his situation, Nadyezhda considers accepting as a lover the son of the shopkeeper to whom she owes money, hoping in some way to escape from her debts while enjoying herself at the same time. Kirilin, too, desires her favors. When the lovers return home, Laevsky tells Nadyezhda that her husband is dead and hurries to Samoylenko, begging for a loan so that he can run away from her. While Laevsky waits for money to flee, Nadyezhda is desperately concealing her own pressing debts from him until a propitious time to confess. As Samoylenko extracts a loan from Von Koren, Laevsky finally admits to himself that his flight will be based on lies: to Nadyezhda, whom he will abandon; to the generous doctor, who will not be repaid in the foreseeable future; to his government superiors; to his creditors; and to his mother, from whom he will get some money, but not enough for his needs.

Meanwhile, because Kirilin has threatened her with exposure, Nadyezhda agrees to give him two more assignations. Angered by the judgmental Von Koren, nearly hysterical with financial worries and his desire to break off his love affair, Laevsky insults his benefactor Samoylenko and his enemy Von Koren, and the zoologist turns Laevsky's unthinking words into a challenge to a duel. Later that evening, consumed with hatred for Von Koren and anxiety about his own situation, Laevsky has a final blow. The jealous son of the shopkeeper conducts him to the room where Kirilin is making love to Nadyezhda Fyodorovna.

Facing himself at last, Laevsky realizes that his life has been both selfish and meaningless, that Nadyezhda has become only what he made her, and finally, that she is the only person in the world for whom he really cares. Although the situation is unchanged, his debts unpaid, he now wishes to live. When Von Koren refuses to accept his apology, Laevsky fires into the air. Still impelled by hatred, Von Koren prepares to kill Laevsky, but a shout from the boyish deacon who is observing from the bushes throws off his aim, and Laevsky is spared, to find new joy in life and in love.

The final revelation comes three months later, at the time of Von Koren's departure. Urged by Samoylenko, Von Koren admits to Laevsky, now married, hardworking, and happy, that he had misjudged him. Laevsky concludes that no human being knows the truth, but that through suffering and misery everyone does more nearly approach an understanding of life.

Themes and Meanings

Throughout Chekhov's story, there is constant opposition between love and hate, between fidelity and infidelity. Whatever speeches the characters may make about values, they are motivated by their emotions. Laevsky and Nadyezhda both blame each other for the failure of their dreams, and both take revenge by infidelity—on her part, physical unfaithfulness, and on his part, the planned desertion. Although they talk, they do not confide. Von Koren himself, hating what Laevsky stands for, is anxious to kill him, and Nadyezhda's other two professed lovers are willing to blackmail her into having sexual relations with them and to betray her to her husband. Only Samoylenko and the deacon are truly good-natured.

Yet the movement of the story is toward reconciliation. Laevsky's suffering and Nadyezhda's unfaithfulness bring them to a love based on mutual understanding rather than on illusion; Von Koren learns that even men like Laevsky can change and that his own hatred can be turned to liking.

Laevsky's final realization, that human beings proceed like a small boat in high waves, unevenly yet with progress, suggests that the harsh judgments made by Laevsky, Von Koren, and even Nadyezhda in the first sections of the story were erroneous. None of them knew the inmost feelings of the others, which were revealed to the reader by Chekhov; each of them was separate in his own grievances and in his own dislikes, which culminated for the men in the duel and for Nadyezhda in her rendezvous with Kirilin. From a distance, human hatred can be as laughable as the young deacon found it; it can also be as wrong as the tolerant Samoylenko, the reconciling and forgiving force, insisted. Given the wrongs of which all human beings are capable, neither high-minded speeches nor destructive actions make sense. Yet even mistakes—like the duel—can produce reform.

Style and Technique

Because Chekhov often deals with the ironic difference between what man thinks and what he does, and because in this complex story he is dealing with several different major characters, he proceeds by exploring first the actions and thoughts of one character and then those of another. For example, after several sections in which Laevsky plans his escape from the woman whose heart he thinks he will be breaking, Chekhov moves into her mind, to reveal her own guilt, boredom, and deception, even her own relief because Laevsky has by his harshness provided her with an excuse for what she had already done. In other cases, too, both the ironic humor of the story and the thematic emphasis on human isolation come from Chekhov's penetration of the minds of his characters—of the innocent deacon's dreams of priestly power, conflicting with domestic bliss, for example, or of the scientist Von Koren's joy at the prospect of killing a man whom he hates, a joy which is concealed within the ritual of the duel.

Finally, theme and technique merge in a clear didactic statement which is not characteristic of Chekhov. Because no one can know the heart of another, and because human beings can change for the better, like Samoylenko one should reserve judgment, act in kindness, and hope always for human progress.

Rosemary M. Canfield-Reisman

DUEL

Author: Richard Matheson (1926-   )
Type of plot: Suspense-allegory
Time of plot: A Thursday in April
Locale: A highway to San Francisco, California
First published: 1971

> *Principal characters:*
> MANN, a middle-aged traveling salesman
> KELLER, a truck driver

The Story

"Duel" is based on a simple but provocative premise: What if an ordinary man, a salesman, were driving along a highway minding his own business when a truck driver, for no discernible reason, suddenly challenged him to a duel of machines? The task the author poses for himself is to develop fully the potential of this premise, to dramatize its limited but exciting and suspenseful narrative possibilities.

Heading west on a two-lane highway through the mountains, Mann, a middle-aged traveling salesman, sees very few vehicles. Because he must maintain his routine speed of fifty-five miles per hour if he is to keep his appointment in San Francisco, he casually passes a truck that is pulling a gasoline trailer. This action somehow sets off a hostile response in the faceless truck driver. The truck passes him, Mann passes the truck, it passes him again, and he begins to realize that an unusual situation has developed, one the truck driver intends to control. An intricate series of actions and reactions ensues, with Mann's own emotions escalating from bewilderment to mild irritation to ordinary anger to mortal fear to combative rage.

There are three major turning points in the narrative. As he climbs a steep grade, Mann is able to pass the truck, but he blares his horn derisively. Soothed by a reverie about his wife and children, with music on the car radio as background, he settles into the delusion that the incident is over. Yet on the steep, curving downgrade, the ugly, square truck tries to ram him from behind, and Mann realizes that the driver intends to kill him.

The second turning point comes when Mann decides to evade the truck by pulling over into the lot in front of Chuck's Cafe, and to placate the driver, who may or may not have entered the cafe while Mann was trying to calm himself with rationalizations in the rest room. Back on the highway, however, the truck resumes its deadly game, stopping and starting and blocking the highway in response to Mann's evasive maneuvers.

Mann's impulsive decision to outrun the truck and his indulgent joy in the race is the third turning point. In this pastoral setting, he is forced to accept the fact that he cannot withdraw from this duel. Two emotions new to his experience—uncontrollable rage and terror of imminent death—enable him to draw on resources that he had not known he had. His overheated car having barely made it to the crest of a steep grade ahead of the truck, he must elude his opponent on the steep downgrade. When the motor fails, he makes a sudden turn onto a side road, timed so that if the truck driver surrenders to an instinct to follow, he will lose control. When the truck disappears from his rearview mirror, Mann stops, gets out of his car, and walks back down the road just in time to see the truck crash in a ravine and explode. Mann looks down, too stunned to feel anything. Then he cries exultantly, like a beast over his defeated prey.

Themes and Meanings

Rising above the story's surface of detailed realism is an allegory of irrational male aggression that reaches back through history beyond the era of dueling to prehistory, when men slew one another out of mere instinctual territorial combativeness. Mann is Everyman, from the first man to man at this moment to man in the future. For the first half of the combat, strange in a modern, civilized setting but commonplace in the jungle, Mann's antagonist is more an alien mechanical force than a person: "He visualized the truck as some great entity pursuing him, insentient, brutish, chasing him with instinct only." After Mann sees the driver's face and learns his name from the printing on the side of the truck—Keller (read "Killer")—the duel is between two men but reduced to the level of their primeval ancestors, bereft of human empathy and intellect, a function of animal reflex and instinct.

In the first half of the story, in the Chuck's Cafe rest room, a hostile oasis, Mann can reflect on the way in which modern society suppresses the knowledge that man's aggressive instincts have survived more than two thousand years of the civilizing process; each person is so dependent on the illusion that he and his fellowmen are civilized that when the primitive, irrational violence erupts, he is totally unprepared to understand logically or react effectively to it: ". . . suddenly, the jungle is in front of you again. *Man, part animal, part angel*." Ironically, Mann thinks that only the driver of the truck is an animal, and that he is its "prey."

Early in the second half of the story, the allegory that equates modern man with his primeval ancestor converges with an allegorical element that is secondary to it but inseparable from it: The animal-angel elements in man are trapped and forever warring in the body of a nonhuman beast. Before Mann saw the driver's face, the truck had been "the embodiment of unknown terror," which appeared to him earlier as a "leviathan," which now is a "purple-silver relic" (of primeval eons), and which later is a "looming gargantuan shape," a "ponderous beast." Ecological conditions and smaller creatures destroyed mammoth creatures in primeval times; Mann-car destroys, by strategy and accident, Keller-trailer-truck. In the final paragraph, Mann and Keller as combative primitive men are submerged in nonhuman beast imagery: "The cry of some ancestral beast above the body of its vanquished foe." Thus Matheson's allegory, based on a detailed realism with which his readers can identify (and which they can fully experience on that level), simultaneously subjects his reader to a reversion to the murderous behavior of his primeval human ancestors and of the beasts out of which man evolved.

Yet the significance of that dual-level allegory is made much more forceful when one considers that it has a present-day and futuristic correlation: In the history of life forms, the human invention of mechanical locomotion occurred only a second ago, and machines are currently engaged in an armed duel, heading, on the two-laned highway of life, west, the direction symbolic of death. Matheson's simple allegory has impressive scope in time and space, illuminating man's predicament as it illuminates the nature of each of his readers.

Style and Technique

Matheson is an interesting example of the commercial writer who is so in command of his craft that he achieves, in this profound allegory, through the controlled use of various techniques and a style almost perfectly suited to it, a work of art.

Except for a few lapses, the narrative point of view is third-person, central intelligence. Serviceable phrases such as "Mann's expression froze in terror," "with haunted eyes," and "his face a mask of animosity" violate that point of view by giving the reader external views of Mann, through whose perceptions all elements of the story are otherwise centralized. Perhaps Matheson the screenwriter intruded at these points; "Duel" appeared in *Playboy* only months before Matheson's own adaptation, directed by then novice Steven Spielberg, showed up on television, becoming a cinematic as well as a literary classic. The very mechanics of the situation as it develops help Matheson to control his basically commercial-literary style, which now and then produces such lines as "He eyed the truck with cursory disapproval." Given the already well-controlled Mann point of view and the ongoing context of terror, it is not necessary to follow "He's going to kill me" with "Mann thought, horrified."

The reader experiences Matheson's simple, precise, fast-paced plot structure as if he were being carried forward, simultaneously terrified and exhilarated, inside a swift, smooth-running machine. The reader intimately shares Mann's emotional, imaginative, and intellectual reactions as they escalate from mild irritation to sheer terror to instinctive murderous rage. The reader experiences a process in which an ironic reversal turns Mann-the-victim into Mann-the-victor.

To enhance Mann's reactions to the aggressive behavior of the truck driver, Matheson uses vivid descriptive detail, imagery, and the devices of parallel and contrast. "Sunlight on his arm and lap" is a detail that enables the reader to drift with Mann into reverie. Later, Mann sees "the back of the truck driver's left hand on the steering wheel," a detail that helps make the driver seem mysterious. That Mann can see only the lower half of the square radiator grill focuses his sense of the menace rushing after him. Matheson makes Mann's response to everything that he sees along the highway very lively: "Who the hell is Will Jasper," he wonders, looking at the name painted on a rock. "What would he think of this situation?" The author offers a grotesquely comic parallel to the deadly serious situation when Mann notices the "Night Crawlers—Bait" sign and thinks of monster films. More effective as contrasts are Mann's responses to the music on his car radio and to the pastoral scenery framing the highway. Yet music finally lacks the power to soothe the savage instincts provoked in his breast, and scenery as relief from terror becomes an irritant, a mocking contrast to his perilous predicament.

Another enhancement of Mann's basic predicament is the sense of isolation that Matheson creates. At the start, and now and then throughout, Mann notices that few cars are on the highway. Even the drivers in Chuck's Cafe are shadowy figures. He feels the driver has isolated him from all other possibilities for this duel. Imagining his wife at the supermarket performing her domestic chores only makes his isolation more intense. When Mann sees two lovers parked in a car, not even noticing him as he passes, the reader shares his poignant isolation. At the sight of a pet cemetery, he wisecracks, but the sight later of flowers and a "Funeral" sign makes him imagine the final isolation—his own death.

By endowing all elements with a sense of immediacy, Matheson enables the reader to follow even Mann's developing, ambivalent meditations with no lag in pace. For example, Mann draws on his lifelong preconception that truckers are cautious; then he decides that this driver must be an independent who lives by his own rules; finally, he will see that the man is lawless. Mann's interrogation of aspects of the mystery, as when he is in Chuck's Cafe, enhances the reader's enjoyment of the fast-paced sequence of actions. There is a rare congruity between the character's questions and the reader's as both try to understand why, in this case, the driver behaves so irrationally. As the truck driver manipulates Mann's behavior, the writer manipulates the reader's responses. "Duel" is an unusually clear demonstration of how, in many effective stories, the main elements become a metaphor of the storytelling process itself—of the dynamics of the writer-reader relationship.

David Madden

THE DUNWICH HORROR

Author: H. P. Lovecraft (1890-1937)
Type of plot: Horror
Time of plot: 1913-1928
Locale: "Dunwich," Massachusetts
First published: 1929

Principal characters:
OLD WHATELEY, an elderly Dunwich resident suspected of
sorcery
LAVINIA WHATELEY, his daughter
WILBUR, her son
DR. HENRY ARMITAGE, the librarian at Miskatonic University

The Story
The birth of Wilbur Whateley in Dunwich is obviously an ominous event. On the night he is born, strange noises rumble through the hills, all the dogs in the vicinity continuously bark, and a hideous screaming is heard. In fact, the whole Whateley family is rather bizarre. Lavinia, Wilbur's mother, is a deformed, unattractive albino. Lavinia's father, Old Whateley, is feared by the local populace for his practice of black magic, while the father of Wilbur is completely unknown.

This ominous note continues as the child grows. Wilbur is described as "goatish" in appearance, although he possesses the Whateley trademark of a chinless face. He can already walk at the age of seven months and talks at eleven months. He is very particular about keeping his body well covered with clothes, unlike the rest of the Whateleys. Every May Eve and Halloween, the boy and his mother are seen going up to the top of Sentinel Hill and apparently practicing weird rites, to the accompaniment of bursts of flame and underground rumblings.

At the same time, the boy's grandfather has been playing an active part in his development. He teaches the boy ancient lore, incantations, and formulas from the old books that he keeps. He continuously buys cattle with a never-ending supply of ancient gold pieces, yet the size of his herd never increases. He also feverishly rebuilds the second floor of the house and constructs a wooden ramp leading up to it from the ground. The few visitors to the house are invariably disturbed by extremely odd noises upstairs.

After Old Whateley dies and his daughter disappears, there is a shift of scene, as Lovecraft affords the reader a view of Wilbur, now fourteen years old and eight feet tall, resembling a huge, dark gargoyle, at the library of Miskatonic University in Arkham, hurriedly copying some missing formulas that he needs out of a rare book, the *Necronomicon*. The alert librarian, Dr. Henry Armitage, reading the Latin text over Wilbur's shoulder, sees references to the Old Ones, beings who apparently are ready to "break through" and destroy the earth. He associates this with the mysterious happenings in Dunwich and the dim, hideous aura of Wilbur, and he immediately refuses him further access to the book.

There now occurs the first climax of the story, which serves as a preview of the real Dunwich horror, which the reader has yet to see. Wilbur is desperate to get the formula he needs, although he seems fearful of being away from the farm for too long for some reason. He finally breaks into the library in an attempt to steal the book, but he is killed by the watchdog. As he lies on the floor with his clothes torn away, Dr. Armitage sees him as the monster he really is—tentacles with red, sucking mouths protruding from his stomach. Dr. Armitage and the reader realize that, terrible as this is, something far worse waits in the farmhouse in Dunwich.

In the final section of the narrative, the horror has already broken loose. The Whateley farmhouse, which has previously had all its inner partitions removed by Wilbur so as to make one huge, two-story space, has literally been blown apart by the monster, nourished by its steady diet of cattle (the reason for Old Whateley's ramp). It soon becomes evident that the thing which has escaped is invisible, although its myriad footprints, resembling a herd of elephants, can be seen. A reign of terror in the surrounding area has already begun, with houses being flattened at night and people and cattle disappearing.

Dr. Armitage has exhaustively studied the *Necronomicon* and as a result has learned more about the strange evil threatening the world and has managed to discover several formulas which might possibly defeat the present evil. He comes to Dunwich with two colleagues from the university, and he hopes to get close enough to the monster for the formulas to have effect when he recites them.

In the concluding scene, Dr. Armitage has tracked the monster to the top of Sentinel Hill, on which is a circle of stones in Stonehenge fashion, along with a huge altar. This confirms his worst fears, for he knows that the monster will try to communicate with the beings from beyond. Dr. Armitage gets close enough and begins to recite the formula while his two helpers spray a powder which gives a brief glimpse of the monster, causing the onlookers far down the hill to scream in terror. As the monster cries out in a thunderous voice, it is obliterated by a lightning bolt, and the situation is saved.

In the course of this final scene, two facts have been revealed. The huge monster, with its Whateley face barely discernible among the tentacles, eyes, suckers, and feet, is evidently the twin brother of Wilbur, born at the same time as he, while the father of both Wilbur and the monster is one of the mysterious beings from the otherworld.

Themes and Meanings

H. P. Lovecraft believed that the oldest and strongest fear of mankind is fear of the unknown. This belief was an important force behind the idea that he gradually developed over many years that the earth was once inhabited by a race of beings from another world or dimension who, while having lost their hold on earth, are waiting to enter again. This is the major theme in "The Dunwich Horror."

This idea develops slowly as the story unfolds. Dr. Armitage has realized that "unseen things not of earth—or at least not of tri-dimensional earth—rushed foetid and horrible through New England's glens, and brooded obscenely on the mountaintops." Old Whateley on his deathbed tells Wilbur that only the beings from beyond, the Old Ones who want to come back, can make the monster multiply. The *Necronomicon* relates that the Old Ones broke through long ago, and they shall break through once again.

Lovecraft was indebted to the English writer Arthur Machen (1863-1947) for the inspiration of this idea, but he carried the idea much further and in a different direction, for while Machen's otherworld is populated by a mixture of little people and nature deities (sometimes fearful), Lovecraft's otherworld, or dimension, is completely terrifying and threatens the continued existence of this world. Lovecraft built up these ideas into an entire body of myth known as Cthulhu Mythos. The names mentioned in the *Necronomicon*, such as Yog-Sothoth, Cthulhu, and Kadath, are beings or places important in the myth.

An interesting and related idea in the story is the ominous feeling imparted by great age. The beings from beyond are described as the oldest things in or around earth. Old Whateley is extremely aged, and the rapid aging of Wilbur is emphasized. The entire village of Dunwich is seen as old, decadent, and unsettling in appearance, while the stone circles (where evil rites are practiced) are of great antiquity, going back at least to Indian times.

Style and Technique

This is one of Lovecraft's most tightly constructed stories, largely as a result of his use of linking elements which give subtle clues and anticipate developments. The climactic scene in which the monster on the hilltop cries out to its father is presaged by Old Whateley in the beginning, when he tells the loungers at the general store that a child of Lavinia's would call for its father on Sentinel Hill. The constant rebuilding and expansion of the farmhouse are clues to the existence of the horror within and its growth. Smell is important, for the similar odors of the upstairs room (where the monster is growing), Wilbur, the top of Sentinel Hill, and the rampaging monster at the end serve to provide clues to the identity of Wilbur. Even sound is utilized, for the whippoorwills always cry in concert before a death.

Some of Lovecraft's strategies are reminiscent of Edgar Allan Poe—not surprising, since he once referred to Poe as his god of fiction. These devices include the conscious use of archaisms and a tendency to use many adjectives. Dr. Armitage "seemed to sense the close presence of some terrible part of the intruding horror, and to glimpse a hellish advance in the black dominion of the ancient and once passive nightmare." This style, mannered and obtrusive in Lovecraft's earlier prose, was more successfully utilized for narrative effect in his later fiction, such as "The Dunwich Horror," in which the story is related in almost reportorial fashion.

James V. Muhleman

THE EARTHQUAKE IN CHILE

Author: Heinrich von Kleist (1777-1811)
Type of plot: Dramatic novella
Time of plot: 1647
Locale: Santiago, Chile
First published: "Das Erdbeben in Chili," 1807 (English translation, 1946)

> *Principal characters:*
> JERONIMO RUGERO, a Spanish tutor
> DONNA JOSEPHE ASTERON, his lover, the daughter of one of
>   the city's wealthiest aristocratic families
> PHILIP, their infant son
> DON FERNANDO ORMEZ, the son of the city's commandant

The Story

The story opens at the moment of a fatally destructive earthquake, just as the young Spaniard Jeronimo Rugero is about to hang himself in prison. Jeronimo despairs at the fate of his beloved, Donna Josephe, who on this day is to be beheaded for having borne a child on the steps of the cathedral while she was a novice in the Carmelite convent. Her father had sent her to the convent upon learning of her secret love for her tutor, Jeronimo. Later, Jeronimo managed to gain access to the convent garden, where their love was consummated.

Upon hearing the bells accompanying Josephe to her execution, Jeronimo tightens the rope that would tear him away from his wretched life, when suddenly the ground trembles under his feet. The earthquake destroys the major part of the city and rips apart the walls of the prison. Barely conscious, Jeronimo escapes through an opening between the fallen buildings and reaches the nearest gate to the city, where he is filled with feelings of ecstasy and thankfulness at his deliverance. Yet depression soon overwhelms him again when he remembers Josephe. He searches for her in vain among the fleeing crowds, then at sundown discovers a distant, solitary valley. On reaching it, he catches sight of a young woman washing her child in a spring. It is Donna Josephe.

The earthquake miraculously rescued her as well, as the falling buildings scattered the gathered crowds and the procession of her executioners. She returned to the convent just in time to rescue her son from the flames engulfing it. Before leaving the city, she noticed that all the seats of power and authority had collapsed, including the prison. Believing Jeronimo dead, she sought out the isolated valley to pray for his soul.

Their first night back together is idyllic, as they exchange stories of their imprisonment, enjoy their incredible good fortune, and plan on departing for a new life in Spain. The next morning their reveries are interrupted by a young nobleman, Don Fernando Ormez, carrying his infant son. Since his wife is badly wounded, he asks Josephe to breast-feed his son. After initial hesitation at meeting someone familiar with her history, she agrees, whereupon Don Fernando invites the lovers to join him and his family for breakfast. Both are overwhelmed by the warm reception of their new friends and quickly forget the horrible events of the recent past. The human spirit appears rejuvenated, as the different social classes mingle easily with one another and everyone helps to ease the pain and deprivation of their neighbors.

Blinded by the general goodwill that they see all around them, Jeronimo and Josephe decide not to go to Spain, but rather to become reconciled with those who had condemned them and their illicit love. Word spreads of a solemn thanksgiving mass in the Dominican church in Santiago. Despite the warnings of Don Fernando's sister-in-law, Josephe insists on attending the mass and immediately sets off for the church with Jeronimo, the two infants, Don Fernando, and Donna Constanza, another sister-in-law.

In the crowded church, an elderly prelate begins a sermon of praise and thanksgiving, then quickly turns to condemning the city's moral depravity and alludes to the scandalous event in the convent garden. Before Don Fernando and his party can escape from the church, voices call out that the godless couple are among them. Saved temporarily by Don Fernando's presence of mind, the lovers slip out of the church, with Don Fernando, freshly armed with a naval officer's sword, holding the two infants. No sooner, however, do they reach the square in front of the church than someone, who cries out that he is Jeronimo's father, slays both Jeronimo and Donna Constanza, who was at Jeronimo's side. Don Fernando manages to fend off the violent crowd, in particular a fanatic shoemaker, but Josephe sacrifices herself in order to save the children. The shoemaker then snatches away Don Fernando's son Juan and ruthlessly smashes him against a church pillar.

Don Fernando does rescue Philip, the son of Jeronimo and Josephe, and later adopts him. When he compares Philip to his own son and thinks of how he acquired him, it seems to him almost "as if he had to rejoice."

Themes and Meanings

The terrible destructive force of the earthquake levels both buildings and human institutions. At the same time that it kills scores of people, it liberates Jeronimo and Josephe from the bonds of the old hierarchical social and political order. The Rousseauistic promise of a new, egalitarian social order based on the natural goodness of humanity, however, deludes the lovers into desiring to return to the city immediately—to the one building left standing where the old power structure could reassert itself and incite people to return to their old ways. The earthquake, Heinrich von Kleist suggests, brings out the best and worst in everyone, and the evil that triumphs in the Dominican church is an evil upheld by a Church governed by a powerful need to protect its own authority and interests. Kleist's sympathies clearly lie with Jeronimo and Josephe, yet the purity of their love is no match for the far stronger social conventions and structures that ultimately destroy them.

The world is the staging ground for vast, unpredictable forces—whether natural, human, political, or religious. It is chance that saves the lovers at first, chance that brings them together at the spring, chance that they are recognized and slain outside the church, and, finally, chance that saves their son. If there is no final certainty, only a universe governed by irrational forces and a God who is incomprehensible and largely absent from everyday life, how should one act? Jeronimo, Josephe, and Don Fernando all act with a natural grace and dignity in the face of turmoil, yet each pays dearly for it. Kleist's deep pessimism about the nature of human behavior and institutions leads almost inevitably to tragedy. Don Fernando embodies Kleistian moral character and provides the story its small yet persistent hope that a more just moral order might yet prevail.

Style and Technique

The narration of the events of the story is extremely compressed and full of dramatic irony and twists. The narrator, although anonymous, is not completely objective in his report, for he betrays his own attitudes toward religious hypocrisy in his subtly sarcastic language, and he clearly does not believe in the lovers' sinfulness or guilt. The serene and idyllic middle section of the story is surrounded by scenes of continuous action, in which details are piled up like the rubble of the fallen buildings and often are not easily separated from the whole. The sudden appearance and disappearance of people and voices underlie the haphazard encounters of friends and enemies. There is little causal explanation: Things simply happen, and the characters react as best they can. If the narrator believes in any grander order, he does not reveal it and couches his own metaphysical uncertainties in a series of speculative, "as if" statements: When the earthquake hits, it is "as if the firmament collapsed"; when Josephe rescues her child from the collapsing convent, it is "as if all the angels of heaven protected her"; when the pair are reunited, it is as if they were in the valley of Eden.

The narrative impatience and uncertainty is counterbalanced by a dramatic structure which is exemplary in its economy and power. After plunging immediately into the dilemmas of the story in the first sentence, the narrative unfolds impetuously, with hardly a pause for reflection until the climax of the sermon in the church, from which point the hideous finale is played out with breathtaking rapidity. The ending, with its coda of Don Fernando reflecting on the tragic fate of his friends and son, resolves little and leaves open the question of the proper human response to apparent divine intervention.

Peter West Nutting

EDWARD AND GOD

Author: Milan Kundera (1929-   )
Type of plot: Philosophical farce
Time of plot: 1958-1960, with reference to events "a number of years" later
Locale: A small Czech town
First published: "Edward a Bůh," 1969 (English translation, 1974)

>   *Principal characters:*
>   EDWARD, the protagonist, a young schoolteacher
>   EDWARD'S OLDER BROTHER, a farmer
>   ALICE, a devout young woman whom Edward pursues
>   MISS CHEHACHKOVA, the directress of Edward's school

The Story

At the beginning of the story, Edward, a recent graduate of a teachers' college, is visiting in the country with his amiable farmer brother. Although now happily settled into his new existence, Edward's brother was once expelled from Edward's own college for laughing at a fellow student's exaggerated grief over Joseph Stalin's death. That student, who later denounced Edward's brother to the authorities, is now the directress of a school in a small town. Edward's brother advises him that since "she was always after young boys," Edward should apply to her for a position. Edward calls on Miss Chehachkova, the directress, whose very "ugliness" puts him at ease, and soon he is teaching at her school.

Edward is indifferent to his teaching duties, but soon he is pursuing the beautiful young Alice, who lives in the town. Alice, however, is reserved, and one day asks Edward if he believes in God. Unwilling to admit that he does not, Edward says that he does believe but is "bothered by doubts." Edward attends church with Alice, but as he is leaving he is seen by the directress. He later excuses his behavior to the directress by claiming an interest in "the baroque interior of the cathedral." During the following weeks, Edward continues to pursue Alice but is frustrated by her sexual puritanism. For tactical reasons, he begins to read the Bible, study theology, and "exaggerate his religiousness."

At school, Edward is soon called in for "a friendly and unofficial talk" with a panel that includes the directress. Deciding that the momentum of events makes it impossible to tell the truth, Edward untruthfully says that he does believe in God, although quite unwillingly. The directress, disarmed, praises him for his apparent honesty, and says that she personally will oversee Edward's future intellectual development. Visiting her apartment on a required visit, Edward finds the directress well-disposed toward him, but he also has an uncomfortable vision of the sadness and intense loneliness of her life. They exchange expressions of regard, and before he leaves, Edward even says, untruthfully, that he finds her "pretty."

Confident that he is now safe from official displeasure, Edward attends church again with Alice. She seems "somehow different" and proud to be seen with him. Eventually he realizes that a distorted report of events at his hearing has turned him into a sympathetic public figure. Although he realizes that Alice's new feelings toward him are "an undeserved gift," Edward makes arrangements for them to spend the weekend at his brother's cottage in the country.

Edward later visits the directress, as required. She has cognac set out for him, and as the conversation gradually turns personal, Edward realizes that he is in a changed and "irreversible" situation. It becomes obvious that the directress expects advances from Edward that he fears his physical aversion to her will make impossible. Eventually, seizing on a sudden inspiration, Edward springs away from her, saying that he is afraid of "sin." The directress persists, until Edward, in desperation, imperiously orders her to kneel, clasp her hands, and pray. Momentarily swayed, the directress obeys. This unexpected reversal enables Edward to regain his confidence and overcome his physical antipathy. He succeeds in making love to the directress.

That Saturday, Edward takes Alice to the country and finds that her puritanism has disappeared, along with her religious scruples. Despite Alice's beauty, Edward is obscurely irritated by this, and he begins to see Alice in a new and unflattering way. He also has a disagreement with his brother, who has learned something about Edward's recent life. His brother attacks dissembling, but Edward argues that in a world of madmen, one can hardly afford to tell the truth.

As the lovers return to town, Edward is overcome with a wave of anger and disgust at Alice, at the "shadowy people" he has struggled to accommodate, and at himself. He picks an ugly fight with Alice, whom he cruelly charges with "sin" and a betrayal of her religious principles. He is soon able to precipitate a break.

This "curious anger" passes, but Edward does not seek a reconciliation. He continues to visit the directress, while beginning to pursue "all sorts" of other women. These activities cause Edward to appreciate the "solitary walks" that he has begun to take, which often end at the church. The narrator warns the reader not to be "apprehensive"—Edward is not beginning to believe in God. Nevertheless, as the years pass, Edward begins to long for the "essential" that he has never found in his "unessential" work, love affairs, and thought. At the moment the narrator chooses to take leave of him, Edward is in church, sunk as usual into a deep sorrow over the nonexistence of God. Suddenly, from that sorrow there "emerges the genuine *living* face of God." Edward breaks into a happy smile.

Themes and Meanings

Kundera is explicit about the nature of the "God" of his title, and about the difference between His nature and Edward's merely human one. "God," as the narrator remarks in a difficult but significant passage, "is essence itself. . . . God alone is relieved of the distracting obligation of *appearing* and can merely *be*. For he solely constitutes (He Himself, alone and nonexistent) the essential opposite of this unessential (but so much more existent) world."

Kundera's language here derives from the "basic theological literature" of Edward's studies. Within orthodox Catholic theology, God's "existence" (the fact of His life) and his "essence" (the defining qualities that make Him what He is) are the same thing. God, in other words, is not troubled by the perplexing gap that opens up for Edward between the seemingly arbitrary facts of his actual existence and an "essential" Edward begins to seek for, but in vain.

Because, as the narrator's language insists, the God of this story is "nonexistent." Unpleasant though he may be in many ways, Edward preserves a certain integrity by refusing to set up for himself some false "essential," as do other characters in the story (consider Alice's brittle religiosity or the directress' rather wooden invocations of "the future").

Within the story, it is true, Edward's "straightforward" brother seems to suggest the possibility of a mode of life that is neither tormented nor dishonest. Unlike Alice or the directress, he does not appear to deceive himself; unlike Edward, he does not deceive others. Unlike anyone else in the story, he appears to be genuinely happy.

Nevertheless, in his debate with Edward, it is Edward's criticisms of merely human "truth" that are allowed to stand as the last word. The story's ambiguous ending seems to suggest that, for Kundera, Edward's irresolvable, faintly comic dilemma over God is itself the "essence" or defining quality of the human.

Style and Technique

Irony, in the broadest sense of that term, refers to any perception of the difference between the way things are and the way things seem.

In "Edward and God," the plot turns on the real consequences of a pretended belief, and the story's theme on Edward's real longing for a God he considers unreal.

Yet Kundera's narrative technique also depends upon a use of dramatic irony: the contrast between his narrator's insight into motives and events, and Edward's own painful if sometimes inspired blundering. Thus, the narrator's description of how Edward sees his teaching duties as being "among the fortuitous aspects of his life," something "attached to him like a false beard," foreshadows Edward's own later dissatisfaction with the "unessential." Similarly, Alice is first introduced into the story with language that looks ahead to Edward's own later disillusionment with her: "In his new place of work Edward soon found a young girl who struck him as beautiful, and he began to pursue her with a seriousness that was almost genuine."

Far more clearly than Edward as the reader first encounters him, the narrator can see through the behavior of the story's characters to its actual sources. For example, the narrator realizes that the extreme and opposing attitudes toward religion taken up by Alice and the directress have a common psychological source, the desire to align with one's own side against the enemy and so preserve "the precious sense" of one's own superiority.

In the course of the story, however, Edward's insight into his own motives improves. During his final fight with Alice, for example, Edward realizes that his disgust is partly with himself, and that "even the shadow that mocks remains a shadow, subordinate, derivative, and wretched, and nothing more." Edward, in other words, seems on his way to being able to write a story like "Edward and God."

S. Badrich

THE EGG

Author: Sherwood Anderson (1876-1941)
Type of plot: Regional realism
Time of plot: Beginning of the twentieth century
Locale: A small town in Ohio
First published: 1921

> *Principal characters:*
> THE NARRATOR, a man relating events from his childhood
> HIS FATHER, a failed entrepreneur
> HIS MOTHER, a loving, ambitious wife
> JOE KANE, a customer in their restaurant

The Story

"The Egg" tells the story of a childhood memory that has in a profound way shaped its narrator's moral outlook. The tale centers on the narrator's father, a man "intended by nature to be . . . cheerful [and] kindly," who, through acquiring the "American passion for getting up in the world," loses his happiness. The father's loss engenders in the son a sense of tragedy and irresolution and a conviction that "the egg"—the source and symbol of that loss—completely and utterly triumphs over life.

The narrator begins his story by describing his father's life as a farmhand in the rural Midwest. The older man is content in this position; he enjoys his work and the easy camaraderie of the other farmhands, who gather at a local saloon on Saturday nights. Dissatisfaction does not strike him until, at age thirty-five, he marries. His wife, "a tall silent woman with a long nose and troubled grey eyes," initiates a change in his life. While wanting nothing for herself, she is nevertheless "incurably ambitious" for her husband and for the son born to them—the narrator. At her prompting, the man leaves his job on the farm and, with his new family, moves closer to town to take up chicken raising.

From the chicken farm, the young narrator gains his initial impressions of life. There he sees at first hand the inescapable tragedy of the chicken:

> It is born out of an egg, lives for a few weeks as a tiny fluffy thing such as you will see pictured on Easter cards, then becomes hideously naked, eats quantities of corn and meal bought by the sweat of your father's brow, gets diseases . . . stands looking with stupid eyes at the sun, becomes sick and dies.

The miserable cycle of chickenkind comes to be, for the narrator, a paradigm for human life; the chickens are so much like people that, in his mind, "they mix one up in one's judgments of life." The narrator's primary problem, however, is not with "the hen," the mature bird already locked in its mortal coils, but with "the egg," the source of potential new life.

Against such odds as the narrator describes, chicken raising proves to be a futile struggle. Selling the chicken farm, the family loads a small wagon with their possessions and begins the slow journey to a railroad way station, where they plan to open a restaurant. Along the way, the boy-narrator, noticing his father's balding head, imagines the bare swath of skin as a path going to "a far beautiful place where life was a happy eggless affair." The father, however, carries with him a memento of the chicken days—a collection of "grotesques . . . born out of eggs," alcohol-preserved specimens of two-headed or six-legged chicks hatched over the years on his farm. These he keeps in the simple belief that people like "to look at strange and wonderful things."

After some time in the restaurant trade, the father decides that his lack of success in business derives from his failure to be pleasant enough; he resolves, therefore, to "adopt a cheerful outlook on life." The central event of the story comes of this decision. One night while the father is tending the restaurant, a young man comes in to pass the time. Convinced that this is the moment to put into action his new cheerfulness, the father begins to imagine ways to entertain the customer. His nervousness, however, strikes the young man as odd; the customer believes the proprietor wants him to leave. Before he can do so, the father begins to perform a trick with an egg. When the trick fails to capture the young man's attention, the father brings down from the shelf his collection of pickled grotesques. When this, too, fails to interest the customer, he tries another trick—heating an egg in vinegar so that it can be pushed inside a bottle. He promises to give the customer the egg-in-the-bottle, but again his trick proves difficult. In a final, desperate effort to force the egg into the narrow container, the father breaks the egg and spatters it on his clothes. Already leaving, the customer turns for a moment and laughs.

The father, consumed with anger, fires an egg at the retreating customer. Then, grasping another egg, he runs upstairs to the bedroom where his wife and son are no longer sleeping. The narrator, remembering his thoughts at the moment, imagines that his father "had some idea of destroying it, of destroying all eggs," but instead he lays the egg gently down and drops to his knees, crying. The mother quietly strokes her husband's balding head. The son, troubled by this scene of his father's grief, weeps too. Into the night, the boy ponders the question of the egg—"why eggs had to be and why from the egg came the hen who again laid the egg"—a question that gets into his blood and remains with him unresolved into adulthood.

Themes and Meanings

Given its title and the narrator's statement that his tale "if correctly told will centre on the egg," the egg is unquestionably crucial to Sherwood Anderson's story. As an image, the egg promotes the possibility for new life, as well as the simultaneous fragility and resilience of that life. For the narrator, however, the egg's special power is to condemn the young possibility, the passionate promise of life, to a relentless round of decay and death. He sees this power of the egg operative in his father, whose "new impulse in life"—to leave the farm and make his fortune in the urban world—is ruined by the egg. Ironically, though, at his moment of crisis, the father preserves rather than destroys the egg. Despite his failure, he values the life in the egg just as he values the "poor little things" that he saves in the jars as a source of wonder.

For the narrator, the egg acquires ever larger significance. "Prenatally" involved not only with his father's fortunes but also with the narrator's own moral disposition, the egg of that night in the bedroom is inextricably linked with the innumerable eggs laid and hatched by his father's chickens. Conjoined with the narrator's ability to think and articulate his thoughts—a talent that his father, as a physical man, lacks—the egg gains the power of generality. It becomes for the narrator the source and symbol of the tragic cycle of life so vividly experienced on the chicken farm, a cycle whose most enduring creations are the pitiful monstrosities preserved by his father. Eventually, the narrator's general view of the egg leads him to the ultimate metaphysical question—the "why" of the egg that implants itself in his mind and leaves him with a feeling of irresolution.

Though the narrator cannot solve logically the question of the egg, he does solve it creatively. The irresolution which the egg engenders in him in fact impels him to attempt, through his tale, to articulate his uncertainty in a form that, like the egg, is in itself whole and complete and pregnant with life. The egg—particularly that one which his father holds in his hand when he enters the bedroom—functions as the fertile ovum from which the boy's imagination prepares for the story that he tells as an adult. Focusing as it does the narrator's memory of his and his father's mutual grief at the failing of life to live up to its early promise, the egg gives birth to the new, narrative act. "The Egg," not the idea of the egg, triumphs.

Style and Technique

Much of the power of "The Egg" comes from the narrator's ability to articulate the inner life of his father. This difference between father and son becomes indirectly the subject of a passage in which the narrator explains his father's decision to become cheerful:

> It was father's notion that a passion for the company of himself and mother would spring up in the breasts of the younger people of the town of Bidwell . . . . They would troop shouting with joy and laughter into our place. There would be joy and festivity. I do not mean to give the impression that father spoke so elaborately of the matter. He was as I have said an uncommuni-

cative man. "They want some place to go. I tell you they want some place to go," he said over and over. That was as far as he got. My own imagination has filled in the blanks.

The father's repetitive statement reveals in a rough and untutored way his simple urge toward a better life. Yet he is not more able to carry out this urge in action than he is able to express it in words. In fact, the urge itself, the ambition to rise in life, leads him out of his natural element—the rural and masculine life of a farmhand—and into the urban, feminine, and civilized town life that requires a greater complexity of mind, speech, and social savvy than he possesses.

In contrast, the son imagines in detail what his father could only minimally verbalize. This act of imagination joins the father and son, for in order for the narrator to relate his father's inner life he must himself intimately experience that life. Yet the imaginative act also advances the son beyond the father. The son, grown into an adult, understands what the father only felt. As a narrator conscious of telling a story to "you," his reader, he achieves the ability to communicate that his father lacked. Furthermore, in seeing his father's suffering, the narrator is led to speculate about the complexity of life. In doing so, he becomes a more complex man, a man who gives life in words to his father's mute yearnings. In style, the narrator is true to his father's inner vision, for his sophistication of mind is rendered in simple diction and sentences, in a voice that his father might have used had he been able to speak his heart.

S. Elaine Marshall

EIGHT VIEWS OF TOKYO

Author: Osamu Dazai (Tsushima Shūji', 1909-1948)
Type of plot: Psychological realism
Time of plot: 1930-1940
Locale: Tokyo
First published: "Tokyo hakkei," 1941 (English translation, 1983)

> *Principal characters:*
> A WRITER
> H, a former lover
> MR. S, a former teacher
> T, a young draftee

The Story

It is July 3, 1940. The author has stopped at a small impoverished village on the Izu Peninsula looking for an inexpensive place to stay and write. For ten days he recalls the sordid events of the last decade, writing about a life of poverty and debauchery as a young student in Tokyo. He had moved many times to keep ahead of the law and creditors—hence the "eight views," although he actually records more than eight impressions of his past.

His writing retreat gets off to a bad start. The inn is shabby, and the maid insists on a deposit when she learns that he will stay ten days. That night, however, he gets out his worn map of Tokyo. It reminds him of a mulberry leaf eaten by silk worms. Like the worms, people from all over Japan descend on Tokyo, pushing and shoving, each seeking a desperate living, "females calling to males, males just wandering around half-crazed."

The first "view" is a Totsuka boardinghouse, where he rented a room in 1930 and entered the French literature department of Tokyo Imperial University. From the second semester on, however, he stops going to classes to work as a political activist. He also invites to Tokyo a young geisha whom he had met a few years earlier, who is identified in the story as "H." H was under contract as a geisha, and his family is shamed by the scandal. An older brother is sent to Tokyo to clear up the matter. There is a tense family conference. The writer agrees to send her back to the countryside as long as they are permitted to get married eventually. He sleeps with her for the first time the night before she leaves.

H wrote that she had arrived back, and that was all. The writer, in despair because of her lack of commitment, devotes full time to political work without much success. He begins a short and sordid affair with a Ginza bar girl who falls in love with him. In part to get attention from both H and his family—they were appalled at the H affair—he attempts a double suicide with the bar girl by swimming into the sea at Kamakura, but only she succeeds.

He is put on probation, and his family is reconciled with the would-be suicide. They buy out H's geisha contract and send her back to Tokyo, where he rents a house in Gotanda, the second "view" of Tokyo. By this time, the author is twenty-three and H is twenty. He is supposed to be continuing his studies, supported by the family, but he seldom attends classes, and does nothing but watch H.

That summer they move to the Kanda area of Tokyo, one known for its bookstores and student hangouts. In the fall they move again, and again in the spring they move to Yodobashi as the writer begins to dabble in haiku. Twice he is held by the police and questioned about political activities. He moves again to avoid the police, to a room over a lumber dealer in Nihonbashi. In this sixth "view," the writer takes on a pseudonym to cover his trail. Beset by ennui, he occasionally goes to the university, not to his classes, but to lie on the lawns.

It is there that he learns that H had slept with another man before joining him in Tokyo. He rushes home to confront her, but she coolly denies the allegations, allaying his suspicions. Later that night, however, he reads Jean-Jacques Rousseau's *Confessions* (1782-1789), and comes to the realization that H had lied. He feels betrayed and leaves in disgust and confusion. Lacking another place to stay, he returns home to her, and they make an uneasy reconciliation. Again they move, to a small gatehouse of a ruined mansion. They survive on money sent from the family, which has all but given up on the twenty-four-year-old profligate son.

The writer begins a lengthy last testament, thinking of suicide once again. It becomes his first major work, a chronicle of his evil childhood and adolescence. Having set this period down on paper, he finds that he cannot finish, that he needs to bring it up to the present: "I was being consumed by a demon who eternally beckoned. It was like an ant trying to stop an express train."

By now it is 1933, and the writer is theoretically due to graduate, but he cannot. The next two years he lies to his brother to get more money to live as a "student," repeatedly promising to graduate, and buying time to complete his manuscript. Finally, he finishes and names it *The Final Years*.

The next "view" is a room in a house in Suginami owned by a friend. For two years he continues work on his collection of stories and continues the pretense of going to classes. By this time, he is deceiving even H. He puts on his school uniform about once a week and works on his stories at the school library, returning home in the evening. The burden of this elaborate deception and the increasing impatience of his relatives begin to weigh heavily on the writer. He knows they will cut off his meager allowance if he tells them that he is finishing his last testament.

They move yet again when their friend changes houses to be near his work. Neglecting his health and drinking, the writer finally chooses his best fourteen stories and burns the rest. He settles his affairs and adds two letters to his completed manuscript. He pretends to H that he is busy with graduation preparations, but he knows that he will fail his final exams at the university. It is 1935 and time to end the deception and die.

Since he could not drown himself five years earlier, the writer tries to hang himself in the hills of Kamakura, but once again he is a failure, returning home with a red and swollen neck. Again his family rallies around him. Ironically, a few days later he nearly dies of appendicitis. He has a long and difficult recovery requiring lengthy hospitalization. H takes up residency in the small private hospital with him; three months pass. They move to the seacoast of Chiba Prefecture to continue the recuperation, but another danger appears. While in the hospital, the writer becomes addicted to painkilling drugs, and this new vice is expensive. He becomes dirty and a nuisance to editors in Tokyo, whom he asks for money.

He is finally on the edge of recognition, for his friends have placed several of his stories in good magazines while he was in the hospital. Soon all the stories are sold to pay for his drug habit. As he falls deeper and deeper into debt, his acquaintances begin to avoid him. Finally he reaches the bottom and is placed in a mental hospital. H meets him a month later when he is released. Their reunion is tense and full of suspicion. Nevertheless, he immediately begins to write to pay the bills. His earlier stories were well received, and he has requests from two magazines for more stories. After selling them, he spends the money on a monthlong drunk at Atami. Returning to Tokyo, he is given another shock. H has had an affair with a painter friend of his, and there is no resolution. He and H attempt suicide by poisoning, but fail. She finally leaves him to a solitary drunken existence. His family falls on hard times and he begins a gradual transformation. There is no critical incident, no dramatic turning point, but somehow he decides to become a real writer. He works with great intensity, and soon produces a story about his latest failed suicide, which sells immediately.

This success leads him to a yearlong retreat in the mountains, where he completes more short stories and works on a novel. He also makes a conventional arranged marriage through a mentor—the wife is not described—and gradually works his way out of debt. One evening, in their Tokyo house overlooking the Musashino Plain, he hits upon the idea of writing about his views of Tokyo.

Two final scenes are added. One is a meeting with a former teacher who had almost given up on him during his deranged period. They visit an art museum where a painting by H's painter is displayed. Both agree that it is no good. The other scene occurs when his sister-in-law's fiancé, T, is drafted. His wealthy relatives and employees in their factory all gather at a temple to see him off. When his regiment stops there, T immediately picks out the writer from the back of the crowd. There was a bond between them, since the writer has also faced death. As the troops leave, he calls out, "You have nothing more to worry about!" Several days later, the writer sets out for Izu to write, and the story comes full circle.

Themes and Meanings

Dazai was a leading member of a group of writers called *burai-ha*, or decadents. He wrote about the underside of urban Japan, his life on the fringes of polite society. Dazai rejected the values of society, devoting himself to drink and other excesses which destroyed his health. His lack of a vision or political philosophy—although he was interested in Communism—led to an intense ennui and periodic depression, and he made his first suicide attempt while still a university student. His flamboyant life-style and his troubled search for meaning have appealed to several generations of young Japanese in the way that J. D. Salinger's *The Catcher in the Rye* (1951) has continued to find a readership among young Americans.

"Eight Views of Tokyo" touches on many of Dazai's recurring themes, but the central focus of the story is his vocation: how he became a writer, and the place of writing in his life. The theme of the artist finding his vocation has been treated countless times from countless perspectives; even so, Dazai's version is unusual. For Dazai, quite literally, to keep on living meant to keep on writing. His first stories, he says, were written as a "last will and testament," and it is true that after finishing them he attempted suicide, but as long as he was writing he was deferring death. Later, having recovered from drug addiction and having made for the first time a commitment to a writer's career, he says explicitly that he was "writing in order to live"—and so he did, until his fifth (and finally successful) suicide attempt, in 1948.

It is interesting that Dazai provides no explanation for the decision he made, in the mid-1930's, after several abortive suicide attempts, to go on living; indeed, he makes a point of rejecting "explanations for a man's turning point. . . . Many times," he concludes, "a man simply finds himself walking in a different field before he realizes it."

Style and Technique

Dazai's criticism of society was often a parody; Donald Keene has compared him to the *gesaku* writers of the Tokugawa period (1600-1868), who wrote comical farces. Although he writes of life on the edge of survival and his feelings of despair, there is an appealing bohemian romanticism in Dazai's writing. As personal as his stories seem, Dazai did not write purely autobiographically. Like most writers, he built on his experiences and adorned them; for example, his collected writings include five versions of his first suicide attempt in 1930. Even a story such as "Eight Views of Tokyo," which appears to be straight autobiography, is a complex weave of fact and invention.

Particularly noteworthy in this story is the handling of chronology. The opening scene shows Dazai in the mountain village where he has gone to write; he worries that he may be unable to write anything, that he will run out of money. The bulk of the story rehearses his past, with the conclusion looping neatly back to the beginning, until the reader realizes that this story is itself the "writing" which Dazai was planning in the opening paragraphs. This technical device conveys very effectively the writer's perception of his own life as "material"—a perception which, in Dazai's case, was unusually strong. Thus, style and theme work together: The method of telling the story reinforces the theme of "writing in order to live."

Richard Rice

THE EIGHTY-YARD RUN

Author: Irwin Shaw (1913-1984)
Type of plot: Realism
Time of plot: 1925-1940
Locale: A Midwestern university and New York City
First published: 1941

> *Principal characters:*
> CHRISTIAN DARLING, a clothing salesman and a former athlete
> LOUISE TUCKER DARLING, his wife

The Story

The story opens with an arresting, vividly detailed description of an eighty-yard run made from scrimmage by Christian Darling at a Midwestern university. Immediately after the descriptive passage, the reader learns that Darling made the run during football practice in 1925, fifteen years earlier, and that the episode has been reconstructed in his mind as he stands on the same practice field, the site of his former triumph. Now thirty-five, Darling recalls and retraces his downhill course in life from that moment of triumph and promise.

His fellow players, his coaches, and his girlfriend, Louise Tucker, were impressed and predicted great accomplishments for him. Louise proudly drove him from the field in her convertible and kissed him in such a way that he knew for the first time that she belonged to him. Yet the promise of glory at a major university was not fulfilled. A German boy named Diederich came from the third string and proved a better ball carrier than anyone else around, being named to All-American teams. For two years, Christian, a good blocker, cleared the path for his teammate through the big linemen of Michigan, Purdue, and Illinois. Still, he was considered an important man on campus, and an adoring Louise lavished gifts upon him.

After graduation, Christian and Louise married and moved to New York City, where Christian became a representative of his father-in-law's company, an ink manufacturing firm. While Christian worked, Louise attended plays and visited art galleries. She acquired a taste for modern painters such as Pablo Picasso, Georges Braque, and Paul Klee, decorating their expensive Manhattan apartment with reproductions of their paintings. Christian preferred paintings of animals to theirs. When the economic crash of 1929 came, Louise's father lost everything, and Christian was left unemployed.

With time on their hands, Louise wanted to continue her cultural activities, but Christian had developed no aesthetic or intellectual interests. He began to seek solace in drinking, leaving Louise to pursue her interests on her own. She found a job with a woman's magazine that paid enough to meet their expenses. The best that Christian could do was to land a few temporary jobs that provided no significant income.

Louise's work brought her into closer contact with writers, intellectuals, and artists. At parties with Louise's friends, Christian felt bored and out of place, whereas she found them exhilarating. Christian did not understand the conversations or the references to obscure poets, composers, philosophers, or leftist politicians. Moments of tenderness between Christian and his wife grew more infrequent. In one poignant scene, he embraced her as she was sitting in the bathtub and asked that she not call him "Baby."

When Christian and Louise received an invitation from a labor leader to a performance of Clifford Odets' *Waiting for Lefty*, Christian preferred to remain home drinking and accepted the reality that his wife would attend plays with others. Still too much in love with her to want a divorce, he lived with her harmoniously but distantly. Finally he received a job offer as a sales representative for a clothing firm. The job required traveling, since the major outlets were colleges and universities. Except for holidays, he would be home only once a month. He hoped that Louise would urge him not to accept the offer, but as he expected, she thought that he should take it. Louise now looked on him with "a kind of patient, kindly, remote, boredom."

The narrative returns to the practice field where it began, his alma mater being among the colleges that Christian visits on business. Having reflected on the events of his life over the past fifteen years, he reaches important understandings and realizations. He grasps that he did not practice for the right things. He had no preparation for either the 1929 Depression or the fast-paced and complex life of New York City. He was not prepared for the time when a girl turned into a woman. Tentatively, he perceives that at some point he and Louise were even and that if he had then put all of his effort toward it, he might have kept up with her. He ruefully reflects that while he is standing alone on a practice field in the fading afternoon light, his wife is in another city, having dinner with another and better man, speaking in a different, new language that he does not understand.

Finding himself standing on the same spot where he received the ball before his run, Christian begins to run toward the goal line, making all the cuts and feints, following the same course, of fifteen years earlier. After he crosses the goal line, he sees nearby a young couple who had escaped his notice. They are puzzled by the spectacle of a middle-aged man in a double-breasted suit mimicking a football play. Christian explains awkwardly, "I— once I played here," and leaves for his hotel, sweat breaking out on his face and around his neck.

Themes and Meanings

Set during the exhilarating 1920's and the depressed 1930's, the story depicts character conflict during rapidly changing times. Louise finds the capacity to adjust and grow when confronted with challenge, whereas Christian, considered an important figure on campus during college, finds himself ill prepared for the world that he confronts beyond the university. The hollowness of his character is exposed when he is no longer propped up by Louise's father. By accepting society on its terms, Louise succeeds in the highly competitive environment of New York City. Because he expects society to adjust to him and rejects all activities that he does not enjoy, Christian fails in his environment. The story presents the classic conflict of one character's outgrowing another.

Further, it challenges the usual acceptance of the value of athletic and business success. Christian comes to recognize that his value system, which placed importance on competitive athletics, is flawed. The German boy Diederich, who received the cheers that Christian had expected, went to a professional team and had his neck broken. Louise's father, who has succeeded as a manufacturer, commits suicide when he has to face failure and bankruptcy. The social criticism offered by the story is, however, muted and detached. The reader is reminded that values are not absolute and that adaptability is essential to success.

In addition, poignantly, sympathetically, the story develops the theme of lost youth. Christian attempts to recapture a moment of triumph, of promise, a time when he felt invulnerable and harbored no thought of death. Except for that moment, his memories of his life are recollections of unfulfilled promises, of lost opportunities, of defeats. He has had to scale down his expectations, and his future seems bleak.

Style and Technique

The narrative moves with admirable clarity and economy. It opens with the exquisitely detailed account of Christian's run and immediately shifts to his appearance on the field fifteen years later. The detailed account has been a feat of his memory. The narrative then moves chronologically, essentially from Christian's point of view, ending with his re-creation of the earlier run.

Shaw's style is marked by vivid, energetic description that relies heavily on verbs, verb forms (largely participles), and absolute constructions (largely nominative absolutes). The technique is reminiscent of the styles of Ernest Hemingway and William Faulkner. The following passage illustrates the technique well: "Darling tucked the ball in, spurted at him, driving hard, hurling himself along, his legs pounding, knees high, all two hundred pounds bunched into controlled attack." In the passage the verbs and verbals bear the weight of meaning and create the impression of movement and energy. The stylistic technique is especially effective when a writer is describing a developing or ongoing action. It permits Shaw to craft lengthy sentences that are carefully controlled and balanced.

Stanley Archer

THE EMPRESS'S RING

Author: Nancy Hale (1908-   )
Type of plot: Fiction of manners
Time of plot: 1954
Locale: The South
First published: 1954

> *Principal character:*
> THE UNNAMED NARRATOR, a woman reflecting on an incident
> in her childhood

The Story

The narrator of this story begins with an admission: "I worry about it still, even today, thirty odd years later." The object of her worry is a child's golden ring "set with five little turquoises." It was given to the narrator for her eighth birthday by a family friend of whom she was so fond that she thought of her as her aunt. The ring was special not only because it was purchased especially for the narrator by a favorite relative but also because the ring was said to have belonged to the Empress Elisabeth of Austria.

The ring is so beautiful and precious that immediately the little girl's nurse declares that it cannot be worn outside to play. This only makes the child want to defy her nurse: "For nobody—certainly not she—could understand the love I had for that ring, and the absolute impossibility of my ever losing anything so precious."

She does indeed wear the ring out to play in her playhouse. Attaining a playhouse is "a sort of victory" for the narrator as a little girl. She has envied the playhouse of their only neighbors, which was built especially for their little girl Mimi. Mimi's playhouse is a miniature cottage complete with shuttered windows, a shingled roof, and a brass knocker that says "Mimi." It is furnished with a miniature table and chairs and real Dresden china "with pink rosebuds and gold rims" made just for children's tea parties.

The narrator, too, must have a playhouse, but her family cannot and will not build one to rival Mimi's, for their farm is no longer a working one. Instead, they clean out an abandoned milk house and move some of her nursery furniture into it.

Although the little girl tries to make it a real playhouse, it cannot match the grandeur of Mimi's. Her mother gives her some of her old china, but the narrator yearns for "rosebuds" and "china, made for children." As an adult, she realizes that what she had was much nicer, but as a girl, she recalls, she felt that "nothing . . . would take the place of pink rosebuds." This yearning added to the appeal of the ring, which, like the miniature china and furniture for which she longed, was meant particularly for a little girl.

She loses the ring in her sandpile—a sandpile that is as imperfect as her playhouse. The sand has become mixed with dirt, for unlike Mimi's sandpile, it lacks a frame to contain it. The narrator is scolded for losing her ring, but in childish bravado she announces that it is not lost at all; she knows exactly where it is. Although she searches for it many times, eventually she feels "a hollow, painful feeling inside me because I had lost my precious possession." The loss of the ring haunts her, and she periodically digs for the ring in the sandpile and even dreams of finding it.

As the narrator tells the reader at the beginning of the story, thirty years later she is still thinking of her ring. Now an adult, she retains some of her childhood tendency toward envy and dissatisfaction. Mimi's perfection has been replaced by that of other neighbors, the Lambeths; the narrator is certain that they have "silver tumblers" while her glasses are "a sorry collection, the odds and ends of a number of broken sets."

The narrator consoles herself with the thought that although the old place where she grew up as a child has been sold, perhaps the new owners have a little girl who will dig in the sandpile, if it still exists, and will find the empress's ring.

Themes and Meanings

Coming from a distinguished family of artists, statesmen, and educators, Nancy Hale is well aware of the importance of the past to people. Her forebears extend back through the Beecher dynasty of New England, and a list of her ancestors' acquaintances reads like the table of contents of an American literature anthology. It is no wonder that Hale has said " . . . the fiction-writer uses for material what other people have forgotten—the past, the meaning of the past." The effect of the past on the present is one of the major themes of her work.

In the past are the seeds for future behavior. As a little girl, the narrator believes that her life is inferior to Mimi's; as an adult, she is still comparing herself to others, feeling somehow inadequate—only now it is a new set of neighbors.

Hale has said that the heart of a short story is a crisis—a point at which someone must make a decision. The decision comes for the narrator in that although she may still think of her ring, she knows that she will never find it, but comforts herself with the thought that perhaps another little girl will find it. By reconciling herself to the loss of the ring (and, implicitly, the loss of her childhood), she gives her life a new direction.

Style and Technique

Because this story re-creates a child's experience, Hale uses short, straightforward sentences and simple words: "I had to have a playhouse. I wept." Part of the immediacy and appeal of this story is that any reader can identify with the first-person, unidentified narrator. As children, most readers knew a little boy or girl whose playthings they coveted.

As an artist and a writer about artists, Hale is distinguished by a careful eye for detail. She can sketch a character in the swift strokes of a portrait artist. Hale is often compared to Edith Wharton in her use of specifics to convey a particular segment of society.

Hale has said a short story is "an impenetrably integrated whole." Like the ring in the title, this story is circular, linking the past with the present. The story closes with the hope that "one of the new owner's children will one day really find my ring, for it is there somewhere." The past can and does encircle the present.

Resa Willis

THE ENCHANTED DOLL

Author: Paul Gallico (1897-1976)
Type of plot: Melodrama
Time of plot: The late 1940's and the early 1950's
Locale: New York City's Lower East Side
First published: 1952

> *Principal characters:*
> DR. SAMUEL AMONY, the narrator and protagonist
> ESSIE NOLAN, a young woman who is suffering from a
> mysterious illness
> ROSE CALLAMIT, Essie's cousin and guardian
> ABE SHEFTEL, a shopkeeper

The Story

Although the setting of "The Enchanted Doll" is a poor neighborhood in New York City's Lower East Side, the plot has many of the characteristics of a fairy tale: a handsome young doctor, a beautiful but helpless young woman, and an ugly old harridan. The tale begins when the narrator, Dr. Samuel Amony, sets out to buy a birthday present for his little niece in Cleveland. With a hurdy-gurdy playing "Some Enchanted Evening" in the background, Amony drops by Abe Sheftel's combination stationery, cigar, and toy shop. When the doctor sees a twelve-inch, handmade rag doll with a painted face, he reports that he feels an affinity with the doll as one might feel with "a stranger in a crowded room." The doll seems lifelike, mysterious, and feminine all at once. When quizzed, Sheftel replies that the doll was created by some red-haired amazon who lives nearby. Sheftel cannot quite recall her name, but he thinks that "Calamity" is close.

Coincidentally, Amony gets to meet the redheaded woman when she summons him to her apartment to make a house call. Her name is actually Rose Callamit, not Calamity, but the latter seems more appropriate. Amony reports that her voice is unpleasant, her hair is dyed, her makeup is overdone, and her perfume is both overpowering and cheap. He is offended to think that this vulgar woman is the creator of the charming doll that he sent to his niece. Yet her sitting room is cluttered with dolls, each of which is different but stamped with the same creative genius as the one that Amony first saw in Sheftel's window.

Finally, Rose leads the doctor through a connecting bath into a small back room, where her cousin, Essie Nolan, sits listlessly in her chair. In the best tradition of the fairy tale, Rose illustrates her cruelty by brutally pointing out that Essie is a cripple. The doctor notices, however, that not the lame left leg but some mysterious, consumptive disease is the cause of Essie's illness.

Although puzzled by Essie's illness, the doctor is relieved to discover that the sensitive girl rather than the vulgar woman is the creator of the exquisite dolls, for Essie is surrounded by paints, material, and other equipment necessary for making the dolls. When the doctor looks into Essie's misery-stricken eyes, he is spellbound.

Leaving Essie's sickroom, Rose and Amony have an angry confrontation. When the doctor insists that Essie's deformity can be cured, Rose tells him to shut up. The doctor is convinced that the reason for Rose's reaction is not that she wants to protect her cousin from false hopes, as she says, but that she does not want to lose her lucrative income from the dolls. He apologizes to Rose, however, because he wants to be allowed to see Essie again.

A tonic and ten days' rest from doll making improve Essie's condition, but when Amony prescribes ten more days of rest, Rose dismisses him. Denied access to Essie, the doctor himself falls sick. He is slowly wasting away until he realizes that his disease is love. He is in love with Essie Nolan. That revelation rejuvenates the doctor, and he decides to rescue Essie. With the help of the shopkeeper, who tips Amony off when Rose leaves her apartment, the doctor rushes to Essie's bedside. Reaching Essie just as she is about to lose consciousness, he explains to the young woman that all of her love and hope have been leeched out by Rose, and, declaring his love for her, the doctor persuades Essie to let him take her home with him. She agrees, and he wraps her in a blanket and carries her through the August heat to his rooms behind the doctor's office.

The narrator frames his account by an explanation at the beginning and end of the story that this day is an anniversary for him and Essie. They are married, have one son, and now have another child on the way, but the anniversary that he cherishes the most is the day he first saw the doll in Abe Sheftel's window. He reports that Essie no longer makes dolls because she now has her own family to care for. The implication is that the young couple will live happily ever after.

Themes and Meanings

The enchanted doll of the title is not the doll that the narrator first encounters in Abe Sheftel's store window but Essie Nolan herself. Essie is enchanted in the sense that she is under the spell of her cousin Rose Callamit. Yet there is no mystery or magic in Rose's methods. By constantly harping on the fact that Essie is lame and by insisting that no man will ever love Essie, Rose cripples the young woman psychologically so that she is too embarrassed to leave the apartment. Starved for human contact, Essie begins to create the hauntingly lifelike dolls, which, as the narrator eventually discovers, become Essie's substitute children.

Yet Essie is not allowed to mother her "children." Quick to recognize the commercial value of the dolls, Rose sells them as fast as Essie can make them, symbolically killing Essie's offspring. The cycle of giving but never receiving love and affection eventually causes Essie to give up any interest in life. At the last moment, this spell, Rose's hold over Essie, is broken by Amony. Just as the handsome Prince kisses Sleeping Beauty and brings her back to life, Amony falls in love with Essie and gives her back her will to live.

The theme, then, as explicitly stated in the story, is that all human beings need love. If deprived of love, the soul will eventually wither and die. Given love, body and soul will regenerate.

Style and Technique

Paul Gallico's experience first as a sportswriter and later as a screenwriter as well as his often-stated goal of entertaining his readers rather than encouraging them to think caused him to create stories that rely heavily on plot details and external conflicts rather than on an exploration of psychological subtleties.

The characters in "The Enchanted Doll" are flat, being either totally good or totally evil. Amony is an idealistic doctor living and practicing in a poor neighborhood. Essie Nolan is at once completely helpless and totally loving, while her jailor-cousin is mean and self-serving. The suspense depends entirely on whether Amony will be able to rescue Essie from Rose before Essie gives up her will to live.

The lack of subtlety is further emphasized by Amony's tendency to speak in clichés. Although the narrator warns that he is a doctor rather than a writer and even fears that his story will be "crudely told," one might expect a doctor to be more original than his phrases, "great reservoir of love," "much blacker crime," and "I who loved her beyond words," would indicate.

The least predictable, and therefore the most engaging, feature of the story is its realistic background. The factories belching coal smoke across the East River, the withered cigars and cardboard cutout advertisements in Sheftel's window, and the cheap satin cushions in Rose's bedroom create vivid visual images. The matter-of-fact accuracy of these details enhances what is essentially a formula plot.

Sandra Hanby Harris

THE END

Author: Samuel Beckett (1906-   )
Type of plot: Absurd realism
Time of plot: Sometime in the twentieth century
Locale: Possibly Ireland
First published: "La Fin," 1955 (English translation, 1960)

> *Principal character:*
> THE NARRATOR, an elderly, unnamed man

The Story

If readers expect the contemporary short story to concentrate on a "slice of life," it must be said that Samuel Beckett is inclined to take his cut at the far end of the loaf. "The End" is a good example of the subject upon which he has concentrated in much of his work: the gritty, sometimes offensive experience of the last days of an old man, struggling to survive and, at the same time, willing to die.

There are no tricks, no sophisticated twists and turns in this story. It is simply the tale of an old, unnamed man, thrown out of some kind of public institution (probably a charitable hospital) with a bit of money and not much else. He has, however, a peculiarity which makes him more than a repulsive, stinking bag of bones; he has the capacity to survive, despite crippling physical limitations, a lively curiosity especially about himself, and (like many of Beckett's tramps) something that is often not seen quickly enough: a first-class, witty intelligence and the ability to talk well, if sometimes disgustingly, about his experiences.

This old man goes from pillar to post, leaving the institution reluctantly, being rebuffed in his attempts to find shelter, finally getting himself a basement room from which he is soon evicted after being cheated out of his money. On the streets again in a town which seems to be his home, he passes his son, who tips his hat to him and goes on his way. It is just as well, since the old man despises him. Finally, in his wandering in and out of town, he meets an old friend who offers him shelter in a seaside cave, which he takes for a while and then leaves because he cannot stand the constant tumult of the sea. He is relieved to get away from the friend since he does not need friendship.

He retreats to a wrecked mountain cabin owned by the same man in which, in his weakened and hungry state, he attempts in a comic knock-down-and-drag-out attack to milk a cow on the move. Eventually, he falls, stumbles, and crawls back to town, where he finds shelter in a shed on a deserted estate near the river.

He now sets up to work as a beggar during the day, mindful of his nice problem of eliciting sympathy without at the same time offending donors' delicate noses. He is not without a peculiar dignity which will not allow him to be used by a Marxist street orator as an example of the capitalist failure. He scoops up his coins, unties his begging board, and leaves work early.

In the shed he sleeps in an old boat which he has meticulously fixed up as a home and as a refuge from the local rats. It is here that the reader leaves him, as he is describing his visions, particularly his ultimate vision of floating out to sea and pulling the plug hole in the bottom of his boat in order to make his end.

If the story goes anywhere, it is from bad to worse, as the old man degenerates physically day by day. What does not happen is any loss of the wild, lively, pawky imagination or any cessation of the chattering soliloquy. Self-pity never intrudes, and it is hard not to admire a man, however odoriferous, who can stare his end in the face with such equanimity.

Themes and Meanings

The word "absurd" may sometimes cause a reader to shy away from the most obvious way of reading this story, since that word suggests intellectual complications which are worrying. They ought not to be. Beckett simply believes that life has no meaning, and he occasionally illustrates that belief in somewhat involuted and technically difficult tales. Sometimes, however, he explores it with works such as "The End," which is, in fact, what it looks like. It is a story about an old man, expelled from a hospital into a society which has no interest in him, and in which he, in return, has no interest. He survives despite all, if with less and less physical strength from day to day.

It can, then, be read as a story about an exceptional old bum living hand to mouth—a peculiar subject and one which may not seem to have much appeal. It is certainly a mark of Beckett's perversity as a writer that he often uses the old and how they survive, how they die, or, at least, how they try to die. On that level, there is a gritty reality and tactility in his work, and a fine eye for detail. What is perhaps larger than life is the quality of the old man's mind; he is stunningly bright and knows how to show it. He is dying nevertheless, and the nature of that experience is faced with relentless rigor.

One ought not, however, be satisfied with "The End" simply as sociological art. Beckett uses versions of this old man often in his works, often being ground down to inevitable death. This conjunction of old age and death stands for him in the abstract as a metaphor for the meaningless nature of life, for the fact that the moment one is born, one begins to die.

Death can take a long time in Beckett's work, and even in "The End" it may be that the old man is only dreaming it, dreaming of setting out to sea like an old Viking. He is not quite that far gone as the story ends. This old man's determination to occupy himself with getting ready for death, without self-pity and without any hope of everlasting life Hereafter is, in a peculiarly

Beckettian and Irish way, the author's celebration of man's capacity to accept pain and suffering, thinking and stinking all the way to the end.

Style and Technique

The first-person narrator, whose chief function seems to be to talk to himself, in a prose version of the dramatic monologue, in order to cheer himself up and on—to give himself some identity in a world where he is often confined or in which he is so physically repellent that people avoid him (and he avoids them)—is a common character in Beckett's later works. The reader must not confuse the physical or economic or social state of this narrator with a similar mental condition; he is not mentally destitute. He may not know his name or quite where he is, but he seems to have had an excellent education, and a taste for logic chopping. The casual reference to Arnold Geulincx, a seventeenth century philosopher concerned with the relation of mind and body, comes naturally to the old man in "The End" and is consistent with his attempts to make some sense of his physical degeneration by imposing a lively mind on the question. As a result, the basic vulgarity of a tramp's life, the search for food and shelter, the disarray and mess of clothing and personal belongings, the awareness of the problem of personal hygiene, all the problems of hobo life are shot through with bits of scholarly knowledge, touches of obsessive rationalization, a lunatic sense of humor, and an occasional wide-eyed innocence about the way of the world.

The oral style is personal and unguarded, a constantly shifting mix of high, middle, and low in which defecation and epistemology are likely to show up in the same sentence. There is no decorum, no forbidden subject, no attempt to defend oneself from sheer silliness. The narrator's intelligence cannot save him from the crazy attempt to milk a cow into his hat while she is escaping, or from his dumb, deadpan comment upon the fiasco. That bit of farce and his obsessive, fumbling grasp of detail ought to remind one of old film comics such as Charlie Chaplin and Buster Keaton (whom Beckett once used in a film based on one of his works).

There is pleasure in the quick, furtive, side-of-the-mouth comment, as well as in the dense argument: the way he dismisses the hot air of the Marxist orator, as well as the long essay on the fine art of begging. Every once in a while the prose picks up lyric power, particularly in the descriptions of nature. Tonally it is, then, all over the place, sometimes sad, sometimes lugubrious, often offensive, but also very amusing. It is an example of putting a character at the end of his tether, but with energy enough to pull cheekily on the rope.

Charles H. Pullen

END OF THE GAME

Author: Julio Cortázar (1914-1984)
Type of plot: Psychological realism
Time of plot: Mid-twentieth century
Locale: A country home somewhere in Argentina
First published: "Final del juego," 1956 (English translation, 1963)

> *Principal characters:*
> LETITIA, an adolescent girl
> HOLANDA, her companion
> THE NARRATOR, another adolescent girl
> ARIEL, a young man

The Story

As the title of this story indicates, the characters are playing a game which comes to an end at the close of the narrative. Letitia, Holanda, and the narrator spend their summer vacation thinking of ways either to confuse or to elude the authority figures in their lives, the narrator's mother and her Aunt Ruth. When they manage to escape the watchful eyes of the adults, Letitia, Holanda, and the narrator retreat to their "kingdom," an area near the railroad tracks where they can act out their game and thus enter into a fantasy world of "Statues and Attitudes."

The game consists of deciding on a statue or an attitude that each of the girls will portray, and then striking a pose to express that statue or attitude. The attitudes—Fear, Envy, Jealousy—are done without props, but the statues—Venus, the Ballerina—require the use of ornaments, which the girls have gathered from the house. What begins as an exercise in freedom and liberation from the world of adults becomes a game of the discovery of adolescent sexuality, even though the girls do not understand it as such.

Although there is no specific information in the story about the relationship of the three girls or their age, it is evident that they are cousins or sisters, and that they are probably thirteen or fourteen years old. Holanda and the narrator understand the world of adults, for they know exactly how to create excitement in the house by spilling hot water on the cat, or dropping a glass while washing dishes, or coaxing the two older women into an argument over who should wash and who should dry. Letitia, a quieter, calmer girl, has a slight paralysis which causes occasional back pains and periods of confinement in bed.

The game of Statues and Attitudes takes on a new importance one day when a man on the passing train throws the girls a note complimenting them on their performance. Letitia, Holanda, and the narrator begin to play the game more enthusiastically for the benefit of their admirer, Ariel. At the same time, they begin to invent details about him—his background, the school that he attends, where he lives.

Ariel begins to drop notes each day as the train passes; each day the notes become more intimate, and it becomes obvious that he prefers Letitia over the other two girls. He finally announces that he will get off the train the next day to speak with them. The next day, however, Letitia becomes ill and cannot accompany the girls to the kingdom. Instead, she gives the narrator a note to deliver to Ariel. When Holanda and the narrator meet Ariel, he engages them in polite conversation but cannot hide his disappointment that Letitia is not there. He takes the note and puts it in his pocket for later reading.

The following day, the three girls go to the kingdom and Letitia brings out the jewels that she has taken from the house for her performance. She dresses herself elaborately and performs the most extravagant statue possible as the train passes with Ariel leaning out the window to look at her. The next day, Holanda and the narrator go to the kingdom alone because Letitia is suffering from her paralysis. As the train passes, the two girls see the window empty and imagine Ariel sitting on the other side of the train, "not moving in his seat, looking off toward the river with his grey eyes."

Themes and Meanings

Julio Cortázar is best known for his story "Las babas del diablo" ("Blow-Up), on which Michelangelo Antonioni based his popular film. In fact, the collection of stories in which "End of the Game" first appeared in English carried the title *End of the Game and Other Stories* (1963) and then, after the success of the film, was reissued in paperback in 1967 as *Blow-Up and Other Stories*. "Blow-Up" is more typical of the kind of story that has made Cortázar a popular writer than is "End of the Game," which is more subtle in its blend of fantasy and reality. Yet the fact that the collection in English was first published with "End of the Game" as the title story indicates that Cortázar considered it to be of particular significance.

Cortázar creates his story through the elaboration of the familiar theme of the conflict of fantasy and reality. The three girls engaged in a game that consists of playacting invent a character, Ariel, based on the very limited knowledge that they have of the real person whose face they have seen on the passing train. When the fantastic game becomes real through the confrontation of Ariel, the narrator, and Holanda, the conflict between the fantastic and the phenomenological destroys the invented reality.

Cortázar elaborates the theme of fantasy and reality in such a way that "End of the Game" becomes representative of the ideology evident in all of his fiction—that instinctive behavior is liberating and any constraints on the expression of the individual will are destructive. Of the three girls in the story, Letitia is the most significant because of her physical deformity and because she is the one chosen as the prettiest by Ariel, whose name relates him to the spiritual realm of the Ariel of William Shakespeare's *The Tempest*. Because Letitia avoids the confrontation with the real Ariel, she does not experience the disenchantment suffered by Holanda and the narrator. She maintains a distance from phenomenological reality by writing the letter and then creates the most fantastic invention possible in an extraordinary display of physical prowess despite her paralytic condition. While the story narrates the moment at which all three girls become aware of their sexuality, it concentrates on Letitia's loss of innocence. Not only does she steal the jewels from the mother and the aunt, but she also releases all of her energy in an orgasmic display for the idealized object of her sexual feelings.

Throughout the story, the girls find ways to escape the restraints imposed on them by the adults. The kingdom by the railroad tracks provides them with a kind of childhood freedom, as does the game of Statues and Attitudes. At first, the game is liberating because it provides a means of exteriorizing the interior world of the girls' feelings. It then becomes liberating because it allows the expression of their awakening eroticism.

Style and Technique

The narrative style of Cortázar is distinctive primarily because of its clarity and directness. Although many details of the story are unclear in "End of the Game," as in any Cortázar story, that uncertainty is the result not of the language but of the narrative perspective. As in most of Cortázar's stories, the narrator is a character in the story, and the narrator does not understand the significance of what is happening. Certain details are not clarified, such as the relationship of the three girls or the contents of the letter that Letitia writes to Ariel, primarily because the narrator is not omniscient and does not have the narrative awareness of an objective storyteller.

Through the use of the first-person narrator, Cortázar is able to create a tension between the events as they appear to the character and the perception of the events by the objective reader. The narrator's version of the story is a reflection of her involvement in the struggle to free herself from adult restrictions and express her individuality. In the first part of the narrative, the narrator concentrates on the girls' attempts to destroy the control that the mother and the aunt have over them in the household. As the story progresses, the narrator becomes less concerned with the events in the home and more involved in the impending event—the extraordinary confrontation with Ariel, who represents the liberation from the strictures of childhood. Through this changing attitude of the narrator, the reader perceives that the game of Statues and Attitudes has become symbolic of the process of children growing up. The game playing typical of childhood is transformed into the ritualistic game playing characteristic of the adult world.

Gilbert Smith

THE ENDURING CHILL

Author: Flannery O'Connor (1925-1964)
Type of plot: Comic realism
Time of plot: The early 1960's
Locale: A small Southern town
First published: 1958

> *Principal characters:*
> ASBURY FOX, a frustrated writer returning home from New
> York
> MRS. FOX, Asbury's doting mother
> MARY GEORGE, Asbury's older, unsympathetic sister
> DR. BLOCK, a local doctor who treats Asbury's illness

The Story

Asbury Fox is a failed writer. Leaving behind the provincialism of his small-town Southern roots, he moved to New York to seek his destiny as a playwright, novelist, and poet. His legacy, however, consists only of "two lifeless novels . . . stationary plays . . . prosy poems . . . sketchy short stories." He returns home believing that he is dying of some unnamed disease. He is also out of money.

Met at the train station by his mother and sister, Asbury certainly looks like one about to die, and his mother immediately plans Asbury's recuperation: mornings are devoted to his writing career, afternoons spent helping the black dairy workers milk the farm's cows, and treatment by Dr. Block, the local physician. Asbury immediately balks; he has come home to die— not to take up the life of the country gentleman. If it had been possible to find a cure, a New York specialist would have found it. His school-principal sister, Mary George, however, refuses to pity him. Skeptical of both his malady and his manner, she scorns her ashen-faced brother and his pseudo-intellectualism.

Asbury's plan is simply to spend time in reflection on his tragic life. Amid his unsuccessful manuscripts is the chronicle of his short, unhappy ordeal: a long, explanatory letter to his mother which fills two notebooks. Intending it to be read after his death, he regards it as a letter such as that "Kafka had addressed to his father." In reading it, Mrs. Fox would finally come to understand the degree to which she has been responsible for Asbury's disappointments: how she domesticated him, squelching his talent and imagination, but "not his desire for these things." She left him with the worst of both worlds: a taste for artistic achievement without the means to reach it. While her "literal mind" would not allow her to see the deep significance of his letter, it would, perhaps, leave his mother with an "enduring chill" that would in time "lead her to see herself as she is."

After arriving in Timberboro, he discovers how completely different the atmosphere on the family farm is compared to the rarefied, intellectualized air of his beloved New York. There he met a group of people, including a Jesuit priest, whom he believed grasped "the unique tragedy of his death, a death whose meaning had been far beyond the twittering group around them." By contrast, at Timberboro he is surrounded by people he regards as dull, backward, and incapable of recognizing life's subtleties and challenges. Chief among them is Dr. Block, a favorite of children, who "vomited and went into fevers to have a visit from him." Against Asbury's wishes, Mrs. Fox invites Dr. Block to examine Asbury and root out the cause of his illness. "Blood don't lie," Dr. Block harrumphs as he completes his examination of the exasperated Asbury by extracting a syringe full of blood. "What's wrong with me is way beyond you," Asbury sardonically counters.

Still, Asbury finds some comfort in the company of Randall and Morgan, his mother's two black dairy workers. Since he once spent a year trying to write a play "about Negros," he feels a special camaraderie with these two. He tries to establish his liberal, egalitarian identification with them by sharing cigarettes and by impulsively drinking fresh, unpasteurized milk from a glass from which the black workers themselves have drunk—despite their admonitions not to drink it: "That *the* thing she don't 'low."

As his fever increases and he faces what he believes is his impending death, Asbury convinces his mother to send for the only likely intellectual in the area who might have an enlightened view of life and death, a Jesuit priest. To his surprise, Asbury receives a visit not from a knowing, worldly priest such as the one he met in New York, but a down-to-earth, salvation-minded priest who quizzes Asbury on the catechism. In the midst of his inquisition, Asbury cries out, "The Holy Ghost is the last thing I'm looking for!" "And He may be the last thing you get," the priest fires back.

In the climax of the story, as various workers and relatives file by the stricken Asbury to pay their last respects, Dr. Block enters triumphantly to announce that Asbury merely has undulant fever, which he acquired by drinking unpasteurized milk. The story ends with Asbury alone in his room shuddering from a sudden chill which he recognizes as the Holy Ghost, "emblazoned in ice instead of fire. . . ."

Themes and Meanings

Asbury Fox is representative of the kind of self-styled intellectuals Flannery O'Connor delighted in skewering. Despising their Southern roots, these refugees seek enlightenment in the bastions of Eastern intellectualism, eventually confronting their own pretentiousness and selfishness in a reunion with family or forgotten friends. There are thus some delicious ironies in the career of Asbury Fox, the would-be novelist, playwright, and poet.

Thinking himself some kind of tragic, Keatsian figure, he returns home to receive the pity and respect such a tragic hero should elicit. He has designed his two-notebook letter to convince his mother of her responsibility for his failures; in death, he will triumph over those unable to recognize his potential artistry. Prepared to die, but not to live, he discovers that he has only a recurrent and controllable fever; his egotism and irresponsibility are thus transparent to all by the end of the story.

O'Connor, who imbued most of her stories with the presentation of some unadorned Christian truth, uses Asbury's confrontation with the local Jesuit priest to reveal the hidden, spiritual source of his failures. Seeking salvation in mere secular wisdom and worldly approval, he becomes a narcissistic parody of the wronged artist. The "enduring chill" he intended for his mother becomes his own destiny, both literally in his undulant fever and in his confrontation with the Holy Ghost he shunned earlier.

Style and Technique

O'Connor is at her satiric best in capturing the posturing of intellectuals in their assumed superiority over their backward Southern brethren. From the beginning of the story, Asbury is depicted as a dilettante whose manner—a disdain for simplicity and directness—betrays his phoniness and insincerity, and O'Connor uses several characters as foils to reveal these unpleasant truths about Asbury.

The first is Asbury's sister, Mary George, a no-nonsense, unsympathetic observer of Asbury's eccentricities; she sees through Asbury's pose as a maligned artist and refuses to accept his role as a helpless invalid. Morgan and Randall, the two black dairy workers, are astonished by Asbury's naïveté when he drinks the unpasteurized milk, and, later, when they are asked to say their good-byes to Asbury on his "death bed," they tell him that he looks fine and on the road to recovery. Finally, Dr. Block, the unsophisticated and unassuming physician from Timberboro, deflates Asbury's "tragedy" when he uncovers the real source of the illness that New York doctors could not diagnose. The pomposity of Asbury is thus finally laid to rest.

Bruce L. Edwards, Jr.

THE ENEMIES

Author: Dylan Thomas (1914-1953)
Type of plot: Allegorical sketch
Time of plot: 1934
Locale: "Llareggub," Wales
First published: 1934

Principal characters:
MR. OWEN, the pagan protagonist
MRS. OWEN, his pagan wife
THE REVEREND MR. DAVIES, the rector of Llareggub

The Story

Mr. and Mrs. Owen enjoy a simple life, close to the land, in the fertile Jarvis valley, hidden by hills from the village of Llareggub. They live in a one-story house built in the green fields, and there they maintain a garden and some cows.

As the story opens, Mr. Owen is working in his garden, pulling up weeds, while his wife observes in the tea leaves of her cup a dark stranger. She then peers into her crystal ball and sees a man with a black hat walking into Jarvis valley. She calls out to her husband to inform him of her discovery. Mr. Owen simply smiles and continues with his weeding.

The Reverend Mr. Davies, the doddering rector of Llareggub, meanwhile loses his way among the hills outside his village. Whenever he tries to hide from the strong wind, he becomes frightened by the darkness of the dense foliage and hills. He finally reaches the rim of a hill and sees the Owens' little house and garden in the valley below: "To Mr. Davies it seemed as though the house had been carried out of a village by a large bird and placed in the very middle of the tumultuous universe."

Mr. Owen, meanwhile, smiles at his wife's faith in the powers of darkness and returns to his work. Cutting earthworms in half to help them spread their life over the garden, he says, "Multiply, multiply." Throughout the story, Mr. Owen is consistently related to the earth, weeds, worms, and other fundamental elements of nature and fertility.

By the time Mr. Davies arrives at the Owen house, his hands are covered with blood from the scratches and bruises that he has received from the rocks. Once out of the safe confines of his small Christian village, Mr. Davies is a prey to every natural force surrounding him. Mrs. Owen bandages Mr. Davies' battered hands and asks him to stay for dinner.

As Mr. Davies says grace before the meal, he observes that the prayers of Mr. and Mrs. Owen are "not his prayers," thereby suggesting their mysterious pagan origins. During the meal, Mr. Owen, "proud in his eating," bends over his plate and eats his food with the same natural zest with which he works his garden. Mrs. Owen, on the other hand, does not eat, because "the old powers" are "upon her." A darkness gathers in her mind, drawing in the surrounding light. "Mr. Davies, like a man sucked by a bird, felt desolation in his veins. . . ." The strength of both his physical body and his religious faith is nearly drained.

Mr. Davies recounts his adventures to his hosts, telling of his fear of the dark recesses among the hills. He explains that while he loves his God, he also loves the darkness, where ancient people worshiped "the dark invisible," but that now the hill caves are full of ghosts that mock him because he is old. Hearing this, Mrs. Owen thinks that he is afraid of "the lovely dark." Mr. Owen, however, thinks that he is frightened of the primitive life forces surrounding him in the valley.

Then Mr. Davies kneels down to pray, not understanding his sudden compulsion to ask for deliverance. He continues to pray and to stare dumbfounded at the dark mind of Mrs. Owen and the gross dark body of her husband. The story ends with Mr. Davies praying "like an old god beset by his enemies."

Themes and Meanings

In this story, Thomas contrasts the Christian religion of Wales with its pagan past. Mr. Davies represents the dying force of Christianity, which is overwhelmed by the powerful force of ancient pagan religion, embodied in Mr. and Mrs. Owen. Mr. Owen is associated with the fertility of the land: "the worm in the earth . . . the copulation in the tree . . . the living grease in the soil." Mrs. Owen, with her tea leaves and crystal ball, represents the ancient belief in the occult. Once out of the village, Mr. Davies is at the mercy of the natural forces which, while supportive of the Owens, frighten and nearly destroy him.

During the meal Mr. Davies becomes aware of the failure of his Christian faith and falls to his knees in fear. The name of the village from which Mr. Davies has strayed—Llareggub—is "bugger all" spelled backward. This is Thomas' mischievous joke that warns the reader early that the rector and his village colleagues are clearly out of harmony with the natural order of the physical universe surrounding them.

Although this story may be viewed as one that is self-contained, Thomas clearly intended it to be read along with its sequel, "The Holy Six." In that tale, Mrs. Owen informs six of Mr. Davies' colleagues of his plight. When they arrive in Jarvis valley, they also find themselves in a hostile world. Thomas reveals them all to be hypocrites, comic fools with evil minds. Meanwhile, Mr. Davies' newly acquired devotion to the primitive life force, mixed with his conventional Christianity, turns him into a grotesque figure. By the end of the story he claims to be the father of the child in Mrs. Owen's womb, a notion that is a bizarre mixture of his lust and spirituality.

Style and Technique

There is not much narrative action in this story. The characters of Mr. and Mrs. Owen and Mr. Davies are important primarily for their symbolic significance. Consequently, Thomas devotes a large part of his tale to a description of the symbolic landscape. During the meal at the Owen house, for example, the focus shifts from the three people gathered around the table to a detailed commentary on the scene outside the window. The "brown body" of the earth, the "green skin" of the grass, and the "breasts" of the Jarvis hills are more than simple personifications of the area around the Owen home. The language suggests the primitive sexuality and vitality of nature, powerful contrasts to the desiccated and desolated old clergyman.

In order to develop the poetic descriptions, rich in metaphors, Thomas had to tell his story from the third-person omniscient point of view. By the end of the tale, it becomes clear that the fabric of Mr. Davies' Christianity has been torn away, leaving him frightened and vulnerable in the face of the powers of raw nature. Thomas' description of him as "an old god beset by his enemies" suggests that a faltering Christianity cannot win out against the omnipotence of the pantheistic world of the Owens, a couple in complete harmony with the pulse of nature and the forces of darkness and the occult.

The allegorical nature of Thomas' story (the Owens representing pagan religion and Mr. Davies representing Christianity) is further developed in the sequel. The holy six of Wales bear allegorical names in the form of anagrams. Mr. Vyne and Mr. Stul, for example, represent Envy and Lust respectively.

Richard Kelly

THE ENGAGEMENT IN SANTO DOMINGO

Author: Heinrich von Kleist (1777-1811)
Type of plot: Love tragedy
Time of plot: 1803
Locale: The island of Santo Domingo
First published: "Die Verlobung in St. Domingo," 1811 (English translation, 1960)

> *Principal characters:*
> KONGO HOANGO, the leader of a black rebel force
> BABEKAN, his mulatto wife
> TONI BERTRAND, Babekan's fifteen-year-old daughter by a
>   French merchant
> GUSTAV VON DER RIED, a Swiss officer serving under the
>   French

The Story

As a consequence of the French Revolution, in 1794 the French National Convention declared freedom and equality for black slaves in the colonies, including the French part of the Caribbean island of Santo Domingo. Kongo Hoango, an old West African who faithfully served his white master for years, rebelled with his fellow blacks, massacred the planter and his entire family, and took over the plantation as his base of marauding operations to help drive the French from the island. Kongo Hoango makes it his practice to have his wife, Babekan, and her daughter, Toni, offer sanctuary to fugitive whites during his absence on raiding expeditions, allowing their unsuspecting guests to believe themselves safe from the rebels until Kongo Hoango returns and brutally executes them.

One night in the year 1803, a desperate white man comes to the house asking for assistance for himself, his family, and several of their household servants. They have narrowly escaped death at the rebels' hands in the town of Fort Dauphin and are fleeing on foot and under cover of darkness in the hope of reaching Port-au-Prince, the sole remaining French stronghold, in time to leave the island for Europe. The man identifies himself as Gustav von der Ried, a Swiss officer who was in the French service at Fort Dauphin. The rest of his party, he tells them, is in hiding some distance away until he can return with fresh provisions for their journey. Gustav cannot understand why his family, Swiss citizens, should be as much threatened by the rebels as the French colonists, but he realizes now that it is their race, not their nationality, which puts their lives in peril. Babekan tells him that she and Toni also suffer cruelties at the hands of the blacks, since both women betray their mixed blood by their lighter-colored skin.

It is decided that Gustav should spend the night at the plantation and send for his family the following day. Toni brings supper for their guest, and Gustav is struck by the charms of the girl, who has, after all, been taught to use them in beguiling those unfortunate enough to stray into Kongo Hoango's trap. In the course of the conversation at table, Gustav tells the story of a white planter from Fort Dauphin and a black slave girl whom the landowner had sought favors of and later abused. The girl had her revenge, however, when she became ill with yellow fever and sent word that she would offer the besieged man a hiding place during the rebellion. Only after taking him into her bed did she confront him spitefully with the fact of her deadly contagion. Gustav asks Toni if she would ever be capable of such a vicious deed, and she insists that she would not.

When it is time for Gustav to retire, Toni goes to prepare the room and a footbath for him. In the course of the preparations, he again finds himself enchanted by the girl's beauty, engages her in conversation about her marriage plans, and draws her tenderly into his arms. Toni is torn between her sense of duty to the rebel cause and the rising desire within herself. Gustav confides that he had a fiancée in France and that the young woman sacrificed her own life to spare him execution as an enemy of the Revolution. Toni is moved to sympathy for his grief, and the embrace which follows ends in the consummation of their love.

The next morning Toni protests to her mother the unjust cruelty of plotting Gustav's murder, and Babekan questions her loyalty to the rebellion. Thus, Toni must gain time by pretending to cooperate in the deadly plan, at the same time contriving to put off Gustav's impatience to announce their "engagement" without arousing his suspicions. Babekan intends to keep Gustav in the house until Kongo Hoango's return, when a detachment can be sent to surprise and destroy the group in their hiding place as well. Yet Toni manages to send word for the others to come to the plantation, certain that then she can defy her mother and leave with her betrothed for Europe.

That night she steals back to Gustav's room, determined to reveal the truth to him, and finds him asleep in his bed. In his sleep, Gustav murmurs her name. At that moment noises are heard in the yard; Kongo Hoango's contingent is back. Toni ties the still sleeping Gustav down in his bed, a trick to convince Babekan and Kongo Hoango that she is faithful to them, and the desperate ploy works. Once the commotion has finally died down and all have gone to bed, Toni goes to meet the Swiss fugitives, by now on their way to the plantation, warns them of the danger threatening Gustav and awaiting them, and leads them into the house, where they overpower the surprised rebels. When they cut Gustav free of the ropes on his bed, however, he seizes his pistol, accuses Toni of being a whore and betraying him, and shoots her through the chest. The others tell him how terribly he has misjudged her, whereupon he turns the weapon on himself and puts a bullet through his head.

The remaining members of the family must still think of their own survival. They bury the bodies of Toni and Gustav, having exchanged the rings on the hands of the two lovers, and finish their journey to Port-au-Prince and then home to Europe. Gustav's uncle settles in Switzerland again, "and even in the year 1807 one could still see, amid the shrubbery of his garden, the monument he had erected to the memory of his nephew, Gustav, and the latter's bride, the faithful Toni."

Themes and Meanings

Because Heinrich von Kleist regarded the human individual as a riddle, he made Toni the central figure of this story. She stands at the nexus of turbulent events and conflicting allegiances. As a child of mixed race, she enjoys the confidence and affections of both whites and blacks, but she also suffers the antipathy and mistrust of both. She must be clever and deceitful beyond her years to make the mother believe that her moral principles, not her attraction to Gustav, prompt her to plead for his release. Gustav himself has difficulty fathoming his feelings toward Toni: "if not for her color, which repelled him, he would have sworn that he had never seen anything prettier." His mixed emotions are only more profound and ominous after their lovemaking: "He swore he would never stop loving her, and that it was only in the delirium of his strangely disordered senses that the mixture of desire and fear she inspired in him could have seduced him into doing such a thing."

Kleist need not have made Toni a mere girl of fifteen if the innocence of youth had not been crucially important to her character. She is a riddle as much to herself as to the others in the story and to the author as well (no omniscient narrator questions or probes the reasons for her actions). She is experienced at playing the decoy for many hapless white fugitives up to now, but she is overtaken by love's desire in the encounter with Gustav; in affairs of the heart she is guileless and utterly confused. It is typical of Kleist that the heart takes over where rational deliberation fails, whether the course thus taken leads to happiness or tragedy.

The tragedy of "The Engagement in Santo Domingo" is perhaps that Toni, the individual so placed as to mediate between the opposing sides, fails to do so. As so often in the works of Kleist, much revolves about a question of knowledge—the opposite of innocence, the cause of humankind's loss of innocence and fall from grace. Standing in the eye of the cyclone, Toni alone knows all sides of the desperate situation; knowing more than any of the others, she is threatened on every side and must be the most dissembling. The loss of her virginity is nothing beside the loss of this far deeper innocence.

For Gustav knowledge is paradoxically treacherous because it is imperfect. Having consummated his love for Toni, "he knew that he had been saved, and that here in this house he had nothing to fear now from the girl." He is right, but Gustav overlooks the fact (and so does Toni, though she could never imagine it) that he has everything to fear from himself: In the end he kills her before he can learn the reason for her actions. Throughout the story, in fact, Gustav trusts Toni when he should not and does not trust her when he should.

Style and Technique

Like any number of Kleist's other stories, "The Engagement in Santo Domingo" pulls first one way and then the other on the reader's expectations. It appears that Gustav von der Ried will die as other whites before him have; then, since he has violated Toni, it seems likely that his fate at Kongo Hoango's hands will be unusually cruel. There follows a stretch of frantic but somewhat brighter expectation as Toni works to win freedom for Gustav and herself. (She firmly believes that they can escape together to Europe.) None of these developments prepares the reader for the surprise ending.

Other expectations prove illusory, too. Gustav's story of the black slave girl who lured her former white owner into her fatal embrace with the promise of saving him from the rampaging rebels only appears to foreshadow what Toni will soon do to Gustav, and her denial that she could commit such treachery seems—and surely is intended to be—deceitful of her. The story which parallels it, in which Gustav tells of his own former bride-to-be and her self-sacrifice to the revolutionary mob in France for his sake, unambiguously prefigures Toni's faithfulness. Gustav gradually discovers that it is the European woman to whom Toni bears a mysterious resemblance. The ironic reversal comes only at the end, when Gustav confuses faithfulness with duplicity and takes it upon himself to execute the second of his redeeming angels.

Some of the story's devices belong to Kleist's stock-in-trade: the fateful confusion of appearance and reality; the intoxication—in this case erotic—which abruptly changes the course of characters' actions; and the appearance of the beloved in the blissful escape of a dream vision, such as that in which Toni finds Gustav as he sleeps on the final night of the story. The motif of forbidden love-at-first-sight, the young girl's awakening to the power of love, and the concluding love-death scene are all familiar to readers from the Romeo and Juliet tradition in literature.

It is worth recalling that, in November of the same year in which this story appeared, Kleist carried out a suicide pact with a woman of his acquaintance, firing a bullet through her heart and a second one through his own head.

Michael Ritterson

ENOCH SOAMES

Author: Max Beerbohm (1872-1956)
Type of plot: Satire with parody and fantasy
Time of plot: The 1890's and 1997
Locale: London
First published: 1920

> *Principal characters:*
> ENOCH SOAMES, a failed writer
> THE NARRATOR, a well-known writer
> WILL ROTHENSTEIN, a painter
> THE DEVIL

The Story

The narrator, a middle-aged, well-known author, looks back on his introduction to London artistic life as a young man in the 1890's. He remembers the fashionable aesthetes with whom he became acquainted, figures whom he then viewed with uncritical, youthful reverence. He mentions actual places and people, such as the portrait painter Will Rothenstein. In this historical context, the fictional protagonist of the story appears: Enoch Soames. Soames tries to force his company on the preoccupied Rothenstein at a restaurant table where the painter and narrator sit together. The kindly Rothenstein tries to put the intruder down gently but cannot get rid of him; he joins them and monopolizes the subsequent conversation in a boasting, affected. way. To the narrator, Soames seems to be a comically ridiculous figure; nevertheless, he has published one book, with another on the way. The narrator, himself an aspiring but as yet unpublished writer, is enormously impressed, despite Soames's ludicrous figure and manners.

Soon after this restaurant meeting, the narrator gets a copy of Soames's book. It seems to be drivel, but, after all, it has been published. The naïve narrator does not know what to believe. Some of the acknowledged literary giants of the moment seemed earlier to have been writing nonsense, until established critics validated their genius.

In subsequent meetings between the two men, however, the narrator's judgment about Soames becomes clarified: He is indeed a pretentious fool, with his silly verses about trotting with the Devil through a London square, his fondness for absinthe, his habit of lapsing into bad French, and his haughty disdain for all other creative people.

Meanwhile, the narrator is himself beginning to achieve the kind of literary recognition which Soames craves. The latter, in sharp contrast, goes steadily downhill. His first two books have had few sales and almost no critical notice from the press; his third and last volume must be published at his own expense; it sells three copies. Soames's air of bravado and contempt, the narrator now becomes aware, is a mask for deeper feelings of self-doubt and depression: He suffers intensely from the world's neglect of his literary effusions.

Several years have now passed since the beginning of the story, and the narrator has lost track of Soames. He suddenly notices him, sitting shabbily dressed and alone in an unfashionable little restaurant, itself about to fail—the kind of place in which Soames would never have permitted himself to be seen in the earlier, more hopeful, days. The now successful younger man joins Soames and tries to comfort him by suggesting that posterity might yet come to appreciate his efforts. Soames admits that literary fame means more to him than life itself—he would sell his soul to the Devil for a peek into a library card catalog a hundred years hence, simply to verify that his books have survived.

At this point, a formally dressed gentleman at the next table, overhearing the wish, interrupts them. He is the Devil and he will grant Soames's wish. The pact is concluded on the spot; Soames rushes out into the future, leaving the narrator to await his return later the same day for a reunion in the restaurant.

The round trip is, in fact, successfully completed, but, alas, the only mention of Soames in the library of the future is the less than flattering portrait sketched of him in this story. The Devil drags Soames down to Hell in payment for his futile look.

Themes and Meanings

On one level, "Enoch Soames" is the witty reminiscence of a middle-aged writer looking back over the abyss of World War I to a more frivolous, care-free era. It is a genial satire, a debunking of what Beerbohm had come to see as a time of pretension, of the inflated poses of would-be artists who gathered around such bona fide geniuses as Oscar Wilde, the writer, and Aubrey Beardsley, the caricaturist. Youthful rebellion occasionally produced enduring works of art; often the result was pretentious nonsense—parodied in this story in the fictional figure, manners, conversation, and writing of Enoch Soames.

Although Beerbohm mocks Soames, he does not spare his younger self, Soames's near contemporary, from satire. The narrator's own problem in recognizing Soames's nonsense for what it is reflects on his own overconcern to be thought well of and to have the right, the fashionable opinions on all subjects. Thus, Beerbohm's satire and parody have three objects in the story: Soames; himself as the narrator-character of the story; and his generation's tendency to startle by affectation in dress, speech, food, and drink, but most especially in its artistic opinions.

On one level, then, this is a light, entertaining narrative, a realistic if

nostalgic portrait of a bygone time, brought to climax by the fantastic introduction of the Devil to reduce Soames's craving for success ultimately to
absurdity. Beneath Beerbohm's light touch and surface gaiety, however, is a
serious exploration of important philosophical issues: What is authentic?
What is spurious? How can the difference be satisfactorily determined? The
object in question is the character and ability of Soames. Both narrator and
reader start gaining access to this phenomenon from the beginning of the
story, but the issue of authenticity is muddled by Soames's striving to project
a favorable image, and also by his reputation as a published author. It soon
becomes a question of who is more ridiculous—Soames for being a buffoon
or the narrator for being impressed by Soames.

In the second half of the story, the philosophical issue of authenticity
becomes transmuted to the psychological one of identity. Soames is revealed
as more pathetic than ridiculous in his pursuit of fame, and the narrator, who
becomes successful in exactly the way which Soames craves, ends by feeling
sympathy for the older man's plight. Although the issue is resolved fantastically, with Soames literally selling himself for a peek at what he hopes will
be his posthumous success, the seriousness and relevance of this theme are
clear and more general than Beerbohm's own professional concern. There is
a contemporary ring, with universal overtones, to the character of Enoch
Soames, a hollow man without qualities, for whom existence and façade are
interchangeable.

Style and Technique

One of Beerbohm's striking techniques is combination; he fuses elements
which are often kept separate in different narratives: fiction with autobiographical reminiscence; realism with fantasy, to which he shifts with the Devil's appearance; initially, satire and parody—exaggerated, comic imitation of
1890's affectation in Soames's speech and writing—with a more sympathetic,
psychological view of this character later in the story. These fusions are all
successful, and contribute to an overall richness of effect.

The author's handling of character is also skillful. The two supporting
characters perform functions for the major relationship of the work, that
between Soames and the narrator. Rothenstein is the link which brings them
together at the beginning; the Devil is a device for separating them at the
end: He drags Soames off to Hell while leaving the narrator, and the lesson
of the story, with the reader. In the Soames-narrator relationship, Beerbohm
uses the technique of the double: Soames is the narrator's double in his
overvaluation of literary success. The narrator, unlike Soames, does have
genuine ability and does achieve success even as the older man sinks into failure; it is their similarity which emphasizes the two major themes of the story,
the earlier one of authenticity and the later one of identity. In the earlier
authentic-spurious confusion, both characters are ridiculous; later, in the

growing appreciation of Soames's hollowness, the narrator becomes more sympathetic to the reader. As doubles they both share the temptation to put image before substance.

In addition, much of the entertaining effect of the story derives from Beerbohm's adroit use of the first-person point of view. The 1890's was a colorful time, and the reader is injected into this era easily and intimately, in the company of a masterful guide who has experienced it directly. The satire and parody directed at this epoch is made more acceptable to the reader because the author disarmingly includes himself as a target. There is one further advantage of the first-person point of view: When Beerbohm moves from reality to fantasy with the sudden appearance of the Devil, this potentially disorienting shift is cushioned for the reader by the narrator's own shocked, amused reaction.

Finally, the author's handling of time is ingenious. At the beginning of the story, literary time recedes to the 1890's. Through the device of the library visit fantasy, time then curls around, moving forward to the reader and ultimately leaving him with the illusion of having experienced something much nearer at hand than that with which he started.

Sanford Radner

THE ENORMOUS RADIO

Author: John Cheever (1912-1982)
Type of plot: Fantasy and domestic realism
Time of plot: New York City
Locale: The late 1940's
First published: 1947

Principal characters:
JIM and IRENE WESTCOTT, a "typical" urban couple in their
thirties

The Story

One of the most frequently reprinted of Cheever's stories, "The Enormous Radio" derives most of its initial impact, and subsequent memorability, from the author's ironic blend of fantasy and realism, shadowed by suggestions of the supernatural.

Set during the years immediately following World War II, "The Enormous Radio" is the best known of Cheever's urban tales, foreshadowing in subject matter, theme, and style the suburban stories that would follow. Here as elsewhere, Cheever foregrounds the subtleties and stresses of contemporary marriage against a background of ambition and social mobility.

In the story's opening paragraph, the narrator spares no effort in presenting Jim and Irene Westcott as a typical, moderately successful Manhattan couple, married nine years, with one child of each sex; significantly, the Westcott children are seldom seen in the story and are never mentioned by name. Jim and Irene, observes the narrator, differ from other, similar couples only in their shared devotion to "serious" music, an interest carefully concealed from friends and acquaintances lest the Westcotts appear too "different."

The Westcotts spend many hours together listening to broadcast music, and when their radio falls into disrepair Jim hastens to replace it with an expensive new model in a "large gumwood cabinet" that clashes with their other furniture. The new radio, although quite superior in tone to its predecessor, soon begins picking up sounds from the elevator and from appliances in neighboring apartments; before long it is receiving and amplifying the neighbors' voices as well, providing the astonished Westcotts with a unique opportunity for eavesdropping: Each turn of the dial tunes in the sounds from a different apartment.

On the first evening, the Westcotts go to bed "weak with laughter" after an evening of switching "stations" with reckless abandon. Before dawn, however, Irene rises to take their young son a glass of water and on impulse tries the radio, only to overhear the conversation of an aging couple; the wife, it appears, is probably dying of some undisclosed disease. Thereafter, the conversations that Irene overhears are increasingly sad, violent, or scandalous in tone and content. In the elevator, Irene begins to scrutinize her neighbors, trying to match the faces that she sees with the voices that she hears. Returning from lunch with a friend, she tells the maid that she is not to be disturbed as she listens to the radio; with the approach of nightfall, the conversations that she hears, interspersed as before with the quaint recitations of a British nursemaid, become increasingly provocative and frightening.

Irene becomes obsessed with the odd revelations emanating from the radio; soon, she urges Jim's intervention in righting the various wrongs of which she has lately been informed: Mr. Osborn, she tells Jim, is beating his wife, and the elevator man suffers from tuberculosis. Faced with Jim's apparent indifference, she further tells him that Mrs. Melville has heart trouble, that Mr. Hendricks is about to lose his job, and that a female neighbor, as yet unidentified, is having an affair with "that hideous handyman."

Heedless of her husband's advice to turn off the radio, or at least to stop listening, Irene hysterically seeks Jim's reassurance that they, the Westcotts, are different from the other couples in the building. "You love me, don't you?" she asks. "And we're not hypercritical or worried about money or dishonest, are we?" Despite Jim's immediate efforts to calm her, it develops not long thereafter that the Westcotts are at least all those things, and possibly more. Once the radio has been "repaired," at Jim's insistence, he begins complaining about the radio's initial cost, simultaneously chiding Irene for leaving clothing bills unpaid. Immediately if not sooner, he observes, they will have to begin cutting back on expenses, as business is not good.

In the story's closing paragraphs, Irene cautions an increasingly irate Jim to lower his voice lest they be overheard through the newly repaired radio. Jim, gathering momentum in his anger, proceeds to denounce Irene for stealing from her mother's estate, cheating her sister out of the sister's rightful legacy, ruining another woman's life, and undergoing an abortion, doubtless illegal, without misgivings or remorse. When Irene turns on the radio, hoping at least to hear the comforting voice of the Sweeneys' British nursemaid, all she receives is the "suave," "noncommittal" tones of an announcer informing his listeners of the current news and weather.

Themes and Meanings

Here, as in his more mature work, Cheever shows a nearly obsessive concern with the instability of modern marriage, a condition sustained and prolonged by the seemingly infinite human tendency toward self-delusion. Beneath the Westcotts' immediate predicament lurks the author-narrator's own preoccupation with the proximity of death, reflected in the darker conversations that Irene overhears.

Intent on getting and spending, like the rest of the postwar population, the Westcotts have in fact sublimated their true humanity in their common fondness for music—an avocation which, in the case of other couples, might well be replaced by hiking, golf, tennis, or any other imaginable shared activity. The Westcott children, although perhaps a source of pride at times, remain all but invisible, obscured by their parents' determination to find themselves conventionally happy. Jim Westcott, despite his omnipresence throughout the story, gradually diminishes in importance before the gathering force of Irene's imagination; his emotional outburst at the end of the story merely underscores the power and eventual dominance of Irene's self-delusion, fueled in turn by her increasingly active imagination.

Arguably, the entire action of the story takes place in Irene's mind, at a moment when she begins to doubt both the force and the extent of a conjugal "bliss" based mainly on a shared interest in classical music. Assuming Jim's accusations to be true, Irene seeks justification for her past behavior in her perceived superiority to those around her; her pleasure in the radio's revelations, a pleasure initially yet only briefly shared with Jim and followed by intimations of mortality, soon gives way to a massive access of insecurity, which she knows to be quite justified. Like Neddy Merrill, the title character of Cheever's later story "The Swimmer," Irene has managed to survive only at the considerable cost of nearly total self-delusion.

Style and Technique

Later acclaimed for his skillful use of often "unreliable" first-person narrators, Cheever in "The Enormous Radio" confines his narrative voice to the third person, presumably omniscient yet, like the radio itself, unable (or unwilling) to pass judgment. The style is generally noncommittal, like the voice of the announcer, save for the increasingly animated and thought-provoking dialogue; only gradually does the reader come to suspect that he might be participating in a fantasy generated and perpetuated by Irene. Notwithstanding, the fiction of the "enormous" radio, in which the adjective regains no small part of the force still felt in the substantive "enormity," continues to suggest supernatural possibilities.

To be sure, Jim Westcott's revelations and accusations in the story's penultimate paragraph come as something of a shock to the reader as well as to Irene, unforeshadowed by any preceding action or description. Later in his career, particularly in such stories as "The Swimmer" and "The Scarlet Moving Van," Cheever would perfect the technique of "fitness," amply preparing for the climax through clues and gradual revelation; in the present case, the ending appears to have been borrowed from O. Henry or Guy de Maupassant. Nevertheless, "The Enormous Radio" ranks among the more impressive of Cheever's earlier efforts, encouraging readers to expect, and to appreciate, the even greater achievement of his suburban stories during the years to follow.

David B. Parsell

ENTROPY

Author: Thomas Pynchon (1937-   )
Type of plot: Allegorical realism
Time of plot: February, 1957
Locale: A suburb of Washington, D.C.
First published: 1960

Principal characters:
MEATBALL MULLIGAN, the proprietor of the lower floor of the house in which the story occurs
SANDOR ROJAS, a former Hungarian freedom fighter
SAUL, a friend to Meatball
CALLISTO, a nihilistic philosopher
AUBADE, the female companion to Callisto

The Story

The narrative opens with an evocation of the fortieth hour of Meatball Mulligan's lease-breaking party, complete with drunken revelers, much debris, and loud music. The latter awakens the upstairs tenant Callisto from an uneasy sleep, and the scene shifts to his apartment, which is a kind of sealed hothouse luxuriating in plants and protected from the wintry weather outside, where it has been, the reader learns, precisely thirty-seven degrees Fahrenheit for three days running (despite announced changes in weather by the newscasters).

Callisto has been nursing a sick bird back to health, attempting to keep it alive with the warmth and energy from his own body—as if their continuous existences were a single system, an enclosed heat engine (into which the tropically warm room has, in effect, been made). For several pages, the story shifts back and forth from the thoughts and occasional audible remarks of Callisto to Meatball's party downstairs. The latter includes a brief conversation between Meatball's friend Saul, whose female companion Miriam has recently left him, the intrusion of a group of drunken sailors on shore leave and in search of a party, and the eventual decision by Meatball to attempt to quell the anarchy which ultimately breaks out and to attempt to keep the party going for several more hours. In the meantime, Callisto reflects upon the concept of entropy, on the possibility that the universe will ultimately suffer heat death and cease to act at all (the first sign of which is the constant thermometer reading outside his window), and on the possible implications of the laws of thermodynamics for social existence (this with some help from those investigators who had appropriated the term "entropy" from physics to information theory). The story ends with the death of the bird and with Aubade's breaking the glass that separates her and Callisto from the cold

outside, as the two of them await the equilibrating of the temperatures between outside and inside, the ultimate consequence, for them at least, of the
principle of entropy.

Themes and Meanings

Pynchon himself has remarked, in the introduction to *Slow Learner*
(1984), the collection of his short fiction in which "Entropy" is included, on
the comparative aridity of this story, upon the mistake he made (he attributes
it to his youthfulness at the time of writing) in believing that a story could be
generated directly out of a theme or symbol or abstraction—in this case, the
concept of entropy evoked in the title and explored theoretically in Callisto's
musings and the conversation between Meatball and Saul, as well as practically in the actions of Meatball and Aubade at the end. In fact, for even
such a brief tale as this one, there is comparatively little action, virtually no
characterization of any significance, and the thematic concerns of the nature
of entropy in thermodynamics and in information theory almost completely
dominate the story. If one were to characterize the story in classical,
Aristotelian terms, it would almost certainly fall under the heading of a plot
of thought.

The controlling trope or idea of the story, entropy, remains, as Pynchon
attests once more in his introduction to *Slow Learner*, a very slippery concept. In thermodynamics, it is a measure of the disorder in a system, and it
was the theorem of Rudolf Clausius that the entropy of any closed system
tends toward a maximum. If, then, like Henry Adams (whose autobiography
provides the model for the memoirs that Callisto is dictating to Aubade during the course of the story), one conceives of the entire cosmos as a closed
system, then it follows that the universe is inexorably heading for ultimate
heat death, the ceasing of all motion which is prophesied at the end of this
story, the outward and visible sign of which is the steady state of the
thermometer outside Callisto's window.

The concept of entropy, however, has also been imported into information
theory, more or less illegitimately, as a measure of disorder in systems of signals. Entropy is roughly the measure of noise, of meaningless sound in any
given string of communicative signals. This meaning of the concept is
deployed in a conversation between Meatball and the recently jilted Saul
(the latter is a computer technician, which makes the conversation margin-
ally more plausible, since Meatball knows nothing about entropy in either
sense of the term, being merely a likable, dumb slob trying to keep his party
from getting out of hand). It is impossible to summarize this conversation, so
it will simply be quoted here:

> Saul jumped down off the stove . . . "Tell a girl: 'I love you.' No trouble with
> two-thirds of that, it's a closed circuit. Just you and she. But that nasty four-

letter word in the middle, *that's* the one you have to look out for. Ambiguity. Redundance. Irrelevance, even. Leakage. All this is noise. Noise screws up your signal, makes for disorganization in the circuit."

Meatball shuffled around. "Well, now, Saul," he muttered, "you're sort of, I don't know, expecting a lot from people. I mean, you know. What it is is, most of the things we say, I guess, are mostly noise."

"Ha! Half of what you just said, for example."

"Well, you do it too."

"I know." Saul smiled grimly. "It's a bitch, ain't it."

Pynchon would ultimately do better with this kind of game in his novels, particularly in *Gravity's Rainbow* (1973), where the technical matter is brilliantly integrated into a masterfully executed plot that turns on some possibilities suggested by probability theory and operant conditioning of subjects in behavioral psychology. Here the conversation does illustrate the principle in question (entropy as a measure of noise in a communication system), but the joke, at least to some ears, falls rather flat.

What does work, however, is the portrayal of Meatball as a kind of counterentropic force in the universe of the party, a sort of primitive resistance against the cosmic pessimism of Callisto. For Meatball does resist the entropic tendencies inherent in his own party at the end, and in that sense he gives the lie to Callisto's resignation to the cosmic fate which he has contemplated and passively endures when Aubade breaks the window in the final paragraph. To the extent that Meatball's cheerful attempt to set things straight in his chaotic household succeeds, it stands as Pynchon's hopeful rebuttal of cosmic pessimism, a potentially bright spot in the otherwise gloomy historical forecast that the concept of entropy seems to project.

Style and Technique

From a technical point of view, this story is not very interesting. The only device worth remarking is the use of a double plot line in the stories of Meatball and Callisto—stories which, as suggested above, are meant to unite (or at least come into contact) at the level of theme. In every sense, "Entropy" is a youthful production, an apprentice piece by a precocious but still technically immature writer. The rich range of different registers (from the snappy slang of postwar urban America, to the lyricism of post-Symbolist fictions such as William Faulkner's, to the almost forbiddingly technical language of scientific manuals, to the humorous song parodies) that characterize Pynchon's mature fictions is confined here almost exclusively to a single voice, interrupted only occasionally by the dialogue of characters such as Meatball and Saul. In short, "Entropy" is a production of a writer who has yet to master his craft; it is of interest chiefly as a prelude to what is to come.

Michael Sprinker

ENVY
Or, Yiddish in America

Author: Cynthia Ozick (1928-   )
Type of plot: Comic satire
Time of plot: Mid-twentieth century
Locale: New York
First published: 1966

> *Principal characters:*
> EDELSHTEIN, an elderly Jewish intellectual who writes and
>   lectures and is trying to save the Yiddish language
> BAUMZWEIG, his friend, editor of a Yiddish periodical
> PAULA, Baumzweig's wife
> YANKEL OSTROVER, a famous author, envied by Edelshtein
> CHAIM VOROVSKY, a drunken lexicographer
> HANNAH, Vorovsky's niece

The Story

The basic premise of this novella-length, seriocomic story is Edelshtein's envy of the success of the writer Yankel Ostrover and his obsession with sustaining Yiddish as a language. Parallel to this plot line is the contradiction involved in Edelshtein's ironic need for a translator, without which he can never achieve success as a writer, but with which he cannot really sustain Yiddish. Although Edelshtein finds American writers of Jewish extraction such as Philip Roth, Bernard Malamud, Norman Mailer, and Saul Bellow puerile, vicious, and ignorant, he reserves his most passionate vituperation for Ostrover, who seems patterned after Isaac Bashevis Singer in some ways and Jerzy Kosinski in others. Ostrover is a writer of stories in Yiddish which, when translated into English, have become highly popular. For Edelshtein and his friend Baumzweig, editor of a Yiddish periodical, Ostrover's Yiddish is impure and his subject matter is pornographic. They call him "Pig" or "Devil" or "Yankee Doodle." With his focus on an imaginary Polish village named Zwrdl, however, Ostrover is considered "modern" by contemporary critics. Free of the prison of Yiddish, he has burst out into the world of reality. Taking Anton Chekhov and Leo Tolstoy as his literary gods, he has been published in *The New Yorker* and *Playboy*.

There are other reasons for Edelshtein's hatred of Ostrover than his envy of his success. Thirty years earlier, Ostrover had an affair with Edelshtein's wife; Edelshtein blames Ostrover for the fact that he and his wife have remained childless. It is the envy which gives the story its title, however, that most eats at Edelshtein. He writes Ostrover's publishers asking them to provide him with a translator so he might show them that there are Jewish writers other than Ostrover. The irony of Edelshtein's position is indicated by the publisher's response that reputation must precede translation, to which Edelshtein replies that without translation there can be no reputation. Edelshtein then writes to a spinster hack who translates for Ostrover, from whom he receives a long reply arguing that she is the one that makes Ostrover modern, although, like a wife, she has the passive role.

When Edelshtein goes with Baumzweig and Baumzweig's wife, Paula, to hear Ostrover read, Ostrover reads a story about a poet who sells his soul to the Devil in order to get a translator and then, when he still cannot find success, is condemned to Hell to write poems that are immediately consigned to oblivion. The story is an obvious allegory about Edelshtein and his desire for a translator, and it serves only to infuriate Edelshtein more. It also enrages Edelshtein that Ostrover responds with jokes to the homage he receives. He believes that the Jewish intellectual, in the modern world, is reduced to being a comedian. At the reading one is also introduced to Chaim Vorovsky, a mad lexicographer who, after completing seventeen years' work on his dictionary, began laughing and could not stop, and then began wetting himself. Now alcohol has cured the laughter but not the incontinence. Edelshtein also meets Vorovsky's niece, Hannah, who knows his poetry from her grandfather, and he begins his efforts to make her his translator.

The climax of the story comes when Edelshtein goes to Vorovsky's house and finds that he has reverted to his laughing madness. Still, Edelshtein tries to convince Hannah to be his translator, telling her that she will be like a messiah to a whole generation. She, however, recognizes him as merely another jealous old man from the ghetto, looking not for a translator but for someone's soul to suck out like a vampire. When she tells him that Ostrover is not of the ghetto but in the world, Edelshtein comes to the realization that for him the ghetto is the real world and the outside world only a ghetto. Hannah attacks him with the accusation that he is a cannibal who hates imagination, magic, and God. When he leaves, Edelshtein calls the number of a fanatical religious organization with whom he argues about the values of Judaism and Christianity. Finally, the religious fanatic calls Edelshtein a kike and Yid. Edelshtein shouts into the telephone that the whole world is infected with anti-Semites who have caused him to lose everything, and most tragically, to fail to have a translator.

Themes and Meanings

Because "Envy" is both a satire, written in broad comic strokes, and an ironic treatment of a serious theme—the isolation of the American Jewish intellectual who clings to his old European tradition—it is a story that is difficult to perceive as a unified totality. Edelshtein scorns what is "modern," particularly if that term means the rejection of the old values. He rejects what he calls the mere storytelling of Ostrover in favor of the true art of poetry. He rejects English in favor of Yiddish and laments that his language is dying. Yet he longs to have Ostrover's success, desperately seeks a translator who he thinks will make this possible, and knows great dejection in his loneliness and despair. The story is less a theme story than a comic satiric story that lashes out through Edelshtein at the Americanized Jewish writer, yet at the same time makes fun of Edelshtein's Old World self-pity and bitter jealousy.

For Edelshtein, the loss of Yiddish is the loss of an entire world. In reading the story, however, one is not always sure whether a world will be lost or only the narrow intellectual world of Edelshtein will be lost. The conflict of the story is summed up in the final dialogue between Ostrover and Hannah, in which Hannah seems to see Edelshtein correctly as a ghetto Jew who refuses to accept the modern world. Even as one rejects the narrowness of Edelshtein, however, one cannot accept the triviality of the vision of Ostrover and Hannah. Thus, there is no answer to the dilemma here. Ultimately, what "Envy" seems to be about is the loss of Jewishness, its absorption into what is American and what is modern. Thus, although Edelshtein is right at the end of the story—that the whole world is infected with anti-Semites—the seriousness of the charge is undercut by his comic cry that because of the anti-Semites he has no translator.

The more serious aspect of the search for a translator focuses on the symbolic need of an intermediary between the Old World and the New. Edelshtein is an isolated figure, like an Old Testament prophet crying out in the wilderness for someone to communicate his cultural values to the modern world; he feels himself surrounded by infidels and traitors to both his society and religion. He is, however, also a comic figure—ineffectual, pathetic, absurd. What he wants is both valuable and worthless at once. Ozick's tragicomic story hovers uneasily between these two opposing points of view.

Style and Technique

Style is more important to "Envy" than theme; the point of view of the story and its rhetorical structure are the most obvious sources of its interest. Ozick maintains an ironic and satiric perspective on Edelshtein, even as she sustains a point of view that reflects Edelshtein's values. The language of the story is comic and ironic, combining the conventions of Yiddish folktale with the style of the upbeat Jewish comic; even as it makes fun of the Americanized Jewish idiom and folktale devices, it makes use of them. Its structure, made up of various kinds of rhetorical patterns such as letters, stories, and debates, is far from straightforward. This highly stylized and self-conscious structure and style make the story somewhat difficult to fix in the reader's mind, depending primarily neither on plot nor on characterization, but rather on purely rhetorical devices and erratic shifts in tone and perspective.

"Envy" is a satiric comment on the nature of Jewish literary culture in

America. Although Edelshtein's view that without the Jews there would be
no literary culture in Western civlization may be an extreme one, it is obvious
that the success of Jewish writers in America is a result of their willingness to
give up the strict traditions of their culture as well as their language. Moreover, the success of such writers as Malamud, Bellow, and Roth is largely the
result of their willingness to make their Jewish characters the butt of an
extended Jewish joke. Roth especially has written novels that reflect on this
capitulation for the sake of popularity. The basic punch line of Ozick's joke
about this dilemma of the Jewish writer is "You can't have it both ways"; that
is, the Jewish writer cannot maintain his language and culture and be read at
the same time. The technique of Ozick's story is to maintain the seriousness
of this problem even as it must be seen from the perspective of satiric humor.

Charles E. May

ESTHER

Author: Jean Toomer (1894-1967)
Type of plot: Character study
Time of plot: Early twentieth century
Locale: Rural Georgia
First published: 1923

> *Principal characters:*
> ESTHER CRANE, a black girl growing up in a small town
> KING BARLO, a charismatic black man

The Story

"Esther" is divided into three parts. The first, titled "Nine," describes the main character, a young black girl who lives in Georgia, at that age. She is first seen walking from her home to her father's grocery store. Esther Crane is almost pretty; her hair does not have enough shine, and her face is too unemotional. Her skin is pale, so that she could be taken for a white girl. As she walks, a strange things happens. King Barlo, a huge, well-proportioned black man, drops to his knees in the street in an area where men spit tobacco juice. White men continue to spit at the spot, hitting Barlo, but he does not notice, as he is in a religious trance. After hours of kneeling in this place, Barlo begins to speak to the large crowd which has gathered to view this unusual scene. He speaks to them of a vision he has had from Jesus, who has told him to tell of an inspired black man of Africa, who, while rapt in a religious concentration similar to Barlo's, was captured by white men and taken to America to be sold as a slave. The blacks in the audience are excited and urge him to continue. Barlo stands up and urges those present to turn to the Lord and greet a new awakening of spirit. That night Barlo leaves town. There are rumors of miraculous events, but all that is known for certain is that a black woman drew a picture of a black madonna on the courthouse wall. Esther is told of these rumors, and her young mind fixes on Barlo as an image of strength.

The second section of the story deals with Esther's adolescence in two sections, titled "Sixteen" and "Twenty-two." In "Sixteen," Esther has two dreams. In the first, she sees the red sunlight on the windows of McGregor's notion shop. She imagines that the shop is burning, and when the fire department puts out the fire, a baby is found, which Esther claims as her own. She cannot think of any way that she might have had the baby except by immaculate conception, but she knows that this thought is a sin, so she stops the dream and replaces it with another, in which people spit tobacco juice on the flames, causing the area to stink. Black and white women lift their skirts to reveal their underwear. Esther rushes in to save the baby and is at first repelled by its blackness but begins to love it as it nurses. The townspeople make fun of her, but she interprets their jeers as envy and is happy with her baby. In "Twenty-two," Esther's daily life as a clerk at her father's store is described. Although her father is the richest black man in town, Esther's emotional life is limited. A young black boy with whom she had an affair while she was in school rejected her because she was cold to him. A white man who was attracted to her dropped her after he found out who her father was. Esther decided that it is the powerful Barlo to whom she is attracted, and she resolves to tell him that she loves him the next time he comes to town. Meanwhile, she grows older, grayer, and plainer.

In "Esther Is Twenty-seven," Esther finally brings the elements of her various dreams together and meets King Barlo. He has returned to town a rich man, having made money on cotton during World War I, and is surrounded by a bevy of beautiful black women. Esther realizes that she will be possessed by an ordinary man if she does not make some sort of advance toward Barlo, but as her resolve increases she begins to be considered strange by the outside world, and people wonder if she is going crazy. Esther sets out at midnight to visit Barlo, who is staying at Nat Bowle's house. She leaves in the middle of the night so that her parents and the other townspeople will not know what she is doing. As she passes McGregor's notion shop, she again imagines that she sees flames in the windows, even though it is night. At Bowle's house, she is sickened by tobacco fumes but goes to the upstairs room containing Barlo and his entourage. She is about to faint, but she revives and sees Barlo before her. She tells him that she has come for him, but Barlo says that this is not the place for her and asks her why she has come. Esther says nothing, but the crowd around Barlo infers her sexual intent and laughs at her. She sees Barlo as an ugly drunk and thinks that conception of a child with such a man would be a sin. Pursued by the jeers of the crowd, Esther goes down the stairs and into the street to discover that the street and the town have vanished.

Themes and Meanings

To the familiar literary theme of the repressed, young, middle-class woman who is both excited and frightened by her sexual desires, Jean Toomer in "Esther" adds the theme of the person of mixed blood struggling to come to grips with an ethnic heritage which is also both exciting and frightening. Esther Crane looks more white than black, so her fellow blacks reject her. Her black suitor said that "for sweetness he preferred a lollipop," but a white suitor also rejects her because of her blackness. Esther is not torn between two worlds; rather, from the beginning, she can fit into neither.

As befits a middle-class shopkeeper's daughter, Esther's sexual desires are carefully hedged round with the disguises of housewifely duty and religious fervor. Although Esther thinks that she loves Barlo, her dreams disguise his identity in the form of a fire so that even her subconscious can interpret her desires to her conscious mind only in the form of a wish for a baby whose blackness at first repels her. She can accept sexuality only if it is disguised as a component of a respectable life. Barlo first appears in the story as a religious messenger, telling a story of a new age to be led by a new black man. Barlo is as powerful as a god, and the black madonna drawn on the courthouse wall is Esther, who, she imagines, will bear Barlo's child. Tellingly, when she first dreams of having a child with Barlo, she does not even think of sex with him but instead explains her desire through church morality: The baby she bears will be the result of an immaculate conception. Yet the same morality that invents a way around the thought of sex traps her again and reminds her that a thought of similarity to the Virgin is sinful. In her second replay of this dream, she sees herself rescuing a black baby from the flames, skipping over the idea of sex altogether.

With such confusion over her motives, Esther's one attempted sexual encounter with Barlo is doomed to disaster. She is reminded of her rejection of half of her heritage when the other blacks, easily accepting sex, make fun of her attempt, saying, "So thats how the dictie niggers does it." When Esther steps into the empty street, it is not the town but her dreams and her future which have disappeared.

Style and Technique

"Esther" is heavily freighted with symbols, the first of which is the main character's name. The Esther of the Bible presented herself to a Persian king at his court and was selected to be his new queen. The Esther of Toomer's story also presents herself to a king but is rejected, or perhaps more accurately, does not have the courage to understand and act on her deepest desires and is thereby rejected as not being queenly enough.

There are also echoes of Dante's *The Divine Comedy* in the presentation of Esther at the ages of nine and twenty-seven. Dante saw Beatrice, the inspiration for his great poem, when she was nine, again when she was eighteen, and once again after her death, in a vision, when she would have been twenty-seven. As all these numbers are multiples of the Trinity, religious significance is added to the fact of Beatrice's beauty by their use. Esther Crane is also seen at nine, but she is merely a witness to a person who is having a vision. She visits Barlo when she is twenty-seven, when Dante's Beatrice was dead; thus Toomer reinforces the fact that Esther is emotionally and sexually dead, a point he makes by extending the section dealing with Esther's adolescence until she is twenty-two, almost an old maid by rural black standards.

Perhaps even more powerful than the other symbols in the story, including the fire which Esther imagines to represent Barlo's sexuality and blackness, is Toomer's use of images that are not symbolic but which are meant to confront the reader directly with their own emotional impact. Just before Esther goes to visit Barlo, Toomer states, "Her mind is a pink meshbag filled with baby toes," an image which is tender and horrific at once, exactly like the mental state of Esther herself.

James Baird

ETHAN BRAND
A Chapter from an Abortive Romance

Author: Nathaniel Hawthorne (1804-1864)
Type of plot: Fantasy
Time of plot: Sometime before 1850
Locale: Western Massachusetts
First published: 1850

> *Principal characters:*
> ETHAN BRAND, a philosopher-scientist, formerly a lime-burner
> BARTRAM, a lime-burner
> JOE, his young son
> OLD HUMPHREY, the father of a girl destroyed by Brand's experiments
> THE DOCTOR, a former acquaintance of Brand
> THE JEW, an itinerant German diorama exhibitor, suspected of being the Devil

The Story

Old Bartram and his young son are burning marble into lime in their isolated kiln when they are disturbed by a strange, mirthless laugh. Soon the laugh is followed by the appearance of a mysterious man who identifies himself as Ethan Brand. Bartram recognizes him instantly, as he has heard village tales of a man by that name who left the village eighteen years earlier in search of the Unpardonable Sin. When Bartram asks if his search has been successful, Brand ruefully confesses that, after all of his wanderings and inquiries, he found the Unpardonable Sin in his own heart.

The lime-burner dispatches Joe to the village tavern to alert the "jolly fellows" there that Brand has returned. Left alone with the stranger, he feels acutely aware of the sins in his own heart responding to this man who "had committed the only crime for which Heaven can afford no mercy." Sins, Hawthorne writes, are "all of one family; they went to and fro between his breast and Ethan Brand's, and carried dark greetings from one to the other." The legends of Brand which seemed comic to Bartram now seem deadly earnest.

Brand, whose search for the Unpardonable Sin actually began with thoughts and speculations during his lonely hours as a lime-burner, stokes up the fire as Bartram recalls tales that he is believed to have evoked the Devil from the fire of his furnace. Brand silences his fear by telling him that he no longer has need of the Devil, who concerns himself only with such halfway sinners as Bartram. Finishing his chore with the fire, Brand announces that he has looked into human hearts hotter with illicit passions than the fiery furnace, but that he did not find the Unpardonable Sin there. In answer to Bartram's query as to what the Unpardonable Sin might be, Brand announces with pride born of madness,

> It is a sin that grew within my own breast. . . . A sin that grew nowhere else! The sin of an intellect that triumphed over the sense of brotherhood with man, and reverence for God, and sacrificed everything to its own mighty claims! The only sin that deserves a recompense of immortal agony! Freely, were it to do again, would I incur the guilt. Unshrinkingly, I accept the retribution!

Bartram is relieved by the appearance of the villagers, summoned by Joe's account of Brand's return. Brand meets again his old companions from the tavern, who implore him to join their pursuit of the black bottle "in which, as they averred, he would find something far better worth seeking for, than the Unpardonable Sin." Brand is offended by this offer of companionship and rejects their overtures with disdain, but not without momentary doubts that his life has been given to a delusion. The Doctor, spokesman for Brand's old tavern friends, tells him he is crazy—a fit companion for Old Humphrey.

Old Humphrey is a pathetic old man who wanders about the hills in search of his daughter, who is believed to have gone off with a circus. Confronting Brand, Humphrey asks if in all of his travels over the world he has seen the girl and if he knows when she is coming back.

> Ethan Brand's eye quailed beneath the old man's. That daughter, from whom he so earnestly desired a word of greeting, was the . . . very girl whom, with such cold and remorseless purpose, Ethan Brand had made the subject of a psychological experiment, and wasted, absorbed, and perhaps annihilated her soul. . . .

After this encounter with Humphrey, Brand's self-doubt vanishes and he concludes, "Yes . . . it is no delusion. There is an Unpardonable Sin!"

An old German Jew carrying a diorama now enters the scene. He amuses the crowd more by the shoddiness of his exhibit than its quality. When he has finished his show, he invites Brand to look into the box. After doing so, Brand claims to recognize the old man. When this mysterious figure complains that it was a hard task to carry the Unpardonable Sin over the mountain in his show box, Brand admonishes him either to be silent or "get thee into the furnace yonder," implying that this old Jew might be the Devil Brand once invoked from its fiery bowels. This strange scene ends with an ancient dog madly chasing its own tail to everyone's amusement. Brand, "moved, it might be, by a perception of some remote analogy between his own case and that of this self-pursuing cur . . . broke into the awful laugh, which . . . expressed the condition of his inward being."

The fun over, the crowd departs, leaving Brand alone again with Bartram and Joe. He sends them to bed, promising to tend the kiln while they rest. During the night, he recollects his earlier speculations by the fire that gradually turned him from reverence for humanity and pity for the human condition to his search for the Unpardonable Sin. As his intellect grew through isolated philosophical speculation, his heart failed to keep pace and gradually the Idea consumed his whole being. In Hawthorne's words, his heart "had withered—had contracted—had hardened—had perished. It had ceased to partake of the universal throb. He had lost his hold of the magnetic chain of humanity." Brand became a cold scientific observer of humanity, manipulating people to serve the needs of his experiments. "Thus Ethan Brand became a fiend. He began to be so from the moment that his moral nature had ceased to keep the pace of improvement with his intellect."

Having finally found in his own heart the Unpardonable Sin, Brand has no further purpose. Unable or unwilling to rejoin the "magnetic chain of humanity" that might offer him salvation, he chooses instead to consign his body to the flames of the furnace. When Bartram and Joe awaken next morning, they first believe that Ethan Brand has left, allowing the fire to burn down. When the old lime-burner opens the furnace, however, he sees in outline form, on top of the heap of burned marble, the skeleton of Ethan Brand. "Within the ribs—strange to say—was the shape of a human heart."

Themes and Meanings

Two of Nathaniel Hawthorne's recurrent themes are the violation of a human heart or soul and the tragic subordination of the heart or emotions to the intellect. "Ethan Brand" represents one of the most important expressions of these themes because it is in this story that Hawthorne identifies the Unpardonable Sin—the one sin man might commit for which he cannot be forgiven—as the destruction of another's soul. Ethan Brand is a philosopher-scientist, motivated only by his intellect. His heart has been so subordinated by his thirst for ultimate knowledge that he acts without regard for the sanctity of other people's beings: He is a man without conscience or human sympathy. Thus, while he sets out to find the Unpardonable Sin in the breast of others, whom he apparently manipulates into crimes through his experiments, it is finally in his own breast that he finds what he sought. His own ruthless behavior is the ultimate sin.

Brand himself is a recurrent type in Hawthorne's work. These scientist-philosopher figures—of whom the best known is Chillingworth in his novel *The Scarlet Letter* (1850)—are driven by a coldly empirical curiosity which, if not mitigated by human feeling, can drive them to a form of madness in which the Idea consumes their entire beings. No excess is then too great, no experiment beyond their scope in the pursuit of their goal to achieve ultimate knowledge. Like Ethan Brand, such figures are not bound by the natural sympathy that unites mankind.

Style and Technique

"Ethan Brand" is subtitled "A Chapter from an Abortive Romance," which may account for its fragmentary nature. More important, however, the subtitle is a reminder of Hawthorne's concept of the romance as a neutral ground where the worlds of reality and fantasy could meet in a dreamlike setting. Thus, against the prosaic world of New England lime-burning, which is presented in realistic detail, there is the story of Ethan Brand's search for the Unpardonable Sin accompanied by such Gothic elements as the old Jew, who seems a Devil figure, and the fantastic ending, which reveals Brand's heart of marble. It is this careful blending of the real and the fantastic that gives much of Hawthorne's work its unique flavor, and earns for him his reputation as America's greatest romancer.

William E. Grant

EVELINE

Author: James Joyce (1882-1941)
Type of plot: Naturalism
Time of plot: 1900
Locale: Dublin
First published: 1904

> *Principal characters:*
> EVELINE HILL, the central character, a nineteen-year-old
> Dublin shopgirl
> FRANK, her fiancé, a man who has seen the world and wants
> to take Eveline with him to Buenos Aires
> MR. HILL, her father, a drunk who forbids his daughter to see
> Frank
> HARRY HILL, her brother, in the church-decorating business

The Story

The story, a psychological study in frustration, is about a young woman who longs to escape from the tyranny of her father and from the responsibilities of surrogate motherhood, thrust upon her after the death of her own mother. When she is offered an avenue of escape, she discovers that she lacks the spirit, the courage, and the strength of character to take it.

Although only nineteen years old, Eveline Hill lives in the past, her mind occupied with the way things "used to be" as she sits by the window of her father's house. The world around her has changed, just as the neighborhood has changed. A land developer from Belfast has constructed brick houses on the field where "other people's children" used to play. One of the children who used to play there is now dead, and others have left the area; some have even left the country. Eveline remains. Her brother Ernest, who was "too grown up" to play, is now dead, as is her mother. Her father has turned to drink and is given to violence, particularly on Saturday nights.

Eveline works as a shopgirl at "the Stores," earning a miserable seven shillings a week, which are then given over to her father. She promised her dying mother that she would "keep the house together," rearing the two younger children and contending with her father's bad temper and the drinking that has worsened since her mother's death. She dreams of escaping the dull, routine existence that circumstances have forced on her.

Eveline meets a young man named Frank, who has sailed around the world and represents a means of escape for her. He wants to marry her and take her with him to Buenos Aires, halfway around the world from Ireland. Although she has accepted his offer of marriage and he has arranged her passage by ship, she has second thoughts on the day of her scheduled departure.

At first her misgivings at home are centered on a remembrance of her past, as she sits by the window, clutching the letters that she has prepared for her father and brother in order to explain her departure. At the end of the story, she discovers that she is in fact unwilling and unable to leave Ireland. She is a captive of the past; she has no future; finally, she cannot leave.

Themes and Meanings

If what Joyce intended to demonstrate in all the stories in *Dubliners* (1914) was the squalor and spiritual impoverishment of typical Irish lives, then "Eveline" is unquestionably in keeping with this general intent. Although still a young woman, Eveline dwells on the past, on the debilitating nostalgia of how things were when her mother was still alive and when her father was "not so bad." She takes solace in childhood memories, dwelling on playmates and siblings who are now either dead or gone. She cannot fully imagine a future away from her family, her neighborhood, or her nation, and when it comes time for her to take her life into her own hands, she is paralyzed and unable to act.

The theme of escape will be a familiar one for those who have read Joyce's semiautobiographical novel, *A Portrait of the Artist as a Young Man* (1916) or its earlier and even more personalized version, *Stephen Hero* (1944), written between 1904 and 1906 and ultimately published as a fragment after Joyce's death. "Eveline," also written in 1904, was inspired by one of the writer's neighbors when the Joyce family lived at 17 North Richmond Street in Dublin. Eveline Thornton, the daughter of Ned Thornton, fell in love with a sailor, whom she married and with whom she ultimately set up housekeeping in Dublin, according to Richard Ellmann, Joyce's biographer. Not only did the prototypical Eveline marry her sailor, but also her mother outlived her. Joyce was writing fiction, however, not biography, and the principal difference seems to be that the husband and wife who served as Joyce's models both ended up being trapped in Dublin.

Joyce turns the sailor into a romantic exile, one who has seen the world and has chosen to live far from Dublin. In other words, Frank in the story becomes a reflection of the young Joyce himself. For Joyce, any young Irishman had to choose between living a life of limited opportunity in Ireland and having to scale down one's expectations, adjusting to the dismal realities and traditions of Irish life, or going out into the world beyond Ireland, which Joyce saw as a world of opportunity and promise.

Buenos Aires, then, represents the ideal of escaping Ireland, of making a clean break with one's nation and family ties, the sort of break that Joyce's own wife, Nora, would make in 1904 when she left her family to go with the writer to Paris. Just as Joyce's *A Portrait of the Artist as a Young Man* romanticizes, with ironic embellishment, the escape of a young man from Ireland, so "Eveline" extends the theme of escape to the case of a young woman who is not nearly so sophisticated as the protagonist of Joyce's novel and who might understandably fear the unknown world that awaits her.

The plight that is described in this story, that of a young woman, over-worked and harried by her attempts to hold her family together, Joyce could have observed at home by watching his own long-suffering and tolerant mother, and by also observing the families of his friends and acquaintances. In the story, Eveline is relatively young but is "tired," worn down, old before her time, and very much a captive of routine, conditioned by her father's ty-rannical ways. She is offered a means of escape and self-fulfillment, but it is not in her nature, finally, to accept it. She is given a choice between life and a sort of metaphoric death, a new life abroad, or a living death in Ireland, tending after a dying family that, presumably, no longer needs her (even though her father, who is "becoming old," depends on her and for that rea-son "would miss her"), and working in a demeaning and subordinate position at "the Stores."

Style and Technique

"Eveline" is an example of naturalistic fiction in which the protagonist, described at one point as a "helpless animal," responds to internal anxieties and environmental forces, particularly the influences of family life and the responsibilities to which she has been conditioned, and of a working life in Ireland, with its impoverishment, as Joyce imagined it. The way that "Eve-line" and other stories of *Dubliners* reflect the details and concerns of every-day life closely observed and raised to significance through art suggests the influence of the Russian writer Anton Chekhov, but Ellmann notes in his biography *James Joyce* (1959) that Joyce claimed not to have read Chekhov at the time that he wrote those stories.

The purpose of Joyce's realistic fiction, however, was not simply the close observation of banal detail. The details are carefully crafted and arranged so as to accumulate in such a way as to give meaning to the story's climax, in keeping with the young writer's theory of the "epiphany." The progression is dramatic in Aristotelian terms, in that the central character is brought to a point of recognition and discovery, as suggested by Aristotle's *Poetics*. Eveline's self-discovery comes at the very end of the story. Her revelation is that she lacks the commitment and perhaps the courage to act on her dream of escape. When forced to choose between staying in Ireland and going to South America, she is also forced to confront her true feelings about Frank, who is "beyond the barrier" at that point, urging her to board the ship: "Her eyes gave him no sign of love or farewell or recognition." Eveline is reduced to a frightened, "helpless animal," as Joyce describes her at the end, who is incapable of exploring "another life with Frank."

James M. Welsh

AN EVENING PERFORMANCE

Author: George Garrett (1929-   )
Type of plot: Sketch
Time of plot: Mid-twentieth century
Locale: The rural Southern United States
First published: 1959

> *Principal characters:*
> STELLA, a high diver and a mute
> A LAME MAN, who accompanies her
> ANGEL, a young girl who accompanies Stella and the lame
> man
> A MERCHANT, a local man who sponsors Stella's performance

The Story

This brief story opens with a description of the promised performance: High atop a tower rising to the clouds stands a plump woman in a spangled bathing suit, poised to plunge into the flaming tub far below. Posters bearing this picture proclaim that "ONE OF THE FABULOUS WONDERS OF MODERN TIMES/ STELLA THE HIGH DIVER" will dive one hundred feet into a "FLAMING CAULDRON." The posters appear suddenly; some are torn down by grumbling citizens and policemen; a few remain for several weeks, silently enticing the residents of the quiet rural town.

Then, one cool and gray October evening, a battered truck parks at the local fairground, and a sagging army-surplus tent rises beside it. Three people have come in the truck: a limping man; a little girl named Angel, shining always in white and unbelievably clean; and a broad, sturdy, red-haired woman who smiles uncomprehendingly and speaks only with her hands. The man does his trading in the town, whose residents watch the family curiously for several days. One morning, the lame man begins to build what appears to be a drilling derrick on the center of the field. Local men gather to watch the stranger working furiously, and the local policeman asks what he is doing. Curtly, the lame man responds that he is building a tower for Stella's dive. Upon being told that he must purchase a twenty-five-dollar permit to produce an exhibition, the man falls still. As he prepares to admit defeat, a local merchant offers to buy the license for him in exchange for half the profits from ticket sales. The lame man grudgingly agrees and schedules the show for the following evening if the weather is good.

By midafternoon of the following day, the lame man has finished preparations for the evening's performance. Then, a wind rises, bringing rain; the tall, rickety tower sways in the wind. Yet wet weather does not keep away the crowd. At dark, a large crowd gathers in a ring around the tower, but Stella

refuses to carry out her dive. The merchant, when informed of her unwillingness, insists that she dive despite the risky conditions. Declaring that there
must be a trick to the dive, the merchant dismisses danger. The lame man
explains simply that the dive is no trick; it is quite dangerous, and Stella hates
doing it. Upon hearing this, the merchant asks in exasperation why they put
up posters, build towers, and sell tickets. Because someone must, is the lame
man's reply. The merchant gives him five minutes to begin the show.

The lame man turns on the lights around the tower, and Stella appears
before the crowd, walks to the foot of the tower, and takes hold of the rope
ladder. The lame man addresses the crowd, introducing the woman and
explaining that her performance is not magical or mysterious, but based on
skill; anyone with "the heart and the skill and the nerve" can do the same.
Stella's dive will be "proof of the boundless possibility of all mankind." She
climbs the rope ladder to the top of the tower and unfastens and tosses down
the rope. As the tower moves in the wind, she signals to the man, who lights
the gasoline on the water in the tub below. As he does so, she jumps. She
seems to hang gracefully in the air before sliding smoothly into the fiery
water. The crowd waits quietly, and she emerges from the water smiling and
unhurt. She returns to the tent, followed by the lame man and the merchant.
The merchant complains that the brief show seems hardly worth the fifty
cents each member of the crowd paid. The lame man responds that Stella's
risking her life ought to be enough for one evening; the crowd should be
pleased. After failing to change the lame man's mind, the merchant takes his
share of the profits and leaves. The crowd departs also.

The next day, all traces of the three strangers are gone, but the memory of
the evening performance haunts the small town long afterward. Preachers
denounce it, and storytellers embroider upon it. A crippled old man says that
it was bad for the people because it made them sophisticated, dissatisfied
with common marvels. Then the narrative voice, which has recounted only an
objective view until now, takes on omniscience and agrees with the old man,
who could not even imagine the dreams of unfortunate women now smilingly
dreaming of diving from a high tower into a pool of flame.

Themes and Meanings

The epigraph to George Garrett's short-story collection *In the Briar Patch*
(1961), in which "An Evening Performance" is the final story, contains two
scriptural passages, the first from Isaiah, and the second from Hebrews:

> We roar all like bears, and mourn sore like doves; we look for judgement, but
> there is none; for salvation, but it is far off from us.

> Let brotherly love continue.
> Be not forgetful to entertain strangers: for thereby some have entertained
> angels unawares.

Garrett, a Southern writer with a firm Christian understanding of the world, often deals with religious themes in his poetry, novels, and short stories. In "An Evening Performance," Garrett has combined the values of this Christian vision with the regional setting common to his earlier works to produce a short story with a parabolic quality.

The poster which appears at the beginning of the story heralds a coming wonder and is soon followed by the mysterious appearance of three strange travelers who remain curiously aloof from the townspeople. In appearance, the three are far from average: The man limps; the child with the beautifully pure features, Angel, is radiant in her starched white dress (kept oddly fresh and clean despite a nomadic existence); and the strange-looking woman cannot speak. They are not received kindly by the natives, who hinder and challenge them in their efforts to mount the performance.

The lame man's explanation of why he and Stella, despite her hatred of the dive, continue to travel and perform clearly points toward the lesson which Stella's dive holds: Someone must bring to the lives of ordinary people the possibility of great deeds. As the lame man tells the crowd, anyone—with courage and skill and will—can perform a feat such as Stella's. The merchant's petty reaction to Stella's performance indicates his misunderstanding of the value of life itself; in his obsession with the temporal, he cannot appreciate the spiritual. Still, the performance leaves its mark on the town. With a narrow vision typical of restrictive, organized religion, local ministers decry the strangers' show as the work of the Devil. The egocentric drunkards and tellers of tales use the performance as a backdrop for stories of themselves and thereby render themselves trivial.

One "wise man," notably a man with a physical deformity, dimly realizes the true nature of the performance; it was an occurrence which eclipsed the rest of life for the townspeople. No ordinary, safe marvels will satisfy them now. In the end, only the understanding narrator can point out the truly lasting effect of the performance; in their dreams, those who grow older and know no love may see themselves as capable of an act of greatness. The townspeople, like the speakers in the passage from Isaiah, look for judgment and salvation but cannot see the way to either. They have seen among them an Angel and did not understand what they saw. Some needful few, however, retain the vision of the performance; they sleep contentedly with the knowledge that they, too, possess those qualities which allowed Stella to dive gracefully from a great height into the lake of flame.

Style and Technique

Although "An Evening Performance" possesses enough development of plot and character to be classified as a short story rather than a vignette, it may be referred to fairly as a sketch. As the title indicates, the story focuses on a single event, one evening's performance; all delineation of characters, all lines of action lead toward the one moment which is the heart of the story. In pointing his reader toward that moment and the lesson contained in it, Garrett writes in the style of the poet that he is. He counters richly evocative language with sparely outlined action.

The story begins with the fiery image of the poster, and as time passes the image dims, "teased by the wind and weather, faded by the still summer-savaged sun and the first needling rains of autumn, the red letters blurring and dribbling away, fuzzy now as if they had been written by a shaking finger in something perishable like blood." When the three people suddenly appear in town, their images rise suddenly in the story, but the reader receives a description of them which seems merely physical, the recollected observations of a narrator who was witness to the scene. The characters remain nameless with the exception of the presciently named Stella (meaning "star") and Angel. Clearly, the reader must derive his understanding of the story's events from the descriptive details that the narrator supplies.

The performance itself is the point toward which the narrator is always working. The relating of the act takes only a few pages, but those few paragraphs contain more specifically recounted actions than any other part of the story. Following the performance, the narrator describes local reaction summarily and focuses on a detailed vision, which he projects into the imagination of faceless local women who possess true understanding of the performance's purpose. They see themselves descending in triumph from a "topless tower into a lake of flame."

Beverly A. Findley

EVERYDAY USE

Author: Alice Walker (1944-   )
Type of plot: Social realism
Time of plot: The late 1960's
Locale: Rural Georgia
First published: 1973

> *Principal characters:*
> THE NARRATOR, a middle-aged black woman
> MAGGIE, her younger daughter
> DEE, her older daughter
> DEE'S MALE COMPANION

The Story

"Everyday Use" is narrated by a woman who describes herself as "a large, big-boned woman with rough, man-working hands." She has enjoyed a rugged farming life in the country and now lives in a small, tin-roofed house surrounded by a clay yard in the middle of a cow pasture. She anticipates that soon her daughter Maggie will be married and she will be living peacefully alone.

The story opens as the two women await a visit from the older daughter, Dee, and a man who may be her husband—her mother is not sure whether they are actually married. Dee, who was always scornful of her family's way of life, has gone to college and now seems almost as distant as a film star; her mother imagines being reunited with her on a television show such as "This Is Your Life," where the celebrity guest is confronted with her humble origins. Maggie, who is not bright and who bears severe burn scars from a house fire many years before, is even more intimidated by her glamorous sibling.

To her mother's surprise, Dee arrives wearing an ankle-length, gold and orange dress, jangling golden earrings and bracelets, and hair that "stands straight up like the wool on a sheep." She greets them with an African salutation, while her companion offers a Muslim greeting and tries to give Maggie a ceremonial handshake that she does not understand. Moreover, Dee says that she has changed her name to Wangero Leewanika Kemanjo, because "I couldn't bear it any longer, being named after the people who oppress me." Dee's friend has an unpronounceable name, which the mother finally reduces to "Hakim-a-barber." As a Muslim, he will not eat the pork that she has prepared for their meal.

Whereas Dee had been scornful of her mother's house and possessions when she was younger (even seeming happy when the old house burned down), now she is delighted by the old way of life. She takes photographs of the house, including a cow that wanders by, and asks her mother if she may have the old butter churn whittled by her uncle; she plans to use it as a centerpiece for her table. Then her attention is captured by two old handmade quilts, pieced by Grandma Dee and quilted by the mother and her own sister, known as Big Dee. These quilts have already been promised to Maggie, however, to take with her into her new marriage. Dee is horrified: "Maggie can't appreciate these quilts!" she says, "She'd probably be backward enough to put them to everyday use."

Although Maggie is intimidated enough to surrender the beloved quilts to Dee, the mother feels a sudden surge of rebellion. Snatching the quilts from Dee, she offers her instead some of the machine-stitched ones, which Dee does not want. Dee turns to leave and in parting tells Maggie, "It's really a new day for us. But from the way you and Mama still live you'd never know it." Maggie and her mother spend the rest of the evening sitting in the yard, dipping snuff and "just enjoying."

Themes and Meanings

The central theme of the story concerns the way in which an individual understands his present life in relation to the traditions of his people and culture. Dee tells her mother and Maggie that they do not understand their "heritage," because they plan to put "priceless" heirloom quilts to "everyday use." The story makes clear that Dee is equally confused about the nature of her inheritance both from her immediate family and from the larger black tradition.

The matter of Dee's name provides a good example of this confusion. Evidently, Dee has chosen her new name ("Wangero Leewanika Kemanjo") to express solidarity with her African ancestors and to reject the oppression implied by the taking on of American names by black slaves. To her mother, the name "Dee" is symbolic of family unity; after all, she can trace it back to the time of the Civil War. To the mother, these names are significant because they belong to particular beloved individuals.

Dee's confusion about the meaning of her heritage also emerges in her attitude toward the quilts and other household items. While she now rejects the names of her immediate ancestors, she eagerly values their old handmade goods, such as the hand-carved benches made for the table when the family could not afford to buy chairs. To Dee, artifacts such as the benches or the quilts are strictly aesthetic objects. It never occurs to her that they, too, are symbols of oppression: Her family made these things because they could not afford to buy them. Her admiration for them now seems to reflect a cultural trend toward valuing handmade objects, rather than any sincere interest in her "heritage." After all, when she was offered a quilt before she went away to college, she rejected it as "old-fashioned, out of style."

Yet a careful reading of the story will show that Dee is not the only one confused about the heritage of the black woman in the rural South. Although the mother and Maggie are skeptical of Dee, they recognize the limitations of their own lives. The mother has only a second-grade education and admits that she cannot imagine looking a strange white man in the eye. Maggie "knows she is not bright" and walks with a sidelong shuffle. Although their dispositions lead them to make the best of their lives, they admire Dee's fierce pride even as they feel the force of her scorn.

Taken as a whole, while the story clearly endorses the commonsense perspective of Dee's mother over Dee's affectations, it does not disdain Dee's struggle to move beyond the limited world of her youth. Clearly, however, she has not yet arrived at a stage of self-understanding. Her mother and sister are ahead of her in that respect.

Style and Technique

The thematic richness of "Everyday Use" is made possible by the flexible, perceptive voice of the first-person narrator. It is the mother's point of view which permits the reader's understanding of both Dee and Maggie. Seen from a greater distance, both young women might seem stereotypical—one a smart but ruthless college girl, the other a sweet but ineffectual homebody. The mother's close scrutiny redeems Dee and Maggie, as characters, from banality.

For example, Maggie's shyness is explained in terms of the terrible fire she survived: "Sometimes I can still hear the flames and feel Maggie's arms sticking to me, her hair smoking and her dress falling off her in little black papery flakes. Her eyes seemed stretched open, blazed open by the flames reflected in them." Ever since, "she has been like this, chin on chest, eyes on ground, feet in shuffle." In Dee's case, the reader learns that, as she was growing up the high demands she made of others tended to drive people away. She had few friends, and her one boyfriend "*flew* to marry a cheap city girl from a family of ignorant flashy people" after Dee "turned all her faultfinding power on him." Her drive for a better life has cost Dee dearly, and her mother's commentary reveals that Dee, too, has scars, though they are less visible than Maggie's.

In addition to the skillful use of point of view, "Everyday Use" is enriched by Alice Walker's development of symbols. In particular, the contested quilts become symbolic of the story's theme; in a sense, they represent the past of the women in the family. Worked on by two generations, they contain bits of fabric from even earlier eras, including a scrap of a Civil War uniform worn by Great Grandpa Ezra. The debate over how the quilts should be treated— used or hung on the wall—summarizes the black woman's dilemma about how to face the future. Can her life be seen as continuous with that of her ancestors? For Maggie, the answer is yes. Not only will she use the quilts, but also she will go on making more—she has learned the skill from Grandma

Dee. For Dee, at least for the present, the answer is no. She would frame the quilts and hang them on the wall, distancing them from her present life and aspirations; to put them to everyday use would be to admit her status as a member of her old-fashioned family.

Diane M. Ross

EVERYTHING THAT RISES MUST CONVERGE

Author: Flannery O'Connor (1925-1964)
Type of plot: Tragicomic realism
Time of plot: The 1950's
Locale: The urban South
First published: 1961

> *Principal characters:*
> JULIAN CHESTNY, the protagonist, a self-centered young man
> MRS. CHESTNY, Julian's mother
> A BLACK WOMAN AND CHILD, bus passengers

The Story

A middle-aged working woman, the remnant of a once aristocratic, slave-holding family, prepares to go to her Y.W.C.A. exercise class, recommended for her high blood pressure. She insists that her son accompany her on the bus, for she is afraid to ride the buses alone as they have become integrated. The young man, superficially educated in liberal ideas, is contemptuous of her racial bigotry and fancies himself vastly more enlightened and intellectual than she.

As the story opens, she is undecided as to whether she should wear the new green hat with the purple velvet flaps she has recently bought or take it back to the store. After all, that seven dollars and fifty cents would pay the gas bill. Julian, her son, whose viewpoint dominates the story, thinks the hat is hideous; nevertheless, he insists that she wear it to expedite their departure. His mother, still doubtful, says that at least she will not "meet herself coming and going"; that is, the hat establishes her uniqueness, as befits a lady of quality. The hat attains symbolic importance as an emblem of her true station in life when, much to her son's amusement, a huge black woman boards the bus with her small son and plops down in the seat facing her. The black woman is wearing the exact duplicate of his mother's absurd hat. Julian exults at this magnificent put-down, even though his mother's red face suggests a sudden rise in blood pressure.

His mother, however, seems to recover. She makes up to the little boy, with that peculiar combination of condescension and sentimentality that considers all small black children adorable. The black woman fairly bristles with suppressed anger as the dumpy little white woman fumbles in her purse for a nickel. Nemesis arrives when both women leave the bus and Julian's mother, unable to find a nickel, offers the boy a bright new penny. The black woman explodes with anger and swings at the white woman with her purse, knocking her down. Julian self-righteously berates his mother for her stupidity and insensitivity, even as she sits stricken on the pavement. His superiority and exasperation quickly crumble to infantile panic, however, when his mother shortly after dies of a stroke on the sidewalk.

Themes and Meanings

This tragicomic tale of social bigotry and fake liberal sentiment is the title story of Flannery O'Connor's last collection of short stories, written before her untimely death at the age of thirty-nine. It displays the author's unique talent for ironic social commentary and grim humor.

With her consummate skill at revealing ordinary people with small minds, she reduces some of the traditional ingredients of Southern fiction to the miniature, without sacrificing an iota of their reality. Generational conflict, racial confrontation, sudden death—they are all there, but stripped bare of any aura of honor and glory, displaying themselves either as tawdry and mean-spirited or as absurdly comic.

In spite of Mrs. Chestny's mental and moral limitations, she is a more sympathetic character than her son, and not simply because she, in one sense, dies for her sin of racial bigotry. Unlike her son, she entertains her mindless notions of social superiority without a trace of actual hypocrisy. She truly believes that she is a member of the upper classes, even as she endures and indeed enjoys her thoroughly middle-class struggle to make her own living and put her callow young prince through college. She has absorbed the middle-class work ethic as unconsciously as she internalized her forebears' pride of family, quite unaware of any contradiction of values. Moreover, before she dies, her stroke wipes out her adult memory and she resumes the innocence of childhood, perhaps an indication, if one considers O'Connor's predilection for themes of redemption, of a wiping out of sin along with memory.

Julian, on the other hand, pretends to the most enlightened democratic attitudes toward blacks, but has no real sympathy or understanding for them. He tries to show his intellectual sophistication by striking up conversations with prosperous looking blacks on the bus, a familiarity usually resented by the recipients of his unwanted attention. He does not realize that his behavior is probably perceived as being as condescending as his mother's giving pennies to black children. He daydreams of offering the ultimate insult to his mother by bringing home a beautiful black girl to marry. Indeed, most of his shallow liberality seems to stem from his resentment of his mother and the fact that they are poor.

Although his mother may chatter on complacently about the aristocratic old home of her childhood, it is Julian who looks back with longing to that time when birth, instead of personal effort, luck, character, or ability, established social status. Suspecting, correctly, that he has none of these qualities, he doubts that he can ever compete in a world where idle luxury is not his birthright.

O'Connor's stories are sometimes like Elizabethan secondary plots that provide comic relief for tragedy. The lowlife reenacts in miniature the sins of the tragic hero, such as Wagner dabbling irresponsibly in magic as his master, Dr. Faustus, consigns his soul to the Devil.

The title comes from the Catholic philosopher Pierre Teilhard de Chardin, whom O'Connor admired. Teilhard de Chardin based his thought on the conception of evolution as the emergence and perfecting of consciousness. As consciousness becomes more clear in individuals, it projects itself toward some hypothetical maximum development which Teilhard de Chardin called the Omega point. Everything that rises in consciousness must converge in spiritual terms as it approaches nearer the Omega point, which is presumably the end of time. Teilhard de Chardin was trying to avoid a simple pantheistic mysticism in which individual egos simply dissolved again into the impersonal stuff of the universe. The superconsciousness developing at the Omega point is greater than its parts without extinguishing the consciousness of individual selves.

The implications of O'Connor's story are ambiguous with regard to Teilhard de Chardin's conception. One might argue that this ridiculous encounter between a person rising to the middle class and one sinking from aristocracy to that class has only comic overtones, suggesting the not especially lofty homogeneity of the new social order in the South. In this sense, the story may be a parody of Teilhard de Chardin's principle of spiritual convergence in the universe.

Considering O'Connor's propensities for religious themes, however, one suspects that she is suggesting some blundering advancement of consciousness even in such unlikely candidates for wisdom as these. Ironically, in the aging white woman, such purification of soul requires the wholesale wiping out of a lifetime of misinformation about social status and the basis of personal worth. What is left after her stroke is certainly a very immature soul, but one relieved of accumulated error. Meanwhile, her son is forced into the world of guilt and sorrow where he might outgrow his selfishness and accept responsibility for his destiny. This possibility for growth is all that O'Connor usually allows to her sadly human protagonists. She does not concern herself with saints.

Style and Technique

Besides the creation of unusual symbols, such as the grotesque hat with one purple flap up and the other down, suggesting the social direction of the wearers, O'Connor is a master of dramatic irony. A paragraph of Julian's internal monologue characterizes not only Mrs. Chestny but also the jaded young man himself, who despises his mother for her unreal expectations and blames her for a social situation in which she must sacrifice herself for his welfare:

She lived according to the laws of her own fantasy world, outside of which he had never seen her set foot. The law of it was to sacrifice herself for him after she had first created the necessity to do so by making a mess of things. If he had permitted her sacrifices, it was only because her lack of foresight had made them necessary. All of her life had been a struggle to act like a Chestny without the Chestny goods, and to give him everything she thought a Chestny ought to have; but since, said she, it was fun to struggle, why complain? And when you had won, as she had won, what fun to look back on the hard times! He could not forgive her that she had enjoyed the struggle and that she thought she had won.

Julian congratulates himself that he has cut himself emotionally free of his mother, as though filial love were some kind of character flaw. He also prides himself on his ability to face facts. His monumental ignorance and immaturity are swiftly brought to a climax in a few sentences, rapidly changing his mode of discourse to one characteristic of childhood. When his mother has a stroke, Julian finds himself "looking into a face he has never seen before."

"Mother!" he cried. "Darling, sweetheart, wait!" Crumpling, she fell to the pavement. He dashed forward and fell at her side, crying, "Mamma, Mamma!" He turned her over. Her face was fiercely distorted. One eye, large and staring, moved slightly to the left as if it had become unmoored. The other remained fixed on him, raked his face again, found nothing and closed.

Only moments before, he had been flippantly lecturing his mother from his pose of wisdom: "From now on you've got to live in a new world and face a few realities for a change. Buck up . . . it won't kill you."

Katherine Snipes

AN EXPERIMENT IN MISERY

Author: Stephen Crane (1871-1900)
Type of plot: Tale
Time of plot: 1894
Locale: The Bowery section of New York
First published: 1894

> *Principal characters:*
> A YOUNG MAN, the protagonist
> THE "ASSASSIN," his companion

The Story

Late one rainy night, a shabbily dressed young man trudges along a New York street taunted by voices calling him a bum. As he reaches City Hall Park, he seeks companionship but spots only well-dressed people on their way home. Moving on to Chatham Square, where the pedestrians' clothes match his "tatters," he sees a saloon sign which advertises "Free hot soup tonight." Moving through its swinging doors, which snap "to and fro like ravenous lips," the youth is served a schooner of frothy beer and a bowl of watery chicken broth. Turning down a second helping, he returns to the street to search for cheap lodging.

The youth is making inquiries with a seedy-looking man when along comes a bushy-haired drunk who appears "like an assassin steeped in crimes performed awkwardly." His eyes have a guilty slant and his lips look as though they have just consumed "some tender and piteous morsel." When he begins begging for some money, the seedy man tells him to "go t' hell," but the youth agrees to give him a few pennies in exchange for finding them inexpensive accommodations.

The "assassin" leads them to a seven-cent dive, a foul-odored den which reminds the youth of a graveyard "where bodies were merely flung." Inside the gloomy room, the faint flame of a gas jet casts ominous shadows. Putting his derby and shoes in a tall locker resembling a mummy case, the youth lies down on a cold cot next to a man who is so still that he might be taken for a corpse. Across the room, his companion is sprawled on his back, snoring through a bulbous nose that shines "like a red light in a fog." Throughout the night, the youth is kept awake by shrieks and moans, the melancholy dirge of a forgotten underclass. The morning rays of the sun produce a cacophony of curses, snorts, and gruff banter. Naked men parade about casually, looking like "chiefs" until they put on their ragged clothes, which exaggerate their deformities.

Out on the street, the youth offers to buy the assassin something to eat at a run-down basement restaurant whose sign reads "No mystery about our hash!" Six cents purchases two coffees and rolls. While they are eating, the assassin launches into an "intricate, incoherent" personal tale of suffering at the hands of his father and various bosses. Meanwhile, the proprietor prevents an old man from leaving because he is carrying a tiny package of food. "B'Gawd, we've been livin' like kings," the assassin chortles after breakfast. "Look out, or we'll have t' pay for it t'-night," the youth replies.

The two companions make their way to a bench at City Hall Park. Watching people hurrying to their morning destinations reminds the youth of the huge gulf between his present plight and "all that he valued." Guiltily, he pulls down his hat, feeling like a criminal. A babble of tongues roars heedlessly, and behind him multistoried buildings cast their pitiless hues. They seem "emblematic of a nation forcing its regal head into the clouds, throwing no downward glances . . . [at] the wretches who may flounder at its feet."

Themes and Meanings

The point of the story is that the misery of poverty is so immobilizing that victims do not have the will to overcome their wretchedness. Crane is elusive on the issue of cause and effect: whether the poor are responsible for their fate or are merely tragic pawns in an immutable world. The experimenter rapidly sinks into a state of "profound dejection," concluding finally that "there no longer could be pleasure in life." Misery loves company, as the saying goes, and the youth feels like an outcast among the well-dressed and purposeful, preferring the company of those who trudge aimlessly, stare dolefully, loiter patiently, get swallowed up by the saloon, and heave on flophouse cots like "stabbed fish."

Misery also breeds passivity, but there are exceptions such as the little pudgy fellow who curses like a fishwife and the enigmatic "assassin" whose gestures are awkward but extravagant. Claiming to be a gentleman "down on his luck," he begs for coppers in a coaxing voice which resembles that of an affectionate puppy. The youth's handout makes his countenance "radiant with joy." On his cot he snores with "incredible vigor," his wet hair and beard glistening and his nose shining "with subdued luster." Liquor clouds his memory and makes him, at times, incoherent, but a warm breakfast puts a red grin on his face and leads him to declare that "we've been livin' like kings." In his limping step is a "suggestion of lamblike gambols." Unmindful of the youth's warning that they have to hustle to survive the next night, the assassin refuses "to turn his gaze toward the future."

During the 1890's, proper society considered the poor to be a criminal element. Ironically, the youth accepts this indictment as he surveys the bustling crowd from his bench and pulls down the rim of his derby. The refuse of a success-oriented society, the poor lacked motivation or ambition. Their crime was resignation. In Crane's concluding line, the young man's eyes take on a "criminal expression that comes from certain convictions."

"An Experiment in Misery" underscores how wide a gulf existed between the rich and the poor. Behind the park are awesome, shadowy skyscrapers. Streetcars rumble along softly "as if going upon carpet stretched in the aisle made by the pillars of the elevated road."

Crane examines the culture of poverty by describing four haunts visited by the youth: the saloon, the flophouse, the hash house, and the park bench. Most alluring is the saloon, with its delectable advertisement, ravenous swinging doors, frothy schooners of beer, and bewhiskered host dispensing soup "like a priest behind the altar." In contrast, the lodging house is a nightmarish morgue, with unholy odors and demoniac wails, causing the sleepless protagonist to "lay carving biographies for these men from his meager experience." The careworn restaurant has coffee bowls "webbed with brown seams" and tin spoons "bent and scarred from the attack of long forgotten teeth." The final resting place is "sanctified by traditions" and leads the youth to see himself inexorably as one with a class of people cut off from the blessings of the world.

Style and Technique

Stephen Crane has been hailed as America's first modern writer, whose tough-minded realism and symbolic impressionism broadened the parameters of twentieth century fiction. His literary career resembled the passing of a comet, brief but brilliant. His first important work, *Maggie: A Girl of the Streets* (1893), had a motif similar to that of "An Experiment in Misery." Despite its lack of commercial success, Crane began work on *The Red Badge of Courage: An Episode of the American Civil War* (1895), which would bring him international acclaim. The previous year, however, at the time he wrote "An Experiment in Misery," he was a struggling journalist trying to persuade editors to publish his work. The country was in the midst of a depression, and Crane himself was frequently without funds. For the sake of research he even stayed in a flophouse and stood in breadlines; the latter experience inspired an article called "Men in the Storm."

"An Experiment in Misery," like others of Crane's tales of Bowery life, uses an impressionistic style to depict a milieu which is hostile and incomprehensible. The story was first published in the *New York Press* with an explanatory introduction and conclusion which Crane later deleted when it was published in *The Open Boat and Other Tales of Adventure* (1898). In the original introduction, the youth tells an older friend that he wants to discover the point of view of the tramp by living like one: "Rags and tatters, you know, a couple of dimes, and hungry, too, if possible." At the end, the youth reports that while he did not discover the tramp's point of view, "mine own has undergone a considerable alteration."

By deleting the introduction and coda, Crane heightened the story's gloomy mood and its sense of mystery and dread. The youth becomes virtually an outcast, not merely an extension of the narrator. For Crane, realism went far beyond journalistic accuracy. He left to reporters such as Jacob August Riis the task of depicting the poor in *How the Other Half Lives* (1890). He used imagery, color, and symbolism to evoke the culture of poverty. Sherwood Anderson claimed that the impact of Crane's style was like an explosion and that his Bowery sketches were the outpouring of an individualist who felt with every nerve within him.

The most puzzling aspect of "An Experiment in Misery" is the character of the young man. Is he in the Bowery as an experiment or as a victim of nature's fate? In the story's original form, the narrator deliberately dons the identity of a Bowery denizen. Without the prologue and epilogue, Crane leaves the issue unresolved, and the tone of doom is more palpable, although not totally unrelieved.

The shortened form gives rise to a metaphysical interpretation: the young man as pilgrim passing through baptism (saloon scene), Original Sin (flophouse scene), Holy Communion (breakfast scene), and Judgment Day (park bench). Perhaps Crane intended to suggest a parody of the doctrine of predestination. Whatever the case, the shortened form of the story is more powerful than the original. Its technique better reflects the author's naturalistic underpinnings.

James B. Lane

THE FACES OF BLOOD KINDRED

Author: William Goyen (1915-1983)
Type of plot: Domestic realism
Time of plot: c. 1920-1950
Locale: Houston, Texas, and an unnamed Midwestern city
First published: 1952

Principal characters:
THE COUSIN, a sensitive, compassionate, melancholy member
of a large Texas family
JAMES, a wild, mysterious, lonely boy who lives briefly with
his cousin

The Story

"The Faces of Blood Kindred" focuses on the relationship between the protagonist and his cousin James, and on two particular incidents which had a deeply felt and lasting effect on the protagonist. The lives of these two boys are shaped by and characteristic of the larger life of their wandering and suffering extended family. The mystery and profundity of blood ties and the essential sadness of human life are two of William Goyen's primary concerns here and throughout his fiction.

Their story begins as James is coming to stay with the protagonist, who is referred to simply as "the cousin" (both boys are fourteen years old). James's father ran away long ago, and his mother, crippled by arthritis, is hospitalized and unable to care for him. The two boys have little in common other than "their mysterious cousinhood, a bond of nature which they instinctively respected." The cousin is timid, obedient, naïve, and sensitive; James, a "faintly hairlipped" stutterer who had owned and loved fighting cocks, is "wild," "mysterious, wandering," and fiercely independent. In spite of their differences, the boys get along well. James tolerates his cousin's timid and fearful nature with tender disdain; the cousin idolizes James for his daring and experience and pities him for his loneliness and isolation.

One afternoon at James's suggestion, the boys go to a farm at the edge of the city to look at some Cornish fighting cocks raised, trained, bought, and sold (illegally) by a roosterlike man named Chuck. The cousin, drawn by the illicit excitement of the venture, agrees to come, though he is afraid and feels guilty because he "stole away" and "did not tell his mother." The cousin's anxiety and awe increase when James counts out fifteen dollars to purchase a "big blue cock with stars on its breast." He is afraid that they will get into trouble at home, that James will have no place to keep the cock. James assures him that he has a place for the bird, and they hitchhike back to town and go to their grandmother's great, rambling house, where James intends to hide the cock for a night.

The big, old, rotting house of the grandmother is filled with members of the family and appears to be a desolate place full of human misery, chaos, frustration, and waste. The cries of Aunt Beatrice seem to give voice to the collective pain and need of the whole various clan: "Somebody! Please help me, I am so sick." Behind this old house is a small grove of fig trees which conceals "a secret place, a damp and musky cove" known only to the children of the house. James intends to keep his new cock in the dark security of this grove for the night. The bird escapes from his grasp, however, and springs into a fig tree; James shakes the tree violently in an effort to get the bird back. The cousin, overexcited by the disconcerting events of the day, concerned that James will "ruin Granny's figs," and terrified of being caught or getting home too late, panics and hurls a stone at the cock, the embodiment of his anxiety. To his surprise and horror, his aim is true, and the Cornish cock falls at James's feet. The cousin retreats beyond the deep shadow of the tree and watches in despair as he sees James "fall to the ground and kneel over his Cornish cock" and hears him "sob softly." The cousin walks away from his grandmother's house, leaving James and the dead cock under the fig trees. He is overwhelmed by the grief he has caused and by the suffering in the dark house. He cannot understand how his admiration and affection for James could have yielded such agony, or why there seems to be "a doom of suffering over the house of his kinfolks." In his naïveté, he believes that he will understand one day, and he resolves to try "one day [to] save all his kindred from pain or help them to some hope." He returns home to "the benevolent figure of his mother in the kitchen fixing supper." James does not come back, though; he runs away to St. Louis and seeks out his father, whom he has not seen in seven years.

Years later, the cousins see each other once again. The cousin, having attained a measure of success in life, is in a large Midwestern city where he is being honored for his achievements. James appears in the hall and moves forward through the crowd: "There was something James had to say, it was on his face." The cousin is drawn away momentarily to receive the congratulations of some dignitary, and when he turns with trepidation to face James, "to look back into the face of his own secret sorrow, James was gone; and the cousins never met again." This final, failed encounter forces the cousin to shed whatever illusions he has managed to hold on to about his having "answered any speechless question, atoned for the blind failing, the outrage, and the pain on the face of his blood kindred." Man's essential isolation, his inability to communicate, the emptiness of public life, the inadequacies of love, are all borne home on the adult cousin in this moment. He carries from that instant a wound deeper and more painful than the one he opened so many years before on the night he accidently killed the big blue cock.

Themes and Meanings

As the title suggests, "The Faces of Blood Kindred" is concerned with the enigmatic nature of blood relationships. Ancestry and family ties are of particular interest to William Goyen (and many other Southern writers) and form a recurrent motif in his fiction. Other themes which are present here and throughout his work include human isolation, the oxymoronic nature of man and experience (spirit and flesh, good and bad, and so on), and the poverty of modern life.

Goyen's interest in blood kindred takes two forms here: In the foreground is the relationship between James and the cousin, and in the background is the large and diverse family which surrounds them. The boys' family, the dark, teeming life of the grandmother's house as well as the various family members in other cities, is a microcosm of the human family; its variety (its pain, fragmentation, and confusion) is representative of the rich complexity of human life. The story of the cousin and James is clearly but one story among the many; the failed effort of the two boys to give voice to their deep and mysterious sense of connection, to manifest the tenderness, loneliness, and hope of their secret lives, is characteristic of the flawed endeavor of all human beings. The depiction of each of the boys is quite touching, and their inability to establish an open and loving relationship is poignant, especially when it becomes clear, as it does in the end, that adults are generally less hopeful, less vulnerable, less atuned to love or mystery than are children. James's rigidity in the presence of his dying mother, his inability to speak without stuttering, and his fierce love for his fighting cocks all suggest that he is a lonely and passionate youth, full of love, confusion, anger, and need. The cousin is acutely sensitive to the suffering around him and has an instinctive desire to help his kinfolk, to make their lives better, yet he is unable to redeem his people from their misery.

The dual nature of experience and humanity is stressed in "The Faces of Blood Kindred." The cousins are clearly representative of the conflicting element in the human composition: James is fair, inarticulate, isolated, wild, and passionate; the cousin is dark, well-spoken, loved, obedient, and timid.

The isolation of people is everywhere apparent in this story, not only in the delineation of the cousins but in the rendering of their family as well. Perhaps the central image of loneliness here is that of the aged grandmother abandoned by her husband, deaf, sitting in her rocking chair alone and ignored in the midst of her family. The impersonal and sterile quality of modern life is also apparent here. Fay, who works in a shop selling ready-to-wear clothing, is married to her third husband, a listless, violent sailor. Suffering family members are relegated to hospitals and nursing homes; the city is alien and unfriendly to James; and the public life of the successful cousin is empty and unrewarding.

This story, like numerous others of Goyen's tales, has a strongly autobiographical flavor; one last characteristic note which it sounds is a longing for the ability to help others, particularly one's family, to make life more beautiful and more loving. The child resolves to "one day save all his kindred from pain or help them to some hope"; the grown man has no illusions about the possibility of success in such a task but is nevertheless committed to it. All of Goyen's fiction seems an effort to restore and redeem the human family.

Style and Technique

"The Faces of Blood Kindred," in spite of being fairly specifically located in time and space, has a mythic quality. The quiet voice of the omniscient narrator, the namelessness of the "cousin," the phrase "blood kindred," and the "unnamed" city, all serve to give this story a universal dimension. The experiences of the cousin speak to all people who have questioned the unfairness of life and striven to help their fellowmen.

One of Goyen's characteristic techniques is evident in this tale. Although he focuses on particular figures, here James and the cousin, Goyen makes one aware of the rich texture of life around these central figures which both frames and shapes them. It is as if there were a baroque symphony playing quietly in the background and a romantic concerto based on the same basic themes and motifs playing in the foreground. The music is communal, even universal; the symphony never ceases though particular melodies may fade into silence.

Many of Goyen's stories, like "The Faces of Blood Kindred," do not conclude in a conventional sense; they simply end. Like music, they are not quite understandable. One is left with a sense of melancholy, perhaps a sense of longing. Goyen does not believe in simple and complete resolutions. The cousin faces deeper and more perplexing questions at the close of the story than he did as a child.

Hal Holladay

FAITH IN A TREE

Author: Grace Paley (1922-   )
Type of plot: Cultural satire
Time of plot: The late 1960's, during the Vietnam War
Locale: A neighborhood playground in New York
First published: 1967

Principal characters:

FAITH ASBURY, the protagonist, who is up in a tree in a
    playground
RICHARD and
ANTHONY (TONTO), her sons, aged nine and six years,
    respectively
MRS. JUNIUS FINN, Faith's neighbor
KITTY SKAZKA, Faith's closest friend, an unmarried woman
    with several children
ANNA KRAAT, another friend, a beautiful woman with a bad
    character
ALEX O. STEELE, formerly an organizer of tenant strikes, now
    a businessman
RICARDO, Faith's former husband, an explorer and writer
PHILLIP MAZZANO, an attractive man, formerly Kitty's lover
DOUGLAS, a police officer

The Story

Faith Asbury is perched in a tree in a neighborhood playground in New
York although she would prefer to be out in the "man-wide" world or with a
"brainy companion" who could speak to her "of undying carnal love." Below
her, under the tree, are her children, Richard and Anthony. Scores of other
neighborhood children, "terrible seedlings," watched over by their mothers,
swarm about the playground: "Among the trees, in the arms of statues, toes
in the grass, they hopped in and out of dog shit and dug tunnels into mole
holes." There are also men in the park, "young Saturday fathers," and older
fathers, holding the hands of the young children of "a third intelligent marriage." Several characters stop under Faith's tree to chat with her.

As Faith mulls over her past and tries to think about her future, and as
passing characters stop to speak with her, the reader learns that Faith had
been married to Ricardo, who is now in an unspecified exotic country, presumably living with a younger woman who "acts on her principles" the way
Faith had once done. The reader also learns that Faith was reared in a Jewish, socially conscious family, that she has an unfulfilling job by which she

supports her children, and that she really does not know what to do next in her life. Faith is also "up a tree" concerning her beliefs. She notes that

> My vocabulary is adequate for writing notes and keeping journals but absolutely useless for an active moral life. If I really knew this language, there would surely be in my head, as there is in Webster's or the *Dictionary of American Slang*, that unreducible verb designed to tell a person like me what to do next.

Faith leaves her perch briefly to flirt with Phillip Mazzano, an attractive man who was once the lover of Kitty Skazka, Faith's best friend. Formerly a teacher and later with the State Department, he now wants to become a comedian. He forms an instant rapport with Richard, Faith's elder son. Faith, however, returns to her tree limb when Phillip appears to be more interested in beautiful Anna Kraat, another friend who is "not interested in anything."

Up to this point in the story, there has been little or no action: Faith, static in her tree, the others playing or lounging below it. A new group now enters the park, a group composed of men, women, and children together. The children are banging pots and pans, and the adults carry three posters. The first poster, showing a picture of a man and a child, poses the question, "WOULD YOU BURN A CHILD?" The next poster depicts the man putting a burning cigarette to the child's arm and gives the answer, "WHEN NECESSARY." The third poster, carrying no words, shows a napalmed Vietnamese baby "seared, scarred, with twisted hands." The group seems to impose an automatic silence on the others in the playground.

Douglas, a police officer, tries to remove the antiwar protesters, who stop, regroup, and continue their march more sedately, discarding the wooden poster handles to which Douglas has objected. When Anthony, Faith's younger child, protests against Douglas' interference with the antiwar group, the policeman answers, "Listen Tonto, there's a war on. You'll be a soldier too someday. I know you're no sissy like some kids around here. You'll fight for your country." Richard angrily rebels against Douglas, as well as against Faith and the other passive onlookers: "I hate you. I hate your stupid friends. Why didn't they just stand up to that stupid cop." He then writes the question and answer on the sidewalk, using bright red chalk: "WOULD YOU BURN A CHILD? WHEN NECESSARY." Richard's pain and anger over such apathy in the face of cruelty bring Faith to a sudden realization of her place and purpose in life. From this point onward, she moves "out of that sexy playground" and into the world again.

Themes and Meanings

"Faith in a Tree," like many other Grace Paley stories, has, as principal characters, divorced or unwed mothers who tend their children in parks and playgrounds while waiting to find a man who will deliver them from their stymied lives. Forming a counterpoint to these characters are the more bourgeois, financially successful (usually male) characters who sacrifice emotional honesty in order to achieve respectability.

Early in the story, the reader learns that Faith was reared to believe in a "sensible, socialist, Zionist world of the future," destined, as an American child, to be independent and free. Instead, her "lumpen time" and her "bourgeois feelings" are spent caring for her children. Clearly, Faith, like many middle-class children who came of age in the 1960's, was meant for better things. Now, in every sense, she finds herself "up a tree." The people who find themselves with her in the playground are in no better position, although they try to give her advice: Alex O. Steele tells her to "speak clearly, Faith, you're garbling like you used to"; Mrs. Finn cautions, "You answer too much, Faith Asbury, and it shows"; Kitty worries, "Faith, you'll fall out of the tree, calm yourself"; even nine-year-old Richard cries, "Faith, will you quit with your all-the-time philosophies."

The other characters in the playground also seem to be stymied, going nowhere. Steele had once organized tenant strikes. Now he works in the East Fifties (it is unclear exactly what he now does, but he seems to have exchanged his former principles for financial success); Phillip Mazzano, who had once been a teacher and then worked for the State Department, now claims to "make a living. Here. Chicago. Wherever I am. I'm not in financial trouble." He now has aspirations of becoming a comedian, although he is "not funny." Faith's friend, Kitty, who has several children and many former lovers (Phillip is one, and another is also in the playground, selling marijuana), "has made one mistake after another." Anna, although beautiful, has a bad character and is not interested in anything.

That Faith and the other characters find themselves in a playground is a clear reference to the fact that she, and they, are not living their true lives and have not entered the real world. The adults, like the children, are still playing. They are forming liaisons, they are enjoying music, they are climbing trees. When the small group of protesters enters the playground, it is as though the children, banging on the pots and pans, have startled Faith—and, one would hope, some of the others—into attention. They, like Faith's children, give Faith the impetus to leave her limb and reenter life, to be where she can meet "women and men in different lines of work, whose minds were made up and directed out of that sexy playground." Further, that impetus is offered by Faith's children's " heartfelt brains," the necessary combination of reason and emotion, which leads to action. In this sense, it is the children, the "seedlings," who bring back a feeling of faith to the protagonist and, by extension, the other members of Faith's generation.

Style and Technique

Paley uses the first-person point of view in this story, allowing the reader to see the playground and the characters in it from her perspective, which, throughout most of the story, is several feet off the ground. The protagonist is thus "above it all," allowing her to be fairly objective about the other characters, but unable to be really part of the life of the playground: She has not yet come down to earth. The reader is brought to epiphany along with Faith, descending, with her, from the branches and back into the world.

Language is an extremely important factor in Paley's stories. The various ethnic idioms of New York City and the rich use of the vernacular add life and texture to her works. Language is also an important metaphor in the story. Faith is looking for the right vocabulary, the "unreducible verb" that will tell her "what to do next." The other characters seem also to believe that she lacks such a language. Richard says, "That's a typical yak yak out of you, Faith"; Steele accuses her of "garbling"; Mrs. Finn cries "Blah blah. . . . Blah to you." Even Faith's attraction to Phillip seems somehow related to his knowledge of languages. Ironically, however, it is a simple question and an even simpler answer that move Faith's children, and thus Faith, to action.

The most evident metaphor in the story is the tree, on whose limb Faith waits to reenter life. The reference to the children as "seedlings" reinforces this image—it is the children who ultimately bring Faith out of the tree and back into the world.

Finally, it is the pure force of Paley's language that carries this almost static story, entertaining and enlightening the reader. Describing one of the more respectable but less feeling inhabitants of the playground, she writes: "Along the same channel, but near enough now to spatter with spite, tilting delicately like a boy's sailboat, Lynn Ballard floats past my unconcern to drop light anchor, a large mauve handbag, over the green bench slats." Paley, unlike Faith, has no language limitations.

Rochelle Bogartz

THE FALL OF THE HOUSE OF USHER

Author: Edgar Allan Poe (1809-1849)
Type of plot: Horror
Time of plot: 1839
Locale: Unspecified
First published: 1839

Principal characters:
THE NARRATOR
RODERICK USHER, the narrator's friend from childhood
MADELINE USHER, Roderick's twin sister

The Story
Summoned to the House of Usher by a "wildly importunate letter," which "gave evidence of nervous agitation," the first-person narrator goes to reside for a time with the writer of this letter, Roderick Usher. Although Roderick had been one of his "boon companions in boyhood," the narrator confesses early in the story that "I really knew little of my friend"; yet, by the end of this gothic tale, he has learned more about the occupants of the House of Usher than he is equipped to deal with. Indeed, one of these occupants is Roderick's twin sister, Madeline Usher, who is suffering from an unspecified but fatal illness. One of the symptoms of this illness is catalepsy (muscular rigidity marked by a lack of response to external stimuli); significantly, this symptom is crucial to understanding what happens in the course of the story.

His sister's illness is only one reason for Roderick's agitation, one reason for his desire to have the "solace" of the narrator's companionship; it is not the only—or most significant—reason. Usher himself is suffering from a "mental disorder," which is "a constitutional and . . . family evil, and one for which he despaired to find a remedy." Why "evil"? one wonders, until one recalls that, in the third paragraph of this story, even before Roderick has been seen for the first time, the narrator mentions that the ancient "stem" of the Usher family never "put forth . . . any enduring branch . . . the entire family lay in the direct line of descent, and had always . . . so lain." In other words, Roderick and Madeline Usher are the products and inheritors of an incestuous family lineage—one which has remained predominantly patrilineal, so that the name of the family always remained Usher. Roderick's dilemma, therefore, is this: Madeline is the only relative he has left on earth, and the dictates of the Usher tradition require that, to perpetuate the race of Ushers and the family name, he marry his twin sister and—through incest—sire future Ushers. (It should be noted that at no place in the story does Roderick say any of this directly; while it is intimated throughout, his dilemma is made clearly apparent only by careful reading of his and the narrator's words on this matter.) Thus, when Roderick refers to his "family evil," the reader may better understand why the narrator earlier mentions, in the second paragraph of the story, that "of late" the family has received some recognition for "repeated deeds of munificent yet unobtrusive charity." Such alms, it should be understood, have been given penitently, in the hope that they will absolve the "evil" of incest germane to the Usher tradition. Nevertheless, absolution comes to the Ushers in no form other than complete annihilation.

During the term of the narrator's visit with Roderick, they read to each other literature concerning classical myth, penitential rituals, theology, physiology, supernaturalism, and demonism—all of which are meant to indicate to the reader Roderick's preoccupation with anything that might help him understand his and his sister's dilemma. What he comes to feel certain about is that the house itself—because it was built and lived in by his forefathers, and because he believes there is "sentience [in] all vegetable things" (and the house consists of such sentient things)—has a "terrible influence" upon him and Madeline, and that it has "made *him*." In other words, the House of Usher becomes a living, feeling character in Poe's story, and one which, Roderick suggests, may be urging the two remaining Ushers to commit incest; although the narrator attempts to convince the reader that he is too rational and realistic to be taken in by Roderick's hypochondriacal theories, he gradually begins to feel "infected" by his host's condition: "I felt creeping upon me, by slow yet certain degrees, the wild influences of his . . . fantastic yet impressive superstitions." Thus, the stage is set for the story's horrifying climax, beginning one evening when Roderick informs his guest that Madeline is dead.

Rather than burying his sister in the family cemetery some distance from the house, Roderick decides to keep her body for two weeks in one of the many vaults within the house—for, after all, one suffering from catalepsy may seem dead, but not, in fact, be dead; it would be horrible to bury Madeline alive. In short, the narrator assists his host in entombing the body temporarily in, first, a coffin with its lid screwed down, and then in a vault behind a massive iron door of profound weight. There she remains for a week, as Roderick roams through his house aimlessly, or sits and stares vacantly at nothing for long hours. One tempestuously stormy night—a "mad hilarity in his eyes"—Roderick enters the narrator's bedroom, where they sit together, the narrator reading to him and both of them trying to ignore the terrible grating sound they hear coming from below the bedroom (the vault into which they placed Madeline's body is directly below this bedroom, and the heavy door to that vault always makes a loud grating sound when it is being opened). As the sound continues more noticeably, Roderick suddenly informs the narrator that he has been listening to noises downstairs for many days, but—apparently fearful that his sister was still living, and that he would again have to face the evil prospect of perpetuating his family's tradition of incest—he says, "*I dared not speak!*" Abruptly, the bedroom door swings open and Madeline, her white robes bloodied by her struggle to escape the coffin and vault, falls into the room and upon Roderick, who, "a victim to the terrors he had anticipated," hits the floor "a corpse."

The narrator flees the house, and from a short distance away he turns to look back and sees the House of Usher split in two and crumble into the dark waters of the tarn before it.

Themes and Meanings

Although Edgar Allan Poe claimed in his essays and reviews that he was against any didactic motive in literature, and although "The Fall of the House of Usher" is not a didactic story, Poe does communicate a definite moral message here. Importantly, however, the morality with which he is concerned is not that prescribed by any specific religion; instead, he seems to be suggesting that, despite the incestuously twisted and mentally deranged life of the Ushers, there exists an unwritten but operative universal morality that is ultimately as inescapable as the hereditary forces which determine a person's life.

While one may argue that Roderick's angst, as well as his acute hypochondria and seeming madness, appears to be the consequence of centuries of incest, which biologically diminishes a creature's ability to survive, Poe is nevertheless careful to note the "repeated deeds of munificent . . . charity" offered "of late" by the Ushers (presumably by Roderick himself, since the story takes place in the nineteenth century, when men, according to tradition, were in charge of financial affairs). Significant, too, is the pejorative appellation of "evil" that Roderick gives to his family, in itself an indication of his own moral sense. Indeed, it is precisely Roderick's morality that causes the internal conflict he suffers, between his inherited traits and his moral revulsion over them, and it is his morality that prompts him to leave Madeline in the vault even after he discovers that she is still alive. Granted, knowingly allowing his sister to die, when he could save her, is immoral; yet Roderick's sense of right and wrong has transcended concerns for what is good for the Ushers and their perpetuation, and becomes a greater, higher concern for the future of the human race. It is no wonder, then, that when the hereditary forces have succeeded in joining the brother and sister together in the house, itself an emblematic agent of those forces, a greater force prevails as it obliterates the Ushers and their house, truncating the incestuous "stem" of the family for all time.

Style and Technique

In an 1842 review of Nathaniel Hawthorne's *Twice-Told Tales* (1837), Poe discusses the importance of "effect" in stories, and he suggests that a "wise" writer will not fashion "his thoughts to accommodate his incidents; but having conceived, with deliberate care, a certain unique and single *effect* to be wrought out, he then . . . combines such events as may best aid him in establishing this preconceived effect." He also asserts that the first sentence of a given story must contribute to the "outbringing of this effect." Essentially, then, according to Poe a good story need not be believable to be successful, so long as the integrity of its effect is not disturbed. Applying Poe's credo to "The Fall of the House of Usher," the reader must admit that, yes, this story is a success for its effect.

The first sentence sets the mood, begins to create the overall effect, as the narrator describes the day as "dull, dark, and soundless," the clouds hanging "oppressively low." When he arrives at the house, he is struck by its "melancholy" appearance, and his spirit is overwhelmed by a sense of "insufferable gloom." Not only is Poe working to create the story's mood in the first paragraph (as he does throughout the story), but he is also intent upon personifying the house when he has his narrator describe its windows as "eye-like" and the fungi implicitly as hair-like, "hanging in a fine tangled web-work from the eaves." Symbolically, the web of fungi, the house itself, and the "black and lurid tarn," which lies near the house, are all extensions of the Usher family's heritage and psychology; the atmosphere around this family reeks "a pestilent and mystic vapour, dull, sluggish . . . and leaden-hued."

Yet, while Poe's story is a success for its overall effect, the problem that exists in his credo extends into the story—that is, reason and probability are treated as unimportant. How, a reader must ask, does Madeline escape her coffin, the lid of which was screwed on, survive in the airless vault for seven or eight days without nourishment, and then escape the vault by forcing open the immensely heavy iron door? What causes the House of Usher to break in half and crumble into the tarn? No doubt Poe would have dispensed with such questions by pointing to the source of his story's lasting success, its gothic and gloomy effect.

David A. Carpenter

A FAMILY AFFAIR

Author: Guy de Maupassant (1850-1893)
Type of plot: Satiric farce
Time of plot: c. 1880
Locale: Paris and its suburbs
First published: "En Famille," 1881 (English translation, 1903)

>*Principal characters:*
>ALFRED CARAVAN, a fat, aging chief clerk in the Admiralty
>MADAME CARAVAN, his thin wife
>MADAME CARAVAN, his disgruntled ninety-year-old mother
>MARIE-LOUISE, his twelve-year-old daughter
>PHILIPPE-AUGUSTE, his son
>DR. CHENET, formerly a ship's surgeon, now in private
> practice, a friend of Caravan
>ROSALIE, the Caravan maid
>MADAME BRAUX, Caravan's sister

The Story

"A Family Affair" constitutes masterful satire and situation comedy; it roundly lampoons the petty clerks and minor bourgeois who proliferated in nineteenth century Paris. Monsieur Alfred Caravan is an aged chief clerk in a government office; he has trod the same circuit as commuter and drudge for some thirty years, for which service he is awarded a lapel pin by the bureaucracy. He is fat and officious, with an atrophied mind and a deeply ingrained dread of his superiors. One hot July night, he and his friend Dr. Chenet travel from Paris to their home at Courbevoie on the Neuilly steam-tram, as usual; they pause once more to tipple at the café, and part. At home (the story focuses comically and cruelly on the bureaucrat's so-called homelife), in a minuscule apartment, Caravan greets his lean wife, a compulsive housekeeper and cleaner, and later encounters his filthy young children, who usually play in the neighborhood gutter. Tedious talk rehearses Caravan's being passed over—again—for a better job at the office. He is henpecked by his wife, while both in turn are domineered by Madame Caravan, Alfred's quarrelsome ninety-year-old mother, who is housed above them.

The narrator has caustically observed earlier that Caravan's ceaseless round of tedious conduct never alters, that nothing has transpired to disrupt his boring existence. Yet the story is devoted precisely to relating one very unusual alteration, for, as all are sitting down to dinner, Rosalie the maid hysterically announces that Mama Caravan has collapsed upstairs. Dr. Chenet is summoned, the mother is pronounced dead, and a round of hysteria and lamentation commences—mechanical and sincere on Caravan's part, halfhearted and improvised on the part of his wife—and some species of chaos is come at last. All, including the doctor, brokenly attempt to complete their meal, and, absentmindedly, they eat and (especially) drink too much. Caravan and Chenet wander out into the fresh air for relief, Caravan conjures up sentimental remembrances of things past, and he even visits his café to solicit sympathy, but none is forthcoming from the busy customers.

Subsequently, back home and in bed, Caravan submits to his wife's plans. Since Mama has died intestate, and since his estranged sister will want the best leftovers for herself, the two must "salvage" and secure any heirlooms at once, in the middle of the might. They tiptoe upstairs and confiscate Mama's monstrous ugly clock, which depicts a girl in gilt bronze playing cup-and-ball, and a heavy chest of drawers with a marble top. Mama's clothes are summarily packed in a wooden crate. Next day, notices are sent everywhere, and all the nosey neighborhood comes to inspect the deceased; even the children's dirty ruffian friends sneak in and take a peek. Finally, Madame and Monsieur Braux, Caravan's sister and her Socialist husband, are telegraphed and asked to come from Charenton. Exhausted, the whole family sits down to dinner once again; the lamp runs out of oil; and, only twenty-four hours after her demise, it is discovered that Mama (who often suffered from fainting fits) has revived. Pandemonium ensues as everyone rushes upstairs. Dazed and sulky, Mama is back to normal—and hungry. The entire family is courteous beyond measure. Then, as all descend on the crowded stairs, the rival sister and her husband appear. Fighting ensues; Mama demands her possessions back and arranges a visit with the sister. The men quarrel lustily about politics. Dr. Chenet reappears, delighted to encounter in Mama such a medical recovery; he abruptly resumes eating and drinking. Caravan's wife quarrels with the sister and her husband; the tension increases until the relatives depart. The Caravans at the close are left, briefly, alone. Yet they are filled with grief and terror about the renewed presence of Mama, and fearful of Alfred's employers, since Caravan has, in all the hurly-burly, managed to miss a day at the office and now has lost his excuse for the absence.

Themes and Meanings

Guy de Maupassant is best known for his brief, realistic tales of Norman peasantry, of Paris life, and of the insignificant bourgeoisie. Often his stories are notable for their speed, drama, climax, and surprise endings. Moreover, he is usually admired for his shrewd deployment of a persistent irony. All these qualities figure prominently in "A Family Affair." Together with several other stories, such as "The Piece of String," "The Necklace," "The False Gems," and "The Umbrella," "A Family Affair" is one of his best-known pieces.

Unlike some, however, this tale does not feature cool authorial detachment. Rather, it is a scathing frontal assault, sketched with roller-coaster rapidity and acid commentary, depicting a typically trite, rapacious, empty-headed suburban family. Indeed, it provides a behind-the-scenes glimpse of terrible mediocrity; the phrase *en famille* usually indicates domestic privacy and bliss, a cozy being "at home." Perhaps a modern translation of the title might coyly be "All in the Family." Clearly, the title is employed, as is virtually all else in this story, with raw sarcasm.

In such a satire, it is difficult to imagine who is not intended as a target. With widening inclusiveness, everyone and anything is indicted: commuters, doctors, bureaucrats, suburban housewives, mothers-in-law, gluttony, avarice, politics, antiques, children, and death. The very breadth and diffuseness of this list renders the story something of a circus, with various dumb animals performing simultaneously in every ring. Just such overcrowding and excess give the story its absurdity, vitality, and grim farcical humor.

Style and Technique

Maupassant, following in the steps of Gustave Flaubert, is the master of precise detail; he frequently captures with exactitude the minutiae of urban life. In the oppressive July heat, Maupassant observes the city's "white, chalky, opaque, suffocating, and warm dust" in the air, which damply adheres to everything, and he is sensitive to city tenements clustered with small noisome flies. He swiftly caricatures Caravan's restless wife, who compulsively rubs mahogany chairs with a piece of flannel; he sketches dainty family members at table overeating with "a sort of studied inattention"; and he surveys the curious from all over town who file in, "stealthy as an army of mice," to observe the corpse.

Maupassant is similarly the master of exaggeration; his deft overemphasis repeatedly transforms normal actions into melodrama. Thus, Caravan in mourning is portrayed as flinging himself upon the body of his supposedly deceased mother-in-law and as incessantly moaning and weeping. Caravan's inebriated vision of Mama in the past is overpainted—old memories are laid on, as it were, with a trowel; for now, with his loss, he vows that his life has been sliced in *half*, that this separation will be *eternal*, that he will lose *all* recollections of his past. This hyperbolic emphasis discolors the scene, rendering the reader suspicious and amused. Hence, it is no surprise that Caravan feels sated, relieved, and comfortable shortly afterward, so that he can turn his attentions more efficiently to the acquisition of Mama's possessions.

Last, Maupassant undercuts the whole scene he is presenting by injecting sweeping summaries that diminish and debase. Caravan, for example, at his mother's wake stares at the corpse, and the reader is told that he is "revolving in his brain those apparently profound thoughts, those religious and philosophical commonplaces, which trouble people of mediocre minds in the face of death." In fact, the entire world of middle-class bureaucrats in commuterland is handsomely summed up at the tale's very outset. Females on the train are depicted as "stout women in strange toilettes, shopkeepers' wives from the suburbs, who made up for the distinguished looks which they did not possess by ill-assumed dignity." The males aboard fare no better:

> gentlemen tired of the office, with yellow faces, who stooped with one shoulder higher than the other.... Their uneasy and melancholy faces also spoke of domestic troubles, of constant want of money, of former hopes that had been finally disappointed. They all belonged to that army of poor, threadbare devils who vegetate economically in mean, plastered houses, with a tiny piece of neglected garden....

This grotesque painting strikes exactly the right note between comedy and horror; its portrayals are exaggerated, but all too often with just enough of the truth to be bitingly effective. Maupassant's is the brilliant culinary art of heaping on too much and basting it until it is very well done indeed.

                                                                                    John R. Clark

THE FANCY WOMAN

Author: Peter Taylor (1917-   )
Type of plot: Domestic and psychological realism
Time of plot: Probably the late 1930's
Locale: A country home in Tennessee
First published: 1940

> *Principal characters:*
> JOSIE CARLSON, the protagonist, a young, single woman
> GEORGE, who treats her like a mistress
> AMELIA, a black servant
> MR. and MRS. ROBERTS,
> MR. and MRS. JACKSON, and
> MR. and MRS. COLTON, friends of George visiting from
>   Memphis
> JOCK and
> BUDDY, George's sons, ages seventeen and fourteen

The Story

From the opening sentences, the story portrays a mental state as well as narrating a series of events; this emphasis on subjectivity means that the impact of events is at least as important as the events themselves. The story's central consciousness, Miss Josephine Carlson, has been invited by her man George to spend a week at his country place, and the sentence fragments and uncertain grammar of her "voice" hint at both anger and anxiety. In this opening scene, the combination of alcohol and sex with Josie's lack of options in the relationship sets the stage for all that follows. As preposterous as it might seem at the end of the story, this "fancy woman" wonders whether George loves her, whether she might be the social equal of the white Memphis visitors she meets, and whether George is eventually going to marry her. For her, and her only, this is a "love story."

The narrative is divided into twelve sections, and each section makes it clearer that George, even when absent from the scene, controls all that goes on. For him, love and marriage are not the issues. One should, however, also note the contrasts between day and night: The events of three nights and three days make up the story and give a sense of progression.

Sections 2 through 5 narrate the events of the first morning when only George, Josie, and the servants are present. In this isolation, Josie reveals her insecurity and defensiveness about her respectability and her lack of power with George—she seems to have only passivity or the whiskey bottle; when in section 4 she becomes sick to her stomach and falls off her mount, George laughs mockingly and leaves her. In section 5, her vacillations reveal the full measure of her insecurity and ambition: One moment she rejects him, but thinks immediately afterward that "he was lonesome. There was, then, a place to be filled." The sequence reveals George as a single-minded bully and Josie as a would-be manipulator; because of the doubtful reliability of both these characters, it leaves many elements of their relationship ambiguous.

The heart of the story, sections 6 and 7, introduces the three Memphis couples and narrates the afternoon and evening of wife-swapping and drinking. In Josie's shock at learning about their organized adulteries, however, there is a positive note of naïveté; her wanting to dance only with George ("because she so liked to dance with him") and her resolve not to care what the others do make her for a time seem the most genuine person present. Again, Taylor's narrative seeks to maintain ambiguity, to forestall taking sides or condemning too quickly.

In the eighth section, when Josie concludes the next morning that Mr. Jackson had come to her bed during the night and derives from this conclusion the satisfaction that "they're none of 'em any better than the niggers. . . . By God, nobody's better than I am," the strong but by no means dominant theme of Josie-as-victim begins to fade. Her desire to get even with George by flirting with his seventeen-year-old son Jock changes her image completely. In declaring a suicidal war against George, she shows the worst in herself, seeing the boys as "smutty" sexual creatures, dreaming that Jock tries to enter her room (another man—and this time, significantly, one does not learn who or even if Josie knows who—has already used her). Josie's confrontation with Buddy, the fourteen-year-old, takes on gothic overtones: This has become a tale of a lone woman in a house of horror, except that the woman has clearly sought the confrontation. Motives even now are not clear, especially Buddy's motives; the only certainty is George's imminent violence against her.

Themes and Meanings

Taylor's major theme in this early story is the disintegration of the family and the collapse of the values associated with the genteel South. Allied with that is an investigation, showing Freudian preoccupations, of the effects of this disintegration on a lone woman's psyche ("A Spinster's Tale," written about the same time, focuses for the same purpose upon a woman who unlike Josie was reared in the upper-middle class). The results suggest that the social breakdown has revealed sadistic and masochistic elements which appear as twisted versions of the male aggressiveness and female passivity associated with the old, genteel chivalric love tradition.

George, who appears often in the story wearing white, rides horses on his country estate, drinks expensive whiskey in his mint juleps, and is impetuous with his inferiors and sentimental with his children, represents a soulless version of the Southern gentleman. His behavior toward his mistress is summarized as follows: "He either laughed at her or cursed her or, of course, at night would pet her. He hadn't hit her." The organized infidelities of his friends are further evidence of social breakdown; his allowing those friends to share his mistress, and his sons to see her, contrasts with his violent defense of those sons from her supposed advances and adds a final grotesque touch to the treatment of "social standards" in the story.

Of at least equal importance, however, is the related theme of the consequences of social and familial disintegration upon women. Josie is out of her usual social element here—thus her loneliness and eagerness to please a man she barely knows. Taylor, however, avoids the pitfall of sentimentality by characterizing her as an adventurer who thinks she can rise in the world: She will, it seems, suffer anything for George. Her essentially conservative assumption about the need for a wife in this "family" is ironic, and does not serve her well. George feels no such need. Events make it clear that Josie, to promote her own interests, is willing to become a drunk, to prostitute herself, to commit adultery with strangers, and to seek to take advantage of what she suspects to be the worst impulses of George's adolescent son. She matches and perhaps exceeds George's desire to manipulate people. For both George and Josie, freedom is a concept unconnected with responsibility, and this license makes their final confrontation inevitable. It is significant that after her constant worry about respectability, she should be named "fancy woman" by George's younger boy, whose precocious insight is an indictment of all the adults in the story.

Style and Technique

Taylor's artistry is subtle but powerful. "The Fancy Woman" communicates the themes of disintegration by its skillful use of the third-person limited point of view, its adaptation of grotesque elements from the gothic tradition, and its ironic portrayal of social nuances.

Limiting the point of view to Josie, an unintelligent and relatively inexperienced woman now out of her social element, Taylor severely restricts the readers' knowledge about other characters' motives. Josie maintains a hopeful view by grossly simplifying everything, especially human nature: "She'd find out what was wrong inside [George], for there's something wrong inside everybody, and somehow she'd get hold of him." The narrative also reflects her weaknesses by what it omits; for example, no explanations or reflections concerning the strangers in her bed enter the narrative because Josie herself refuses to think about what she has done. The sight of George's boys on the lawn reminds her of "a scene from a color movie, like one of the musicals": She habitually perceives experience in terms of clichés—the only sources of comparison and judgment which she possesses.

The gothic elements are well disguised at first by the dark comedy of

Josie's ignorance and George's callousness. Nevertheless, the vaguely dangerous man, the secretive servants, the isolated house, the mysterious guests, the night visitors to Josie's room, the turning doorknob, her strange dreams, the enigmatic young boys, and finally her isolation with the younger son, whose voice "came from one part of the house and then another," firmly imprint the damsel-in-distress motif on the narrative and prepare the reader for George's violence at the end. Like the use of Josie's flawed consciousness, the gothic elements work largely in the service of irony.

Finally, another very important ironic element is the pastoral scene, used to bring into bold relief the leisure habits of the "quality" people of urban Memphis. In this simplified environment, this Tennessee Versailles, in its freedom from artificial social constraints, the "sophisticated" people can show who they really are, and they do. Josie remains unaware of all this, but the arrangement of events in the narrative creates ironic commentary on all notions of "class." The rituals of conversing, eating, drinking, appreciating nature and the arts (music, poetry, dance, games, and sports)—all communal rituals, in fact—are mocked by these characters. The most dignified persons are the servants. By focusing on a character who is ignorant of these nuances, who misunderstands what is important and concentrates on what is not, the story exposes the hypocrisy and decline of this culture from beneath rather than from above, an approach which places Taylor directly in the tradition of William Faulkner.

Kerry Ahearn

THE FAT OF THE LAND

Author: Anzia Yezierska (1885-1970)
Type of plot: Social realism
Time of plot: The early 1900's
Locale: New York City
First published: 1919

> *Principal characters:*
> HANNEH BREINEH, the protagonist, the mother of six children
> FANNY, her only daughter
> BENNY, one of her sons
> MRS. PELZ, Hanneh's friend and neighbor

The Story

In the first section of the story, the third-person narrator introduces two Jewish women who are neighbors in a tenement. Hanneh Breineh, a self-centered and hyperemotional woman, calls out her window to the kind and somewhat philosophical Mrs. Pelz for help. Hanneh's washer-boiler is broken, and she asks to borrow Mrs. Pelz's.

Hanneh engages Mrs. Pelz in a dreary conversation, but as she is doing so, one of her six children falls from his high chair. The mother characteristically overreacts, rushing hysterically to her son, while the more sedate Mrs. Pelz offers up a superstitious solution for avoiding such future occurrences.

Mrs. Pelz also tries to comfort Hanneh with the thought that, although a burden now, six children will eventually provide much more income when they are old enough to work. Then, Hanneh will live off "the fat of the land." Ignoring this prophecy, Hanneh continues to lament the particulars of her awful life. Suddenly realizing, however, that she is behind schedule, Hanneh rushes to the marketplace, returning later only to find one of her children missing.

Desperately searching the local streets for her Benny, she is shadowed by a crowd of concerned residents. At the end of this search, while Hanneh is reviving from a fainting spell, a policeman appears with the frightened and tearful Benny. Hanneh's earlier tormented concern quickly turns to anger and resentment. Instead of welcoming her son lovingly, Hanneh tells him to sit down and eat, and while eating to "choke."

In the second section of the story, the still impoverished Mrs. Pelz returns to live in New York City, apparently after some time away. She is on her way to visit the widowed and wealthy Hanneh, who now resides in a brownstone with her daughter, Fanny. The brief absence of the servant on this day allows Hanneh the momentary pleasure of eating in the kitchen. She and Mrs. Pelz do so, in a manner reminiscent of their tenement days.

It is true that she is quite wealthy, Hanneh declares, but she then proclaims through tears how wealth has enslaved her. This once envious woman, now the very object of local envy, secretly longs for her poorer days. Interrupting this poignant moment, the servant returns, and the two former neighbors are forced to end their tenement-style meal.

The third section of the story begins as all of Hanneh's children gather in the brownstone one day. The conversation centers on Benny and his successful Broadway play and on the family's plans to attend a performance together. Suddenly, however, Hanneh tearfully starts to chide her offspring for not having invited her to go along with them. Fanny, it seems, thought it best to have Hanneh attend on a different night, and since it was her duty to ask Hanneh to accompany them, the mother never received an invitation. According to Fanny, the ill-mannered and uneducated Hanneh would be a social embarrassment. In addition, she would prove detrimental to Fanny's career if the daughter had to introduce her to the influential Mrs. Van Suyden. In further defense of her actions, Fanny accuses her brothers of abandoning Hanneh, while she, the daughter, has had the difficult chore of living with their mother.

As a result of this disclosure and discussion, the children agree among themselves to provide Hanneh with an apartment of her own. This decision makes Hanneh even more unhappy, since the new apartment is without a kitchen, that one refuge to which Hanneh could always turn in order to stay busy. The idleness that this creates, along with the humiliation of being stared at in the public dining room, intensifies Hanneh's unhappiness. One day, she finds solace by returning to her old neighborhood to bicker and bargain with the vendors there.

Back at her new apartment building, which has strict regulations concerning food delivery, she defiantly enters the front lobby with her bag of groceries, including a large fish. Confronting there the very staid and proper hallman, Hanneh makes a stand. During the ensuing drama, Fanny enters the lobby with Mrs. Van Suyden. Immediately running to elicit aid from her daughter, Hanneh emotionally explains the situation. Instead of providing support, however, Fanny sides with the hall-man. Dejectedly, Hanneh goes to her room upstairs. Fanny apologizes to the departing Mrs. Van Suyden, who suggests that they meet again at some better time.

Blaming her mother for this lost opportunity, Fanny storms into her mother's apartment to deliver a tirade. An argument erupts, with mother and daughter accusing each other of various past and present abuses. When the fish finally arrives at the door, Hanneh flings it across the room and leaves.

Shortly afterward, at Mrs. Pelz's house, Hanneh seeks consolation and a sense of solidarity from her impoverished friend. Hanneh catalogs the unendurable conditions of her current life-style, ending her confession of grief with a request to stay the night with Mrs. Pelz. Yet the uncomfortable bed and the vermin combine to drive the former tenement dweller away. She walks back toward her more comfortable apartment with the realization that she can never return to the arduous, simple life. With bitter laughter, she scorns her original enchantment with those magic words, "the fat of the land," and once again enters the civilized enslavement of her apartment building.

Themes and Meanings

Yezierska's short story deals with the ongoing social phenomenon of impoverished immigrants struggling to become a part of the American success story. In this story, one family from the Jewish ghetto in New York City achieves that dream, only to discover that there is a price to be paid for this success.

On a superficial level, the story depicts the hazards to be found in the extremes of both poverty and wealth. On another level, though, it indicts the hypocrisy of a society in which children grow up to be ashamed of their parents. The price for "Americanization," for success, that Hanneh's children, particularly Fanny, must pay is the denial of their Old World streetwise mother. The price that Hanneh must pay for achieving her desire to live "off the fat of the land" is loneliness and bewilderment. The driving purpose of her life—to survive under difficult circumstances and to ensure the survival of her family—has been removed by wealth, and by a society that places a higher value on social etiquette than it does on familial love and respect. Hanneh's children are Americanized and, in the process, dehumanized.

In particular, Fanny's adoption of the social code of the status-oriented and the success-seeking virtually severs the mother-daughter bond of love and respect. This tragedy leads the mother to recognize that in many ways the affluent are less free than the tenement-dwellers. She is bound by the rules of a rigid social code that she does not understand. The author leaves Hanneh with the dilemma of despising her newly acquired social position and acquaintances while realizing that she cannot return to the degradation of poverty. The reader is also left with a dilemma, or more accurately, an opportunity to draw his or her own conclusion: Does Yezierska simply illustrate one of life's paradoxes, or does the author point out the need for moderation and tolerance in our lives?

Style and Technique

Much of the force of this story derives from the characters' speech. The richly idiomatic language of the immigrant community establishes both Hanneh's character and her environment. Through the dialogue, the characters paint their self-portraits on a canvas of sound, colored by expressions reflecting their social and ethnic ties. Narration is minimal, and descriptive passages, when they occur, are usually sympathetic to Hanneh's point of

view. For example, the hall-man is described as "frigid with dignity," supporting Hanneh's opinion. Thus, through the dialogue and narration, the world
that the reader views is Hanneh's world, rendered in her language.

While the author uses diction to establish character, the story's structure
contributes to its thematic development. Each section is framed by a character's movement to or from a passageway. The only exception is the section
which concentrates on Hanneh's children. This is significant, since the children are attached to this new environment, while Hanneh is not. The movement which either initiates or ends a scene symbolizes the mother's sense of
abandonment. This device is so essential that Yezierska chose to close the
story with Hanneh on the threshold; Hanneh's movement through the doorway is left unfinished, leaving her neither inside nor outside. She remains
framed in the reader's mind in a position symbolizing her inner state. The
woman who has traveled from poverty to affluence has yet to arrive at any
feeling of belonging. She is suspended as it were, between two worlds, at
home in neither one.

Paul Kindlon

THE FATHER'S DAUGHTERS

Author: Muriel Spark (1918-   )
Type of plot: Psychological comedy
Time of plot: 1957
Locale: Nice, France; London and Essex, England
First published: 1961

>   *Principal characters:*
>   HENRY CASTLEMAINE, an eighty-year-old novelist
>   DORA CASTLEMAINE, his forty-six-year-old spinster daughter
>   BEN DONADIEU, a thirty-one-year-old teacher at the Basil
>   Street Grammar School in London
>   KENNETH HOPE, a celebrated novelist
>   CARMELITA HOPE, Hope's twenty-one-year-old daughter

The Story

After having spent thirty-five comfortable summers at Nice, the Castlemaines are faced with poverty. Novelist Henry Castlemaine's name has been forgotten; in fact, people believe that he died long ago. His forty-six-year-old daughter, Dora, who has decided to serve her widowed father and attend to "his needs as a public figure," is worried about money. It has been thirty years since her father was recognized everywhere. Henry insists on patronizing an expensive place near the casino in Nice; Dora protests but relents, chided by her father for being "vulgar," that is, concerned about costs and prices.

One March, when Dora and her father are forced to abandon their expensive hotel, she meets Ben Donadieu, who is vacationing with his friend Carmelita Hope, the daughter of the famous novelist Kenneth Hope, "a shy, thin, middle-aged man" whose creative "magic" Dora admires. Carmelita likes Ben for being an "intellectual," but she thinks that Ben loves her chiefly for being the novelist's daughter. Ben is keenly interested in talking to Carmelita's father, whom she praises for not interfering in her life.

Dora accepts a job as an elocution teacher. Her father objects; he sulks and complains that he is a burden to her and that he ought to "go off and die." It is one of their affectionate quarrels: They are "shrewd in their love for each other." In her job, Dora again encounters Ben, who inquires, to her delight, if she is related to Henry Castlemaine.

Meanwhile, Ben's relation with Carmelita is in trouble; he wants to find out if Carmelita still means anything to him without sex. Carmelita wonders if Ben is "practising a form of cruelty to intensify her obsession." Her father does not want to help Ben for her sake. When Ben mentions his acquaintance with Dora, Carmelita thinks that his interest in the Castlemaines would "make everything easier for both of us." It turns out that this friendship spells the end of Ben's engagement with Carmelita. Henry Castlemaine urges Dora to marry Ben, and Dora accepts this as a kind of "destiny." The father-daughter conspiracy manifests a shrewdness capable of absorbing Ben as "a born disciple."

Themes and Meanings

From the title, one can infer that the narrative will explore the corrupting potential of a quasi-incestuous father-daughter relationship, its unnatural persistence, and its tension with the absent or canceled roles of mother and wife.

Patriarchal power dominates in the Henry-Dora bond: What the father dislikes, the daughter also dislikes. Dora cannot openly tell her father how poor they are. He always uses his formulaic defense against the world: Dora is "vulgar" if she mentions money. She has subordinated her needs to her father in the belief that he stands for a vital interest in life. As he says, "The world is ours. It is our birthright. We take it without payment." He ignores the need for earning money. It is Dora, however, who must solve the problem, even to the point of marrying Ben for his income.

On the other hand, patriarchal authority withdraws in the relationship between Kenneth and Carmelita, even though its effect is registered in Carmelita's personality. Unlike Henry, whose novels deal with "individual consciences" (his vanity, however, seems immune to the claims of others), Kenneth Hope's art opens "bricked-up" windows. Dora is fascinated with Hope's illusory world of adventurous spirits. Unlike Henry, Hope does not visibly interfere with his daughter's life. He refuses to help Ben write an essay about himself; he hates disciples. He thus refuses to help his daughter because he believes that she should be independent and know what she wants.

While Hope presents a "smiling and boyish . . . party face" to society, he conducts an inner struggle with himself during his creative moods, experiencing (as he confesses to his daughter) "a comedy of errors." His daughter is abandoned by Ben, whose quest for a father would sacrifice the erotic pleasure offered by Carmelita for the "marriage of true minds"—as Henry Castlemaine puts it. Hope's inventiveness fails in grappling with real-life problems or empathizing with suffering kin.

Carmelita's belief that there is more to discover in an intellectual type such as Ben exemplifies a blindness, or inadequacy of perception, explainable by her being Hope's daughter. For Dora, on the other hand, Ben represents money and a revival of her father's works, a recovery of youth, and the value of the immediate present. In her anger and despair, Carmelita has a moment in which she intuits the essence of her father's depression, during which he "miraculously wrote the ache out of his system in prose of harsh merriment."

Distanced from her father, the daughter is able to gain this insight.

Separation of kin and respect for individual integrity may be read into the Hope-Carmelita relationship, whereas negation of self and triumph of paternal vanity characterize the Henry-Dora relationship. Dora's liking for Hope's imagination is a symptom of her suppressed life, of her victimization by a puritanical and hypocritical code to which she willingly submits. Her justification of her marriage to Ben as "destiny," or as evidence of a former life, and her gambling in the lottery all testify to her inability to take control of her life.

Muriel Spark satirizes Henry Castlemaine's aristocratic pretense and his phony interest in "individual consciences." She also caricatures the "cultivated type" represented by Ben, whose parasitism of famous authors is a mirror image of Henry's parasitism of his daughter. The main target of Spark's satire, however, appears to be the bohemian foibles of the two fathers: Henry's creed that the true artist's sensibility transcends the world of commodities and money, and Hope's "comedy of errors" resolved by his escapes to Morocco or the Middle East. This self-serving aestheticism is the privileged space for the male psyche guaranteed by the subservience of women.

Where are the mothers in this narrative? The theme of sexual domination through the mind and of psychological bondage—the women's utterances are always being interrupted or sidetracked here—may be conceived as a repression of women's creativity, the stifling of both Dora's and Carmelita's self-fulfilling drives. The fathers can "father" while the daughters minister to their needs. When Dora secures a teaching job, her father is jealous. Carmelita is a sexual object for Ben and is later discarded. The maternal can be discovered in the folds of "vulgarity," in the world of pleasure which the fetishism of art and the mystification of the intellect tend to deny. Perhaps the maternal impulse surfaces and asserts itself in Dora's conception of "destiny," and in Carmelita's admittedly unwilling "liberation" from Ben.

Style and Technique

Spark has often been credited for her whimsical wit and her "crotchety originality." What stands out in this polyphonic blending of voices and scenes, the interweaving of the lives of two daughters and the men who control their lives, and the consistently mistaken interpretations of motives and purposes, is a complete mastery of the banal peculiarities of English family relationships and the petty eccentricities of male writers.

The narrative structure consists of the alternation of scenes involving the couples Henry and Dora, Carmelita and Ben, and Carmelita and Kenneth Hope. Each scene comments on the other and unfolds the ironic implications in the limited knowledge of each character. The impoverished Castlemaines want the past restored, while Carmelita looks forward to a vague future. By juxtaposing the last two scenes—Carmelita's dilemma, her problem of how to satisfy Ben's intellectual ambition, and Dora's hesitation to marry Ben— the narrative exposes Carmelita's pathetic blindness, her self-deception in- duced by her fatal admiration for her father. The third scene functions as a pivotal disclosure of Dora's will to assert herself against her father, suggest- ing that, while she may not be as free as Carmelita (whose fixation on Ben testifies to her father's predominant influence), she can make practical deci- sions within the framework of her symbiotic relationship with her father. Her job epitomizes her ethical limit: "a reformer of vowel sounds."

Spark's critical thrusts are both direct and oblique. Henry tells Dora that she is "a chip off the old block." Dora uses her father's all-purpose epithet "vulgar" to signal their moral and aesthetic superiority to the world. She ad- justs whatever she wants to say to her father's moods and idiosyncrasies. Her thoughts, however, especially about Hope's magic, betray a repressed dimen- sion of her psyche, which is absent in Carmelita. Only at one point does the narrative enact a dialogue in Carmelita's consciousness symptomatic of the split that women suffer in a patriarchal regime, in which women must keep their private thoughts to themselves and assume predetermined roles. By a sudden turn of dialogue or shift in tone, the two women's voices are always drowned or absorbed by the male voices, which invariably impose male opin- ions, caprices, and follies.

Given the montage of scenes depicting antithetical but also parallel lives, the comment by the dark-skinned blonde at the lottery kiosk in Nice seems apt: "Life is a lottery." The wheel of fortune transfers Ben from Carmelita to Dora; a new disciple for Henry Castlemaine appears. Dora's belief in destiny and in a former existence may be an ideological blinder for her submission to her father's wish for a revival of his fame, for her passivity or adaptability; yet it also intimates the larger, overarching structure of economic, political, and cultural institutions, whose impact on individual lives generates such cross-purposes, misunderstandings, and self-deceptions as the narrative ex- poses with acute satiric finesse.

E. San Juan, Jr.

THE FIELD OF MUSTARD

Author: A. E. Coppard (1878-1957)
Type of plot: Realism
Time of plot: The 1920's
Locale: Rural England
First published: 1926

> *Principal characters:*
> DINAH LOCK, a married woman about forty, vivacious and
> sensual
> ROSE OLLIVER, a woman about the same age, more reserved

The Story

On a November afternoon, three "sere disvirgined women" are gathering kindling at the edge of a gloomy forest bordered by a field of mustard plants. Dinah Lock, a "vivacious woman full of shrill laughter, with a bosom as massive as her haunches," teases an old man about a watch which was given to his uncle for "doing his duty"; Dinah says that she "never got no watch for doing that a-much."

Dinah and Rose Olliver, a tall angular woman, leave the woods while the third, Amy Hardwick, remains behind, slowly bundling up her collection of kindling. While they wait for Amy, a "sour scent" rises from the mustard blooms, and the dark woods lie on the hill "like a dark pall over the outline of a corpse." Oppressed by the pervasive melancholy of the scene, Dinah laments that "cradle and grave is all there is for we"; turning to Rose, she says, "I like you, Rose; I wish you was a man."

The two women go on to discuss the dissatisfactions of their lives. Dinah asserts that she is young at heart, while her husband is "no man at all" since an illness. Rose rather bleakly contrasts her childlessness with Dinah's family of four children. Rose takes a clipping from her purse and reads a passage that envisions the world as a beautiful garden filled with cherubic children; when she finishes reading it, she crushes the paper. Dinah says that, while she is willing to sacrifice for her children, she never really wanted any of them: "Somehow," she says, "I've been duped, and every woman born is duped so."

The recollection of her husband's feebleness leads Dinah to reminisce about Rufus Blackthorn, a gamekeeper and a "fine bold man" who was her lover several years before. She recalls how Rufus passed her house while she was working in her flower garden and took her to a wedding where they celebrated boisterously. Thereafter, she was "mad after Rufus" and met him regularly at night.

Dinah has described Rufus as "a perfect devil," but Rose asserts that he was a kind man, particularly toward women. She then tells Dinah a story—

which Dinah had not previously heard—of how Rufus once concealed the body of a drowned gentleman in his bed so that he could collect the reward for recovering the body. When Rose says that Rufus also made her a pair of reed slippers like a pair he made for Dinah, Dinah accurately infers that Rufus was Rose's lover as well as hers. Rose comments, "We was all cheap to him, cheap as old rags; we was like chaff before him." Dinah and Rose again feel the gloom of the day and of the mustard field, but Amy's arrival prevents further discussion of Rufus.

As they trudge home, bearing the heavy burden of the kindling, Rose envisions Dinah's children in a series of sentimental, almost romanticized, vignettes, while Dinah counters with complaints. Rose thinks of the children as waiting eagerly for Dinah and imagines her "setting round your fire with'em, telling tales and brushing their hair," while Dinah only says, "Ah, they'll want their bellies filling." Rose speculates that the children will "make you a valentine, and give you a ribbon on your birthday." Dinah responds that "they're naught but a racket from cockcrow till the old man snores—and then it's worse!" Then Dinah envisions Rose spending a quiet and pleasant evening playing draughts or dominoes with her kind husband, who will, she says to Rose, "stroke your hand now and again."

As the two women part in the windy, threatening evening, Dinah again says, "I like you, Rose. I wish you was a man." Rose, however, does not reply. As the women return to their homes, clouds are blown rapidly across the heavens and "the lovely earth seemed to sigh in grief at some calamity all unknown to men."

Themes and Meanings

As is the case with many stories, the theme of "The Field of Mustard" depends on a series of carefully arranged contrasts and on a revelation that is unexpected, at least by one of the characters. The contrasts begin to become apparent when Rose reads the clipping that describes an idyllic storybook garden, populated with cherubic children. As an image of what the world is like, this garden contrasts sharply with the "actual" world of the story: a dark wood on a gloomy November day and a field of sour-smelling mustard plants. Dinah also mentions that she "loved a good flower" at the time that she met Rufus and wishes "the world was all a garden." This contrast between the world as it is, a sour-smelling mustard field, and the world as the women would like it to be, an idyllic garden, is reinforced by the unfulfilled expectations and the disappointments of the women's lives. Rose is childless; Dinah's husband is "no man at all" since his illness. Although Dinah cares deeply about her children, they are an encumbrance that she never really wanted to have.

Almost certainly, the most fulfilling experience of Dinah's life was her love affair with Rufus, a "fine bold man" whose sensuality and fondness for boisterous fun matched her own. The revelation that Rufus has also been Rose's lover somehow diminishes, for Dinah, her own affair with him: It is evident that she was not as special to Rufus as he was to her. Rose's bitter appraisal—"We was all cheap to him"—is, sadly, more accurate.

The resentment that Dinah apparently feels at this discovery that she was not Rufus' only love expresses itself in her rather irritated responses to Rose on their walk home, but the bleak circumstances of the women's lives impel Dinah to seek the support of Rose's friendship. As "the wind hustled the two women close together, and as they stumbled under their burdens," Dinah reaches out, touches Rose's arm, and repeats that she likes Rose and wishes she were a man. That Rose again fails to respond to this overture of friendship suggests the ultimate isolation of the women, even from each other.

The story's concluding description of the "darkening world" as "windy, dispossessed, and ravaged" and the comment that the "lovely earth seemed to sigh in grief at some calamity all unknown to men" reassert the theme of the desolation of the women's lives. In the context of the story, it seems likely that the final "men" may refer more to the male sex specifically than to mankind in general, for surely the story emphasizes the disappointments that women face because they are women more than the disappointments that are common to all mankind.

Style and Technique

Perhaps the most conspicuous aspect of Coppard's technique is his near-symbolic use of setting and landscape in developing the significance of the story. The melancholy gloom of the November afternoon, the darkness of the wood, and the sour smell of the mustard plants, all mentioned several times in the story, parallel the dismal circumstances of the women's lives. Both Dinah and Rose, at different points in the story, chew on a sprig of mustard flower—Rose, when she contrasts her childlessness with Dinah's family of four, and Dinah, when she begins to contrast her husband's feebleness with Rufus' virility. The mustard flower, while not precisely a symbol, is clearly used to draw attention to the principal disappointment in each woman's life.

Although the "wind hustled the two women close together. . . as they stumbled under their burdens" on their way home, Rose's failure to reply to Dinah's gesture of friendship at the end of the story suggests that even friendship fails as a consolation in the bleak world that is the lot of these women. This view is reinforced by the way Coppard handles point of view, scrupulously avoiding direct revelation of the two women's thoughts. Their thoughts may to some extent be inferred from their words and gestures, but the fact that the thoughts themselves are never directly revealed subtly reinforces the aloneness and isolation of the women's lives.

Erwin Hester

THE FIGHT

Author: Dylan Thomas (1914-1953)
Type of plot: Fictionalized autobiographical sketch
Time of plot: 1928
Locale: Swansea, Wales
First published: 1939

> *Principal characters:*
> DYLAN THOMAS, a fifteen-year-old boy
> DAN JENKYN, his friend
> MR. and MRS. JENKYN, Dan's parents
> THE REVEREND and MRS. BEVAN, friends of the Jenkyns

The Story

In this short story, Dylan Thomas captures the bravado, friendship, and artistic dreams of his youthful days in Swansea. The story opens with the young schoolboy Dylan teasing old Mr. Samuels. The boys from the school keep Mr. Samuels on guard against their throwing apples and balls into his window. While Dylan rudely stares at the old man, suddenly a strange boy pushes Dylan down an embankment. They proceed to fight, the stranger receiving a bloody nose and Dylan a black eye.

Their battle quickly makes them allies as they see Mr. Samuels egging them on. They both throw gravel at the old man and walk off together as comrades. Dylan's newfound friend, Dan Jenkyn, says that Dylan has "the best black eye in Wales," and Dylan admires his friend's bloody nose.

Dylan spends the rest of the day glorying in his battle scar, enjoying the respect of the local girls and the boys at school. The young boys' conversation at school then turns to their dreams of owning expensive automobiles, large houses, and harems with "the girls in the gym," and of smoking fancy cigarettes.

That evening, before he visits his new friend, Dylan describes the small world of his bedroom: It is clearly the room of a young poet, with pictures of William Shakespeare, Walter de la Mare, Robert Browning, Rupert Brooke, and John Greenleaf Whittier (among others) hanging on his walls. He also has a copy of a poem he has published in the newspaper, pasted on his mirror.

As he walks along the street toward Dan's house, Dylan recites aloud his romantic verse. When he sees a young couple approaching, he quickly changes his recitation into a tune and hums his way past them. As he nears the house, he hears music coming from it and expresses his admiration for Dan's accomplishments: "He was a composer and a poet too; he had written seven historical novels before he was twelve."

Dan proceeds to play some musical pieces for Dylan, and the young poet, in turn, reads to him from an exercise-book full of his poems. The two boys seem to enjoy the prospect of an artistic future "spread out beyond the window." While they are waiting for supper to be ready, they imagine that they will edit a magazine together—*The Thunderer*. Then Dan suggests that they look at the bedroom of the family maid. As the call for supper reaches them, Dan promises that one day they will hide under her bed.

Besides Dan's parents, at the dinner table are their friends, the Reverend Bevan and his wife. The two boys enjoy indulging in rather profane thoughts, as when Dylan, struck by the gray-haired and gray-faced Mrs. Bevan, imagines that she might be all gray. He proceeds to undress her in his mind but cannot bring himself to go beyond the navy bloomers to her knees.

When it is revealed that Dylan is a poet, Mr. Bevan asks him to recite one of his poems. Embarrassed by the request, Dylan nevertheless begins to say aloud one of his poems filled with images of lust and violence, until Dan kicks him under the table. Mr. Bevan pretends to content himself with recognizing Alfred, Lord Tennyson, as the influence upon the boy's poem, but he and the Jenkyns are obviously shocked.

Back in Dan's room, the boys discuss Mrs. Bevan. Dan tells him that she is mad and once attempted to jump from the upstairs window of his house. At this point, she enters the room and the boys open the window and coax her to jump out, but she merely sits there awaiting her husband. The boys grow tired of watching her, Dan plays one more tune on the piano, and Dylan says his good-byes and walks out of the house with Dan. They look toward the upstairs window and see Mrs. Bevan's face pressed to the glass. Half afraid that she might jump, they run down the street and say their good-byes to each other. Dan says that he needs to finish a string trio tonight, and Dylan announces that he is busy working on a long poem "about the princes of Wales and the wizards and everybody."

Themes and Meanings

Thomas' chief aim in writing this autobiographical sketch is to capture the happy hooliganism of his boyhood. His head filled with poetry, pranks, and dreams, Dylan discovers a kindred spirit through his bloody little fight with a strange boy. Although surrounded by straitlaced adults, the two boys create and maintain a wonderful world of their own, filled with immense hope and joyful, profane energy that threatens to crush everything in its path, including a maid's privacy and a minister's sense of propriety.

In all of Thomas' poetry and fiction, he consistently praises the joys of primal energy, the life force that drives the blood, and the juices of the grass and flowers. He takes a special interest in children, following the tradition of the Romantic poets, because children best symbolize a natural oneness with the unchartered life force. Still free from the constraints of civilized society and its debilitating rituals, boys such as Dylan and Dan represent the hopes of the mature artist. If the child is father of the man, as William Wordsworth says, then the fifteen-year-old Dylan in this story is indeed the shaping influence of the mature poet, Dylan Thomas, the irreverent singer of the sacredness of life.

Style and Technique

Written from the first-person point of view, this sketch embodies the boisterous and self-assured tone of its fifteen-year-old narrator. Thomas not only captures the headstrong vitality of the boys through his narrator but also manages to maintain an ironic perspective on the boys' untested dreams. Dylan's admiration for Dan's amazing accomplishment of having written seven historical novels before he was twelve reveals not only a youthful mutual admiration society but also a monumental absurdity.

By presenting the adult world through the eyes of a boy, Thomas renders their conversations and attempts to communicate with the youngsters as comic failures. The adults and the boys live in two separate worlds. The adults restrain and repress the vitality of youth, and whenever the boys are alone together, Thomas' language becomes more poetic, unrestrained, and self-indulgent, as if to say here are two boys, artistic prodigies turning their dreams into words and music that the adults cannot fathom or appreciate. The gray Mrs. Bevan, for example, carries in the color of her skin the death of vitality. She is interesting to the boys only insofar as she might be manipulated into a glorious fiction, a madwoman leaping from a tall window. That is excitement, and that is what life and poetry are all about.

Richard Kelly

THE FIGURE IN THE CARPET

Author: Henry James (1843-1916)
Type of plot: Metafiction
Time of plot: Late Victorian period
Locale: London
First published: 1896

Principal characters:
THE NAMELESS NARRATOR, a minor literary journalist
HUGH VEREKER, a novelist of some standing, whose works are
the subject of curiosity and analysis by several of the
characters
GEORGE CORVICK, a friend of the narrator, the husband to
Gwendolen Erme, and the purported discoverer of the
secret of Vereker's work
GWENDOLEN ERME, a minor novelist, the wife of Corvick and
later of Drayton Deane
DRAYTON DEANE, a prolific literary journalist who marries
Gwendolen Erme after the death of Corvick

The Story

Having reviewed Hugh Vereker's latest fiction in *The Middle*, a literary weekly (this a result of the kind offices of his friend George Corvick), the nameless narrator is invited to a country-house weekend, during which he encounters Vereker. The novelist reads the narrator's notice and comments derisively on it, only to relent when he learns the identity of the author. In a gesture of compensation (one supposes), Vereker confides to the narrator that his fictions are all linked by a single idea or scheme which no critic has ever noticed but which is the very secret of all of his work. This is the famous "figure in the carpet" of the story's title, and it is what Vereker sets the narrator to discover.

Upon his return to London, the narrator sets about his work of investigation and analysis, to no avail. He confides his secret to Corvick, who in turn (and with the help of Gwendolen Erme, herself a novelist) pursues the same goal of discovering the elusive design in Vereker's writings. Baffled and unsuccessful, Corvick departs for India, ostensibly on a journalistic assignment, but (one learns later) in actuality with the intention of distancing himself from the immediate engagement with Vereker's books, the better to discover their secret. Corvick succeeds, or so he asserts, as a cable from Bombay to Miss Erme informs her that he has discovered the "general intention" in Vereker. Corvick rushes to visit Vereker in Rapallo, Italy, where (once again the news is cabled to London) Vereker confirms that Corvick has indeed stumbled onto the secret of the fiction. Corvick immediately proposes a long, definitive piece on Vereker, but not before demanding of Miss Erme that she become his bride as the price for his revealing to her the treasure that he has discovered. She consents, her mother (who has consistently opposed the union) conveniently dies, and the two are wedded, while the narrator is called away to Germany to assist an ailing relative.

Corvick's marriage to Gwendolen proves ill-fated, for on their honeymoon, he is killed in a cart accident in the country. The grieving Mrs. Corvick returns to London, where the narrator inquires of her whether Corvick had written his essay on Vereker. He had merely begun it, she admits, but he had nevertheless confided to her the secret itself. The narrator presses her for it, and when she refuses to reveal its nature or even to hint at it, he expresses doubts that Corvick had in fact ever known. Insulted, Gwendolen departs, thus enforcing a more or less permanent break with the narrator.

Six months later, Vereker publishes *The Right of Way*, which will be his last fiction. In an attempt to ingratiate himself with Gwendolen, the narrator delivers his copy to her, only to discover that she has already read it, having obtained a copy courtesy of Drayton Deane, who is reviewing it for *The Middle*. Deane is, in the narrator's view, more or less a hack, and the review confirms his judgment. Yet Deane manages nevertheless to impress Gwendolen so that she consents to make him her second husband. She continues to write novels, and Deane's career as a literary journalist flourishes, while the narrator languishes in his ignorance of the secret of Vereker's work. In the meantime, Vereker dies, as does Gwendolen, as a result of the birth of her second child. Encountering Deane at their club after his wife's death, the narrator inquires whether Gwendolen had ever shared with her second husband the secret confided to her by her first. Deane, expressing first bemusement, then shock that his wife had possessed so momentous a secret and had kept it from him, is left at the end of the story utterly crestfallen—whether at the loss of the precious knowledge itself or at the sense of having been betrayed by his wife is unclear. The narrator, meanwhile, derives a certain compensatory satisfaction for the permanent loss of Vereker's secret in the distress of Drayton Deane.

Themes and Meanings

Numerous commentators, from Richard Blackmur to Tzvetan Todorov, Wolfgang Iser, and J. Hillis Miller, have noted that "The Figure in the Carpet" is a fiction about fiction, a story about the formal properties of storytelling and the interpretation of narrative. What remains unsettled, however, is both the meaning of this curious device (what the figure in the carpet signifies) and the connections to be drawn between it and the overall project of James's writing. Nor is it entirely decided among James's readers and critics whether this tale itself is meant as a joke, a tragedy, or something else entirely. In short, "The Figure in the Carpet" has remained as elusive in its ultimate significance as the emblem in Vereker's fiction that gives the story its title.

What does seem incontestable, however, is that James intended to suggest, perhaps no more honestly than Vereker, that fictions do instance a controlling idea or schema. There is ample evidence in James's letters, notebooks, and nonfictional prose to suggest that exactly such a concept of the architectonic structure linking the works of an author one to another was very much the ideal toward which James strove in his own writing and which he thought characterized the most successful novelists of his and previous epochs. His famous criticism of certain British and Russian novels of the nineteenth century for lacking precisely this controlling intention, for being "loose and baggy monsters," testifies to this. Nevertheless, James remained characteristically vague, scarcely more helpful than the fictional Vereker himself in giving any solid clues to what the overarching idea behind his fictional practice might be. Resourceful scholars have labored toward this goal, but with scarcely more to show for their pains than the narrator in "The Figure in the Carpet" could boast. One might hazard the judgment that James no more intended that they should succeed than, as seems perfectly plausible, Vereker did in the narrator's case. In a sense, in order to discover the secret of a writer's entire oeuvre, one would have to be that writer oneself.

Style and Technique

"The Figure in the Carpet" is somewhat unusual among James's major tales for being written in the first person, rather than in the third-person, partially omniscient mode characteristic of his fiction. This may account in part for the relative directness of the style itself, which, if one compares it to the contemporaneous "The Altar of the Dead" or even to the earlier "The Aspern Papers," seems simple and unproblematic. None of the infamous convolutions associated with the famous "late style" is evident here. Such a stylistic practice does not, however, prevent the story from being an excellent example of that ambiguity and elusiveness which is often remarked in James's most important fiction.

Indeed, the seeming straightforwardness of the tale is a kind of falsely comforting, or purposefully deceptive, device for luring the unsuspecting reader into the labyrinthine difficulties and possibilities presented by the plot and characters. In a world where most of the characters speak comparatively plainly and directly (unlike the later novels and tales, "The Figure in the Carpet" is not clotted with a dense structure of conflicting metaphors and other figures of speech), one is likely to believe that they themselves are, in the end, fairly transparent in motive and straightforward in action. Nothing could be further from the truth. One is never certain whether Vereker is telling the truth when he confides a hint about his secret to the narrator, or whether Corvick did indeed make the discovery he has claimed, or most of all whether he confided his knowledge to his bride. Nor can one be certain of the motive for Gwendolen's silence both in the face of the narrator's importunings and with regard to her second husband—or was she silent with him at all? In a tale so fraught with mysteries and potentially deceptive behavior, one would be foolish to take at face value the narrator's judgment concerning Drayton Deane's ultimate ignorance. It is just such naïveté, which the narrative manifestly defeats in its theme and in its action, that the plainness of James's style invites. It would probably be incorrect to label this disjunction between style and theme a contradiction; it would not be so wrong to discern in it yet another puzzle in this most puzzling of James's major short stories.

Michael Sprinker

FIRSTBORN

Author: Larry Woiwode (1941-   )
Type of plot: Romance
Time of plot: The early to middle 1960's
Locale: New York City
First published: 1982

> *Principal characters:*
> CHARLES, the protagonist, Katherine's husband, a father-to-be and a radio advertising executive
> KATHERINE, the wife of Charles, a mother-to-be
> NATHANIEL, their firstborn
> HARNER, Katherine's obstetrician

The Story

"Firstborn" opens as Charles, the protagonist, is reading from Leo Tolstoy's *War and Peace* (1865-1869) to his wife, Katherine, who is in labor. She has fallen asleep, but he continues to read. He reads the part in which Pierre, realizing his feelings for Natasha, goes out under the Moscow skies and sees the comet of 1812, "a comet that is supposed to portend all sorts of disasters but for him speaks 'his own softened and uplifted soul, now blossoming into a new life.' " This quotation from *War and Peace* foreshadows the course of the story, which moves rapidly into disaster and then, more slowly, into rebirth.

As Katherine sleeps, Charles thinks about their marriage four months earlier. She had been pregnant by then, and he had assumed that the child was his. Later, she confessed that there had been a relationship with another man but that the child was Charles's, that she would not have married him if it were not. At first, he considered divorce, but could not go through with it. Then followed a period of turmoil in their marriage. Finally, two weeks ago, as they were leaving a party, his anger had risen and he had impulsively kicked her and sent her sprawling on the icy sidewalk. The bruises she sustained are still apparent now. He is filled with remorse for his act.

Now, although she is only seven months along in her pregnancy, Katherine is about to give birth. The contractions become more severe, and they leave for the hospital. The events leading to the birth and subsequent death of Nathaniel, their firstborn, follow. Later, after hearing that the child has died, Charles goes to a bar while Katherine lies alone in her hospital bed. Charles, during a chance meeting with Aggie, an aged prostitute, faces what he had previously avoided: He, too, had been having an affair. He hears "a faint whisper at his ear, *Murderer. You'll never quit paying for this.*"

The final section of the story indicates that this incident is being related from the future, from the vantage point of several years and four children. The marriage has survived, but it is only at this point that Charles is finally released from his guilt and "freed into forgiveness, for himself, first, then for her, the rest falling into place."

Themes and Meanings

While the story is most obviously about the birth of Charles and Katherine's first child, it really focuses more on their marriage. Their relationship calls up the comparison with Tolstoy's *War and Peace* in its movement from peace to turmoil and back again. The marriage's precariousness is most shockingly demonstrated in Charles's assault on his pregnant wife, which sets the stage for the story's two central themes, struggle and redemption. The story's primary theme is struggle—out of which joy may possibly emerge. As Katherine is struggling to give birth to their child, the more fundamental conflict between her and her husband is unfolding.

Charles's struggle with himself is the appropriate culmination of a story that has struggle as its central theme. Originating with Nathaniel's struggle to be born, the story reveals the struggle in the relationship between Charles and Katherine. Perhaps the reference to *War and Peace* overstates the difficulties that the couple experience and their significance, but the author's quotation from the Russian masterpiece is justified by subsequent events, which enact the same unnerving, uncanny, and ultimately redemptive combination of objective menace and personal deliverance. Though Katherine is more able to offer Charles immediate emotional comfort, such a resource has to find its own season in him, has to occur naturally, as peace follows war—tentatively, perhaps, but inevitably.

Out of this central theme comes the story's complementary theme, redemption, again evoked by the mention of Tolstoy, who often treated this theme, and by the specific quote from *War and Peace* at the beginning of the story. Yet the most obvious resolution to the theme of struggle is not employed: The birth of the child is no cause for joy, but is rather one for grief. At the end of the story, however, at the point at which true understanding is reached by Charles, he realizes "that the child had always been with him, at the edges of his mind and in his everyday thoughts, as much as any of their living children (*more*, he thought)." By virtue of never having lived, Nathaniel haunts his father until such time as Charles's spirit is assuaged and he can make his peace with his dead firstborn. One of the story's most commanding artistic features is that it neither shuns the metaphysical dimension of its material nor pretentiously exploits it. The dimension arises with persuasive ease out of the material's naturalistic foreground. The story is no more a philosophical speculation than it is an obstetrical case history: It informally declares itself to be an experience lived. The story thus outgrows, though never forgets, the context of the delivery room. More important,

Charles perceives in his closing, consummating moment of acceptance the current of energy common to all living things and which all living things experience.

At the end of the story, Charles undergoes a rebirth. In terms that invoke the imagery of light and vision, Charles "began at last to be able to begin again to see." The inference is that, not only in the aftermath of the firstborn's tragic birth but also in all the events leading up to and surrounding it, Charles has experienced a type of blindness. His stumbling, erratic footwork may be cited as confirmation of his condition. Ironically, however, it is when the promise of life was so insistent, so urgent, that Charles's vision failed him.

Style and Technique

Given its central dramatic occasion, it might be expected that "Firstborn" would positively teem with metaphors concerned with birth, breeding, newness, and succession. In particular, events seem primed for meditations on the miracle of paternity, the joy of motherhood, and the like. The events of the story, however, preclude such obviousness.

The style of "Firstborn" is essentially plain and direct. Occasionally, however, sentences become flamboyant and plethoric, infused, so it seems, with a surge of energy greater than that required to complete the fundamental task of narrative. The unpredictable occurrence of the latter type of sentence is an effective enactment of a central feature of the story, its "moral stamp" (Woiwode applies the phrase to Tolstoy). This feature is the capacity for erratic change exemplified both by Charles and by Katherine, their ability to grow and, ultimately, to outgrow.

In a sense, because of the random interplay of differing syntactical tensions (from directly informative simple sentences to more complex units conveying difficult emotional conditions), it might be said that the author does not possess a particularly distinctive style. While obviously a lover of language, Woiwode does not treat language with very much indulgence. He is ready to use a colloquialism as a verbal gem. One reason for this apparent casualness is that it effectively communicates the sense of improvisation and inconclusiveness that suffuses the central characters. Another reason for the style's comparative lack of polish is that its plainness provides immediate access to the minutiae of daily life, communicating thereby the inescapability of the common lot in its typically mundane context. The stylistic fluctuations of "Firstborn" accurately dramatize the tissue of conflicting experiences upon which the story is premised.

By concentrating on the immediate drama of the birth and the circumstances directly leading up to it, the author imparts a basic momentum to the material. The story's strong sense of pace befits the subject matter. The natural-seeming, though deftly orchestrated, pattern of lurch, stall, rush, and ebb closely engages the reader in the vivid moment at the center of the work. This pattern also reproduces the story's psychology of uncertainty and articulates its problematical idea of consummation.

Complementing the story's variety of styles are its structural features. By concentrating on a basically simple chronological development, a nominal stability is provided. The taut chronological core, dealing with events directly pertaining to labor and delivery, however, has its narrative integrity offset by the story's larger temporal framework. Nathaniel's case provides "Firstborn" with its dramatic pretext. Yet the case is also used to illuminate the quality and trajectory of the energies that went into making it, as well as the burdensome but survivable aftermath. As is true of other aspects of the story, a structural view reveals a mutuality between the intense moment and the accumulation of the years. The long view is latent within the ostensibly discrete episode. Thus, while the conclusion of "Firstborn" may seem somewhat sketchy or condensed, on structural grounds it is crucial to the story's vision. Time's duplicitous but eventually therapeutic duality, which the conclusion tacitly establishes, is the reader's most immediate access to the story's rather generalized but nevertheless genuine philosophical concerns.

George O'Brien

THE FIVE-FORTY-EIGHT

Author: John Cheever (1912-1982)
Type of plot: Psychological realism
Time of plot: The 1950's
Locale: New York City and its suburbs
First published: 1954

> *Principal characters:*
> BLAKE, a businessman and womanizer
> MISS DENT, Blake's erstwhile secretary and onetime
>   "conquest"; also a former psychiatric patient

The Story

Among the more successful of John Cheever's urban tales, extending into suburbia, "The Five-Forty-Eight" recounts the brief but harrowing ordeal of a selfish, thoughtless male executive whose recent past comes back to haunt him in the person of a deeply disturbed young woman lately employed—and dismissed—as his secretary.

When Blake first spots the young woman apparently waiting for him to emerge from his office building at the end of the day, he readily recalls her face but not her name. Only gradually does he come to suspect that she might be following him, yet when her "contorted" face pops into view directly behind his own in the reflection of a store window, Blake suddenly wonders if she might be planning to kill him. In any case, Blake chooses not to recognize her and continues on his way, telling himself that she will be "easy to shake."

Stepping into a bar that caters exclusively to men, Blake locates a well-hidden seat and proceeds to order a Gibson cocktail; as he drinks it, he recalls the few facts that he has ever known concerning Miss Dent, or Bent, or Lent, whom he had dismissed from his service several months earlier after a single night of lovemaking—presumably because of her strangely "undisciplined" handwriting glimpsed by chance during their brief assignation. Crucially and doubtless typically, Blake has failed then as now to draw the obvious inferences: In a person as shy and restrained as "Miss Dent," such disorderly handwriting might well indicate a similarly disordered and even unbalanced personality; Blake has also failed to spot the potential significance of Miss Dent's expressed gratitude for giving her "a chance" after eight months in the hospital. Even now, in the bar, Blake does not seem to wonder in what sort of hospital she might have been.

Upon finishing a second cocktail, Blake observes that he has missed his usual train to the suburbs, the express, and will instead have to take the local, the five-forty-eight of the story's title. On his way to the station, Blake notes with some relief that the woman seems to have stopped following him; once aboard the train, however, he nervously seeks familiar faces, noting with some dismay that the two acquaintances present are no longer his friends. Mrs. Compton, his next-door neighbor, is both a busybody and a confidante of the beleaguered Mrs. Blake. Mr. Watkins, an object of Blake's disdain both because he is an artist and because he rents his home instead of owning it, has long since stopped speaking to Blake thanks to Blake's disruption of a growing friendship between their adolescent sons.

As the train emerges from underground into the fading daylight, Blake hears a female voice addressing him and finally recalls the young woman's name as Miss Dent. In response to Blake's reluctant, perfunctory questions, Miss Dent replies that she has again been "sick" and has been unable to find other work because Blake has "poisoned their minds." When Blake nervously prepares to move toward another car, Miss Dent informs him that she is armed with a pistol and quite capable of killing him, albeit reluctantly; all she really wants, she claims, is his attention to what she has to say.

Pulling an unmailed letter from her purse, Miss Dent forces Blake to read it as she rambles on about her sense of persecution and her need for love. Upon arriving at the Shady Hill station, where Blake normally dismounts, the woman forces him, at gunpoint, to precede her off the train. Marching him north of the station, toward a freight house and coal yard, Miss Dent finally forces Blake to kneel down and put his face in the dirt. Repeating her earlier declarations that she knows more about love and life than Blake does, she continues, "Oh, I'm better than you, I'm better than you, and I shouldn't waste my time or spoil my life like this. Put your face in the dirt. *Put your face in the dirt!* Do what I say."

Taking the woman at least at her word, Blake stretches flat on the ground, weeping as he does so. "Now I can wash my hands of you," declares his unlikely captor, and before long she is gone, the sound of her retreating footsteps resounding in Blake's disbelieving ears. Hesitantly, Blake at last raises his face to discover that Miss Dent is indeed gone, having apparently "forgotten" him, having "completed what she wanted to do." Picking up his hat from the ground, he proceeds on his way home.

Themes and Meanings

Anticipating by at least a decade the developing current of feminist literature, "The Five-Forty-Eight" presents in credible and memorable terms the compelling evidence, and possible means of redress, against the "institution" of male chauvinism as exemplified in the prototypical relationship of "boss" and secretary. The author was himself male, and one potential weakness of the story is that Miss Dent might be dismissed by the reader as merely "crazy." Cheever, nevertheless, has taken care to present her in accessibly human terms, even as his characterization might tend toward Freudian stereotype. Blake, in contrast, remains dehumanized, even in his own mind, by the self-perpetuating masculine stereotype that, according to Cheever and others, tends to prevail, at least in the commercial world. Until the present moment of confrontation, Blake has had little reason to question either the principles or the conduct of his life, even under the continued censure of such individuals as Mrs. Compton and Mr. Watkins. Presumably reared and advanced according to the entrepreneurial conventions of his generation, Blake, to his eventual peril, equates success with domination, even with exploitation.

Faced with the immediate prospect of death, Blake recalls "in a rush" his battlefield experiences during World War II, and the frequent sight of unburied corpses. In counterpoint to Miss Dent's complaints as he believes that she is preparing to shoot him, Blake briefly recalls pleasant memories from his childhood. Cheever, whether deliberately or not, rehearses through Blake's experience the "moment of truth" common to the work of the French existentialists and to that of Ernest Hemingway as well; it is doubtful, however, that Blake will ever learn the lessons implied in his experience: Just as he had forgotten "Miss Dent," whose name is drawn solely from his admittedly defective memory and is never confirmed—and as "Miss Dent" appears to have forgotten him, Blake in all likelihood will forget what happened to him that evening on the local train.

Style and Technique

Narrated throughout in the "affectless" third person, "The Five-Forty-Eight" is notable for the reader's implied identification with "Miss Dent," no doubt certifiably insane, and not with the supposed viewpoint character, similarly identified only by his family name: Apart from Blake's son Charlie, the immediate cause of his quarrel with Mr. Watkins, only Mrs. Compton is identified by her given name, Louise, and then only in passing. Mr. Blake, it seems, is most pleased when so addressed, and when keeping the rest of the world at a similar distance of conventional formality. Louise Compton, apparently, has been mentioned to Blake so often by his unhappy wife that he cannot help but recall her first name. From the unexpected slant of the narration, it soon becomes apparent that Blake, and not the unfortunate Miss Dent (who may, or may not, have made a "dent" upon Blake's consciousness), is truly the more estranged and alienated of the two.

David B. Parsell

FIVE-TWENTY

Author: Patrick White (1912-   )
Type of plot: Psychological realism
Time of plot: The 1960's
Locale: Sydney, Australia
First published: 1973

> *Principal characters:*
> ELLA NATWICK, the protagonist, an elderly widow
> ROYAL NATWICK, the antagonist, her invalid husband
> AN UNNAMED OLDER MAN, the driver of a car which the
>   Natwicks watch daily

The Story

Ella and Royal Natwick, having retired to a small bungalow along Parramatta Road, a decaying suburb of Sydney, are spectators of the modern, industrial world that passes by them. Their chief summer activity is watching the traffic each day from their porch. Royal, a belligerent, insensitive invalid, is confined to a wheelchair; Ella, his lifelong devoted mate, dotes on him, suppressing any display of emotion which might upset him. As they watch one of the frequent traffic jams, Royal singles out for ridicule a man driving a pink-and-brown Holden: The car's color betrays masculinity, and the man's head appears deformed. Ella, without directly challenging Royal, suggests that the man may have a domineering wife and notes that the man passes each day at five-twenty, suggesting that he may be a business executive. That comment brings further slander from Royal, who complains ironically about the lack of achievement by white-collar workers: His own life has been a failure to achieve the status which he now belittles.

One evening, Ella assists the victim of a traffic accident in front of their house. Royal, indifferent to the tragedy of others, worries only about how Ella will wash the blood out of blankets which she has provided; in response, she kisses him on the forehead, immediately regretting her public display of affection for underscoring his powerlessness in the chair. Royal's only concerns are what he is to eat, his illusion of superiority over Ella, her proper care for him, and the habitual flow of traffic, in which Ella always notes "that gentleman . . . in the Holden."

Amid their evening recollections, the omniscient narrator provides fragmented flashbacks over the course of the Natwicks' lives. Royal's family settled in Australia from Kent, and the young Ella McWhirter liked to think that there was a hint of English royalty in those Natwicks who came to New South Wales. Royal's ambitions surpassed those of his bookkeeper father, but he never made them fruitful despite a series of moves from one town to another, until finally settling in Sydney. Ella has always been subservient to

Royal, and, at Fulbrook, she worked as a waitress, nurturing both their savings account and Royal's deluded self-image as a successful businessman. In Sarsaparilla, an outer suburb of Sydney where Royal opened a grocery store, she postponed having a child at Royal's admonishment that starting a new business would not be compatible with starting a new family. Throughout those years Ella defended Royal from customers' complaints and continued her devotion to him. Ignoring a doctor's implicit suggestion that Royal might be impotent, Ella accepted the failure to conceive as her own shortcoming, quietly brooding over "her secret grief."

Upon the Natwicks' retirement, Ella turns her energies to caring for the garden, the house, and Royal's increasingly deteriorating health. With a hernia, heart trouble, and arthritis, Royal becomes incontinent and confined to the wheelchair. The traffic jams, the air pollution, and the man in the pink Holden become their only mutual diversions from drab routine. Indeed, when the man does not drive by for a few days, there is almost a crisis for the Natwicks: "Nothing would halt the traffic, not sickness, not death even." Before he resumes his five-twenty schedule in a new, cream-colored Holden, Ella dreams that she meets the man in her garden, a dream that she does not share fully with Royal. Having repressed her sensuality and her desire for affection for a lifetime, Ella is hardly conscious of her increasing obsession with seeing the man pass by. In a second dream, she drops a double-yoked egg, breaking it on the path in her tunnel of cinerarias in the garden. Only these dreams disrupt the monotony of Ella's life.

Royal's death in early autumn deprives Ella of an object for her devotion. She withdraws into herself; Royal had been all-consuming of her emotions: the "feeling part of her had been removed." She remains compulsive about seeing the man in the Holden pass each evening, but she becomes indifferent to the care of her garden and her house, spending much of the autumn and winter sorting reflectively through a box of keepsakes and changing daily the water in a tumbler that holds Royal's dentures. The traffic and the cinerarias—head-high blossoms of purple, blue, and wine spires—occupy her most devoted attention.

One late winter evening, Ella is walking among the cinerarias when the man in the Holden appears in her garden, asking to use the telephone because of car trouble. She notices that he has a harelip, a deformity that earlier had repulsed her, and that "his eyes, she dared to think, were filled with kindness." Waiting for the tow truck, Ella becomes suddenly exuberant, bragging about her garden, laughing and showing off her cinerarias. As she begins to tell him about them, she "switched to another language," seemingly inarticulate in an "almost formless agonized sound." In response, the man seeks to comfort her, and as they embrace, Ella kisses him, "as though she might never succeed in healing all the wounds they had ever suffered." Before he departs, Ella has invited him for coffee the next evening.

Ella's preparations for her meeting occupy her entire day. She learns how to brew coffee from Mrs. Dolan, her neighbor. She spends a considerable part of the day shopping for cosmetics and applying them, but she removes them when she appears to herself to be mirroring a purple cineraria. She considers hiding Royal's teeth but decides against it. Having made the coffee early, she waits on the porch. When a traffic accident occurs, she remembers helping once before but decides to "save herself up" on this evening. She chats with Mrs. Dolan, but she cannot repress her "lust" for kindness, intensified by the man's late arrival. She realizes that the man does not know that she has measured her life in the passing of his car, and she retires to the garden to walk among the cinerarias. Then she hears him coming into the garden.

Immediately Ella senses that he is sick; his voice fades, and he falters. When she reaches him, she begins mumbling pet names, supporting him in the throes of a heart attack. In her frantic desperation, she tells him that she loves him, even as he slips from her arms to the ground. She covers the dying man with her kisses. Without knowing him or even his name, Ella concludes that "she must have killed him by loving too deeply, and too adulterously."

Themes and Meanings

Just as "Five-Twenty" marks the end of the day, it also marks symbolically the end of Ella's routine of meaningless suffering, yet Ella is left with only an ambivalent redemption at the end of the story. Ella possesses an inherent goodness, embodying Patrick White's belief, expressed in his autobiographical *Flaws in the Glass: A Self-Portrait* (1982), that "only love redeems. . . . I mean the love shared with an individual. . . . [I]t is making do . . . whatever our age, in a world falling apart." There is little apparent reason for Ella's goodness, for her devotion as mate to a brutally insensitive Royal, but her capacity for sharing love is beyond doubt. With the man in the Holden, sharing love becomes a possibility.

Ella's goodness, however, has suffered at the cost of her desire; she has repressed her desire for expressing affection, or receiving it, just as she has given up hope for a child. Royal's frustration of Ella's affections does not, however, succeed entirely: Her obsession with the man in the Holden becomes the blossoming of her desire just as her devotion to the phallic cinerarias signals the coming opportunity for love, for kindness. With the rise of her desire in the wake of her lost object of devotion, Ella becomes a whole person with a last hope for love. The man's own implicit suffering because of his deformities echoes Ella's suffering in her subservience to Royal. In her unconscious fantasy of loving the man in the Holden, Ella achieves wholeness by balancing her devotion with her desire.

As Ella's dream of the meeting gives way to her dream of the double-yoked egg, both become realities: Ella has the chance for new life but loses it (as in "losing" the child) in the man's heart attack, itself an ironic situation of mutual pain, his physical and hers emotional. She has become a whole person, redeemed in love, only to lose the confidence of that love in her presumed guilt that she has "loved too deeply, and too adulterously." Ella, then, is one of "the poor unfortunates" in the epigraph of an early collection of short stories, *The Burnt Ones* (1964). She redeems herself in the free expression of her love only to suffer the greater pain of condemning her own just desire to love and to be loved. Ella's devotion, her very goodness, is the self-constructed prison from which she cannot escape, for it destroys the very balance upon which her wholeness depends.

Style and Technique

White's ability to explore a profound theme underneath the surface imagery of a decaying, superficial urban world rests largely on his use of irony and symbolism. The chief irony is that while Ella is far more deserving of devoted love than Royal, it is Royal rather than Ella or her friend who enjoys the devotion, and he demands it instead of appreciating it. Doubly ironic is the turn of plot that introduces a deformed man to serve as Ella's liberating object of desire when she herself has been emotionally deformed by her lifelong repression of desire, particularly in the recent care of her invalid husband (an emotional invalid far more than a physical one). The crowning irony of the conclusion is that Ella believes she has been adulterous in the explosion of her sensuality, despite her status as widow and Royal's callous indifference to her affection. Instead of recognizing the redemption of love, Ella, in typically self-deprecating fashion, assumes responsibility for her would-be lover's death. The unifying irony of the entire story is that Ella's very goodness is the source of her own undoing.

Through a precise use of images, White further complicates the story by his use of symbols. The traffic jams reverberate with Ella's repressed desire just as the accidents foreshadow both the chance encounter and the man's death. The cinerarias are pointedly phallic in shape and in Ella's perception of them, just as the garden itself becomes her object of desire while she cares for Royal. The garden tunnel, where the cinerarias are located, seems strikingly vaginal as Ella dreams of meeting the man within it. With the use of obvious sexual symbolism, White can suggest something far more important to Ella than sexual fulfillment: the desire for love and the desire to express love freely, not mere sensual gratification. The symbolism, then, becomes a mask for the quest of love. Even Ella's kisses in the mock mouth-to-mouth resuscitation of the final scene symbolize her attempt to love both of them back to life. Ella's attempt to save the dying man is a last attempt to save her own momentary wholeness upon which her goodness rests, and gasps.

Michael Loudon

FLIGHT

Author: John Steinbeck (1902-1968)
Type of plot: Realism
Time of plot: The early 1900's
Locale: Monterey, California
First published: 1938

Principal characters:
PEPE TORRES, a nineteen-year-old farmboy
MAMA TORRES, his mother, a middle-aged widow

The Story

Pepe Torres is a "gentle, affectionate boy" whose only fault is his laziness. Reared by his protective and loving widowed mother, Mama Torres, who struggles to provide her children with a stable emotional environment and a meager material existence on the family farm, Pepe would rather not work. Hour after hour, he plays with his dead father's switchblade, throwing the knife at a post until his aim is extremely accurate.

One day, Mama Torres sends Pepe to town for some salt and medicine. Pepe has never been trusted with such a mission, and he feels proud when his mother gives him his father's round black hat with the tooled leather band and his green silk handkerchief to wear on the journey. After he has left, Pepe's younger brother asks if Pepe has become a man today; his mother answers, "A boy gets to be a man when a man is needed. Remember this thing. I have known boys forty years old because there was no need for a man." Mama Torres' wisdom is sound, but she does not foresee the tragic events which are about to unfold.

Pepe returns home in the middle of the night, only stopping briefly in his flight to the mountains. He tells his mother that in town he was called names he "could not allow" as a man, and that in the subsequent fight, he killed with his knife the person who called him such names. The definition of manhood in his society required such action. The mother understands, declaring, "Yes, thou art a man, my poor little Pepe. Thou art a man." She gives Pepe the father's rifle and his black coat, and when the other children ask where Pepe is going, she states that "Pepe is a man now. He has a man's thing to do." As soon as he leaves, she begins "the high, whining keen of the death wail," for she intuits that he will not be able to survive in the mountains.

The second, longer part of the story follows Pepe into the high mountains, where he attempts to elude the posse. He has no real choice in his actions now: He meets the ordeal that he must endure with "a man's face." His initiation into manhood, which began with his journey into the city, is complete, and he struggles against the forces of society and nature with the status of manhood. Occasionally, he sees dark figures in the landscape watching him:

forms of men who are always faceless, suggesting the formless figures of death.

Although Pepe successfully evades the posse for a few days, one morning his horse is shot out from under him without warning, and in the ensuing gun battle, he is wounded in the hand by a sliver of granite, chipped off a rock by a bullet. Although he does escape into the high barren peaks, he is without water, and soon his hand and arm begin to swell with the wound.

During the course of these events, he loses his father's possessions piece by piece: the hat, the horse, the coat. When his hand and arm become gangrenous, he is almost crazed from pain and lack of water. At last he finds a dry streambed in the bottom of a ravine, digs down into it for a few drops of water, and falls asleep. When he awakes in the afternoon, a mountain lion is watching him from twenty feet away. The beast has no fear of Pepe, for in his present condition, Pepe no longer presents a threat. Pepe is himself a "hurt beast." The lion watches Pepe until evening; it appears that the lion is about to fall asleep, and then suddenly it leaves. A few moments later, Pepe hears the dogs of the posse looking for his trail. He struggles to his feet and once more eludes the posse. Weak from his ordeal, he falls asleep again, near the top of a high, barren ridge. When he awakes and goes on, he realizes that he has forgotten his rifle; he returns, but cannot find it. The last item once belonging to his father is now gone.

In the final scene, Pepe crawls up the slope of the ridge, and as the dawn breaks, he stands up on the top of a big rock on the ridge peak. He cannot actually see the members of the posse, but he knows they are nearby. There he is shot, standing upright to take the bullet. His body tumbles down the slope, starting a small avalanche. "And when at last he stopped against a bush, the avalanche slid slowly down and covered his head." The forces of society have overwhelmed him, but he has died with dignity, achieving a tragic stature in his struggle.

Themes and Meanings

Beneath the surface, realistic detail of this story, John Steinbeck develops the moral allegory of a boy growing into manhood. The opening events resemble the simple plot of a fairy tale: A boy leaves home on a journey of initiation, he undergoes a trial, he returns a man. Steinbeck, however, brings the tale to a new conclusion: In this society, the achievement of manhood can demand the life of the protagonist. Built within the framework of society is a code by which the individual must act—but the individual may well die as a result of this action. Thus, to choose to be a man by society's definition of manhood can have tragic consequences.

That Steinbeck has chosen a *paisano* for his hero is significant. Steinbeck defined the *paisano* as a mixture of Spanish, Indian, Mexican, and assorted Caucasian bloods—someone whose ancestors have lived in California for a hundred or more years. These people are poor by the Anglo's materialistic standards, for, by and large, they do not subscribe to the Anglo work ethic but live in a different moral structure, one in which a man's behavior is much more important than his possessions. The focus in this story is on the nature of that behavior: To be a man can require action that society must condemn, and the paradoxical nature of this requirement is what makes for the possibility of the tragic figure. When that figure struggles against society with honor, he achieves an individual dignity that elevates him to a tragic status. Thus, in his final days in the mountains, Pepe becomes the symbolic tragic hero of his society.

The concept of a powerful society overwhelming the individual—the guiding idea of the literary movement known as naturalism—works its way through this story. Steinbeck viewed society as a huge organism which operated by natural laws, unmindful of the individual's wishes and desires, yet he also viewed the individual as being capable of acts which bring him human dignity. Pepe's story is the result of Steinbeck's artistic exploration of these contradictory truths.

Style and Technique

Steinbeck explores the story's themes using a third-person point of view that focuses on the consciousness of Pepe during his ordeal in the mountains. The author achieves a poetic grace with plain language that is appropriate to the thought processes of his protagonist. Contained in that language is the sharp detail of the physical landscape, which has a beauty of its own. Steinbeck also uses the detail of the physical landscape to suggest Pepe's inner emotions. For example, in the scene before his death, Pepe sees that "strewn over the hill there were giant outcroppings, and on the top the granite teeth stood out against the sky." The stark image of the "granite teeth" works to reflect the emotion that Pepe feels; trapped in his fate, he senses powers that will overwhelm and "devour" him. The images of the landscape provide a backdrop for his final act of defiance, of standing up to be shot down.

The dialogue early in the story between Pepe and members of his family is filled with short, declarative statements and the use of *thy* and *thou*, which gives it a stilted quality. By such devices, Steinbeck—rather like Ernest Hemingway in *For Whom the Bell Tolls* (1940)—was attempting, unsuccessfully, to convey the archaic dignity of his characters' speech.

Steinbeck's technique and style are appropriate to his subject: Pepe's direct, uncomplicated emotions are presented without authorial comment, being placed directly before the reader with a simple honesty that gives this story both power and poignancy.

Ronald L. Johnson

FLOWERING JUDAS

Author: Katherine Anne Porter (1890-1980)
Type of plot: Psychological realism
Time of plot: c. 1920
Locale: Mexico
First published: 1930

> *Principal characters:*
> LAURA, a twenty-two-year-old American who teaches school
> and participates in the revolution in Mexico
> BRAGGIONI, the leader of the revolution and suitor of Laura
> MRS. BRAGGIONI, his wife, who works hard for the revolution
> and weeps for her husband
> EUGENIO, a political prisoner who takes an overdose of
> narcotics, which he has obtained from Laura

The Story

In "Flowering Judas," Laura, after teaching school and visiting Eugenio in prison, comes home to be warned by Lupe, the maid, that Braggioni is waiting for her. Although she detests his presence, Laura, a young American, allows the Mexican revolutionary leader to sing to her. She is afraid of him, as he is known for his cruelty and vanity. As she "owes her comfortable situation and her salary to him," however, she does her best to tolerate him. For the past month he has been spending the evenings with her. Laura is in the precarious predicament of attempting to resist his advances without seeming to do so. His "gluttonous bulk . . . has become a symbol of her disillusions" with revolution and leaders. Braggioni has come to represent the disunion between her idealistic view of life and the life she is actually living.

Born a Roman Catholic, Laura still slips into a church now and then, but can no longer find comfort in it. She instead tries to embrace revolutionary theories, but without much success. Her private heresy is not to wear lace made by machines, even though the machine is "sacred" to the revolutionary forces with which she is working. She fears that she may become as corrupt as Braggioni, who sits before her in his expensive clothes and his great self-love. As he sings his love songs and lectures on his philosophy, Laura wonders why she stays in Mexico. She teaches the Indian children, attends union meetings, visits political prisoners, smuggles letters and drugs, and delivers messages. Yet her motives are unclear.

To the Mexicans who know her and see her in the street, Laura is an erotic mystery. Although she remains aloof she is admired for her green eyes, sensual lips, beautiful walk, large breasts, and long legs. The legendary virginity of the *gringita* spurs Braggioni and other potential lovers into constant courtship—but Laura says no to everyone. Not even the children are able to penetrate her remoteness, and they, too, remain strangers to her. The word "no" becomes symbolic of Laura's entire existence, as she denies to all people and things the chance to affect her emotions. Braggioni, however, believes that he has all the time in the world to break down her resistance. As a teenager, Braggioni was rejected by his first sweetheart, and now he makes every woman pay for the anguish he suffered. His wife is included in this vengeance, despite her devotion to him and to the revolution. She works hard organizing unions for the cigarette factory girls, but spends much of her time weeping for Braggioni, since this is what he prefers. Currently, he is observing a month of separation from her for what he describes as higher principles. Laura, though, envies Mrs. Braggioni's loneliness, since she feels trapped by Braggioni's persistent presence. As he sings on, she reflects on her visit to the prison that day and on Eugenio's condition.

Braggioni interrupts her thoughts by telling of the May-day disturbances he is planning for Morelia, where the Catholics and the Socialists will be having celebrations. He asks Laura to oil and load his pistols, while he speaks of revolution and sings of love. He wraps his fingers around the throat of the guitar as he sings and strokes the pistol in Laura's hands as he expounds on Marxist philosophy and his faith in dynamite. Laura finally hands back his gunbelt and tells him to make himself happy by killing someone in Morelia. When he leaves, Laura feels a sense of relief, but she does not flee, as she knows she should.

Braggioni goes home, ending the monthlong separation from his wife. She continues her weeping at his appearance and even offers to wash his feet. As she performs the task, she begs for his forgiveness. Braggioni happily consents, since her endless tears and humility refresh him.

Laura, meanwhile, prepares for bed. Before she falls asleep, she is concerned about her confusion with love and revolution: her inability to understand what her life is all about. Haunted by the thought of Eugenio, who may be dead by now as a result of taking the drugs she delivered to him, Laura has a nightmare in which Eugenio asks her to follow him. He calls her "Murderer" and offers her flowers from the Judas tree. She accepts them from his fleshless hand and eats them greedily. He calls her "Cannibal" for eating his body and blood. Laura cries no. She awakes and is afraid to sleep again.

Themes and Meanings

Laura and Braggioni obviously live by different sets of values. The latter, who masquerades as a professional philanthropist, loves himself most of all and will exploit the revolution and the people whenever it is to his advantage. He will never die for his principles or his love for humanity. He is an egomaniac who uses people and things for his own benefit. Laura, in contrast, is filled with guilt to the point that she suffers from moral paralysis. She merely goes through the motions of being a teacher and rebel without understanding the reasons behind them. While Braggioni will betray anyone, Laura betrays herself. She is unable to compromise between her concept of life as it should be and life as it is. The chaotic world of revolutionary Mexico overwhelms her.

Braggioni is the primary problem for Laura, who has a romantic view of what a revolutionary leader should be. He does not have the gauntness, the heroic faith, the abstract virtues associated with the ideal leader; his bulk, Jockey Club clothes, selfishness, and indifference to political prisoners offend her. She is also worried by his courtship. The threat of violence is always in the background. He is fascinated by his power, which includes the right to own things and people. He indulges in his love of small luxuries, and Laura fears that she is being placed in that category; he eventually may demand more from her than delivering messages and cleaning his guns. She may be only an interlude for Braggioni, like the revolution itself, but that does not reduce the threat. Braggioni's main concern is to be comfortable, to be flexible in his principles so that he can take care of himself as profitably as possible. He is at perpetual peace with himself, but Laura is lost.

Katherine Anne Porter began her writing career in the 1920's, when the wasteland motif was popular. Stemming from T. S. Eliot's poem *The Waste Land* (1922), and a recurring theme in the work of writers such as E. E. Cummings, Edwin Arlington Robinson, Edgar Lee Masters, Sinclair Lewis, Ernest Hemingway, F. Scott Fitzgerald, and William Faulkner, this concept emphasizes the lack of morality in society. Economic values are more important than moral values. Money and social position are depicted as being the prime goals in life. In "Flowering Judas," Braggioni is an example of a character who prospers in this kind of environment. Laura is an easy victim of those who play by rules that are foreign to her. She cannot come to accept the ugly reality of Braggioni. She is full of romantic error, according to the rebels, who have, in comparison, a strong sense of reality. Thus, Laura is not at home in the world. Like Prufrock, in Eliot's poem, "The Love Song of J. Alfred Prufrock" (1917), she suffers from moral ennui. She acts without thinking, or, when she does think, she is incapable of meaningful action. Indeed, she aids the corrupt Braggioni and helps Eugenio commit suicide; since the values of her former life do not apply, she denies the value of everything. She gives in to her environment and tries to convince herself that things are beyond her control.

This resignation to her fate is a form of self-betrayal. She rejects her old value system but fails to replace it with a viable philosophy. She disclaims the principles of the revolution, the propositions of her suitors, and the love of her schoolchildren. Laura no longer makes moral decisions, and the wasteland claims her.

Style and Technique

In a story noted for its symbolism, the major symbolic patterns involve sex and religion. The sexual emphasis is used primarily to show how Laura is victimized by Braggioni. Under his domination, she yields to a fatalistic view of life in which events are beyond her control. The religious symbolism reveals the self-betrayal of this surrender.

Braggioni represents the potential of sexual violation. His fat body, encased in expensive clothes, calls attention to the power he has over Laura. As he strokes the guitar and the pistol and sings his love songs, his amorous intentions are made clear to Laura. His name, resembling "braggadocio," further suggests his boasting, macho behavior. Laura's aloofness and her attempt to hide her body in heavy material merely add to the challenge that she represents to the rebel leader. His great bulk threatens her physically just as his corruption destroys her romantic illusions. In resisting him physically, however, she yields to him intellectually and morally.

The title of the story suggests its religious symbolism. Judas, the betrayer, supposedly hanged himself from a redbud tree. In Laura's dream, Eugenio offers the flowers of the Judas tree, which she readily devours. The dream indicates the guilt she feels as a result of her amoral activity. The guilt, suppressed during her conscious hours, comes forth in a parody of religious ritual, much like the washing of Braggioni's feet by his wife. Laura's dream thus embodies the story's themes in a highly charged symbolic language.

Noel Schraufnagel

THE FLY

Author: Katherine Mansfield (Kathleen Mansfield Beauchamp, 1888-1923)
Type of plot: Psychological realism
Time of plot: After World War I
Locale: England
First published: 1922

Principal characters:
THE BOSS, the protagonist
MR. WOODIFIELD, a visitor
MACEY, the office messenger

The Story

"The Fly" is a story told primarily through the eyes of "the boss," the protagonist, who is described not by name but by function. The story has two parts. In the first part, Mr. Woodifield (whom the boss thinks of as "old Woodifield"), retired since his stroke and woman-dominated, visits his friend the boss, who though five years older than Woodifield is still in charge of the firm. Woodifield and the boss have one experience in common: Both lost sons in World War I.

The boss enjoys showing Woodifield his redecorated office and benevolently offering him some whiskey. Then Woodifield, who has momentarily forgotten what he meant to tell the boss, remembers. His daughters have been in Belgium to see the grave of their brother, Woodifield's son, and they have also seen that of the boss's son. After Woodifield reports that the cemetery is well kept, he leaves, and the first part of the story is concluded.

Feeling that he must weep, the boss tells the cowed messenger, Macey, to give him a half hour alone. He feels as if he can see his son in the grave. Yet, although he muses that his life has been meaningless since the death of his promising only son, whom he was grooming to take over the business, the boss cannot weep.

At this point, the boss sees a fly in the inkpot, pulls it out, and puts it on a blotter, where he proceeds to torture it, placing one drop of ink on it at a time and repeating the operation every time the fly seems to have extricated itself and gained hope. Even though he admires the fly and cheers it on, the boss continues to drop ink upon it until at last the fly dies. He feels miserable, but he cannot remember what he was thinking about before he began his experiment with the fly.

Themes and Meanings

"The Fly" is a story of death. It begins with a meeting of two men who have lost sons in the war, and it ends with the death of a fly. In a deeper sense, however, there are six deaths indicated in the story.

When the boss first looks at old Woodifield, he sees a man who appears to be totally different from him. Woodifield is retired. He is dominated by his wife and daughters, who keep him in the house every day except Tuesday, when they dress him up and send him out to visit his friends. His passive, infantile life causes the boss to think of him as a baby. He is useful as someone to impress and to patronize. The boss enjoys offering him whiskey, which Woodifield's women deny him; thus, the boss can assert his own power, which elevates him above the rules of Woodifield's own bosses. Even Woodifield's forgetfulness suggests the decline he has suffered since his stroke. Clearly Woodifield is on the downhill road toward death; yet the fact that he could not remember the girls' visit to his son's grave suggests a second death, the death of his son's memory in his own mind.

On the surface, the boss is very different from Woodifield. He is healthy and active. He dominates Macey, his messenger, as a master would a dog. Yet he thinks that his life ended six years ago, when the son for whom he intended the business was killed in the war. In response to his son's death, the boss himself has died, or so he thinks.

Yet now, six years later, he finds himself staring at an unfamiliar photograph, which does not seem to look like his son; worse, he finds himself tormenting a fly rather than grieving; and finally, he forgets why he feels so miserable. If his son has been alive in his memory, he is now unfamiliar and unremembered, and in a sense, dead. Furthermore, if the boss loved only the son who always agreed with him, both father and son died a long time ago. All that is left is the boss's self-pity. His inability to feel for the son, hard as he may try, is like his inability to feel for the fly. Healthy, prosperous, domineering, the boss is, however, dead to feeling, and perhaps he has always been too self-centered to feel anything for others.

A fifth death is the death-in-life to which the boss has reduced his messenger, Macey, who is referred to throughout the story as a dog rather than a man. Macey, too, is old. His boss's attitude toward him is reflected in the thought that everyone, even Macey, liked the son. If Macey has learned to survive by doglike obedience, perhaps, Mansfield implies, Macey and the boss's other subordinates were counterfeiting their admiration of the son, whom the boss remembers as always having been pleasant, but who evidently looks like quite another person in his photograph. At any rate, Macey must have died as a human being at some time in the past, when he became the boss's faithful dog.

Finally, there is the death which gives the title to the story, that of the fly. Godlike, the boss first rescues the fly, then tests it repeatedly, cheering it on, sadistically applying a fresh ink drop just when the fly has survived the last, and finally deliberately putting what he knows will be the killing drop upon the fly.

In "The Fly," perhaps the most pessimistic of Katherine Mansfield's stories, death conquers all. It may be death to feeling or death to memory; it may be death-in-life through self-love or through self-abnegation; it may be the death of will; finally, it will certainly be literal death, as it has been experienced by the two sons and by the fly.

Style and Technique

In "The Fly," Katherine Mansfield typically uses a minimal amount of action in order to reveal human emotions. The real drama of the story involves a dialogue between two men, a direction to a messenger, a soliloquy, the torture and death of a fly, and another direction to the messenger. Throughout the story, the point of view is that of the boss, as he moves from self-satisfaction to inability to feel to preoccupied torture to misery. Because the boss, in contrast to Mansfield's sensitive protagonists, is essentially self-centered, however, the revelation in the story must come to the observant reader, rather than to the protagonist himself.

It is the reader, not the protagonist, who will notice the various parallels which are carefully built into the design of the story. The boss does not notice that he and Woodifield are alike in managing to forget the deaths of their sons. Nor does he realize that Woodifield's stroke and his own life's end, when his son died, have both been followed by a rebirth, by the capacity for pleasure, whether in a day out or in showing off the new furniture.

It is also the reader, not the protagonist, who sees that the fly itself has symbolic significance. Much as the boss may pity himself, in that he has lost the son whom he was shaping to follow him, he does not admit any feelings of identity with anyone or anything—not with Macey, not with Woodifield, certainly not with the fly he kills. Yet the fly can be interpreted to represent every human being, including the insensitive boss. Just as the boss puts blot after blot upon the fly, whatever powers there be put burden after burden upon humanity, whether through nature, through war, through a hierarchical social and economic structure, or through the human need to dominate another creature. The pattern of human life is like the brief ordeal of the fly, which staggers, hopes, and rises, growing weaker each time, until at last it is conquered by death.

If Katherine Mansfield's symbolism in this story is directed toward the observant reader, rather than toward the insensitive protagonist, her language reflects the nature of the boss. There are no incomplete sentences, no fragments of thought, such as are found in Mansfield's indecisive characters. In his conversation with Woodifield, the boss observes himself bending to his inferior: winking, joking, and generously offering the whiskey. Even in his thoughts, the boss moves logically, as if he were arguing a case with the gods. It is only when he begins to torture the fly that he becomes oblivious of himself, so involved is he in the kind of action which has made and kept him "the boss." Even after the fly's death, when he feels miserable, he does not drift into half-sentences, but gives Macey an order. Only three sentences before the end of the story is there a momentary hesitation in the style, when the boss realizes that he has forgotten something. Even then, though, he acts, he wipes his neck, and the final ironic line—"For the life of him he could not remember"—is in a style as self-assured as his whole life.

Rosemary M. Canfield-Reisman

FLYING HOME

Author: Ralph Ellison (1914-   )
Type of plot: Psychological realism
Time of plot: World War II
Locale: Macon County, Alabama
First published: 1944

> *Principal characters:*
> TODD, a black candidate in the army's Flight Training School
> JEFFERSON, an old, black tenant farmer
> TEDDY, his young son
> DABNEY GRAVES, a white man, the owner of the land that
>   Jefferson farms

The Story

Todd, a young black man, a candidate in Flight Training School in Macon County, Alabama, during World War II, is just returning to consciousness after an accident. The narrative soon reveals, in one of several flashbacks, that Todd's "exultation" in flight had carried him away. He had flown "too high and too fast"; the plane had entered a tailspin, and before he could react a buzzard had smashed into his windshield. Panic caused him to lose control. A crash landing has thrown him from the plane and has broken his ankle. Over him stand an old, black farmer, Jefferson, and his son, Teddy. What immediately preoccupies Todd even more than the physical pain in his ankle is the anxiety over his failure as a pilot. His white officers will see the accident as confirmation that blacks are not capable of flying or of aerial combat. Since for Todd, earning his wings and fighting overseas are his escape from social inferiority—and from the stereotypical black traditions that he sees epitomized in Jefferson—the accident is a crisis in his young life.

Jefferson instinctively understands much of what Todd is experiencing. He sends his son to Dabney Graves, the symbol of white civil authority in the region and the owner of the land that Jefferson works, in order to get help, and then tries to take Todd's mind off the pain. He first tells him a brief anecdote about once finding two buzzards inside the remains of a dead horse and comments that Teddy's name for a buzzard is jimcrow. To Jefferson, this identification is both comical and meaningful. He then tells a more lengthy tale about his past life, when he was in Heaven. Though he was a black angel and required to wear a harness, he violated the rule and showed off his extraordinary powers of flight. His daring, however, became dangerous and offensive to God. As punishment, God took away his wings and sent him to Macon County, Alabama. This myth of origins again prompts Jefferson to laugh hilariously, but Todd, interpreting the two stories according to his own egotistical fears, accuses him of mockery. Todd takes the buzzards and the flying black angel to be satiric representations of himself. Jefferson had no such intentions and can only express his regret and empathy for Todd's painful situation.

Somehow, Jefferson's attempts to distract him, the empathy, and the physical pain succeed in taking Todd outside himself and releasing memories from his childhood. He recalls in detail his early obsession with airplanes and his attempt once, when he was getting a fever, to grab from the sky a real plane, which he mistook for a toy. In his feverous state during the next few days, he dreamed of capturing planes just beyond his grasp and of hearing his grandmother warn him about his arms being "too short/ To box with God." After a brief conversation with Jefferson about the plight of black people in a white society and after Jefferson's warning about the fickleness of Dabney Graves, Todd in painful delirium recalls another childhood moment. He was walking down a street on election day. Black faces peered fearfully from the houses, and one person seemed to be begging for his aid or perhaps warning him of danger. He saw a shower of leaflets descend from a plane high against the sun. When he picked up one of them, his mother took it and read a warning from the Klan: "Niggers Stay Away From The Polls." He awakens from the dream to see three men approaching. Dabney Graves and two hospital attendants put him in a straitjacket, intended for Dabney's crazy cousin Rudolph but placed on Todd by Dabney as a joke. When Todd comes to full consciousness of what is happening, that the men have also laid him on a stretcher and are about to carry him away, he rebels. He steps out of the role of the inferior "nigger" and demands that they not touch him. Incensed by such independence in a black man, Dabney kicks him in the chest. The physical violence suddenly transforms Todd. It causes him to observe the entire situation with objectivity. He now sees his salvation in Jefferson. As Jefferson and Teddy, at Graves's command, carry him off to the "nigguh airfield," he loses his sense of isolation. Jefferson's care and the confrontation with the white bigoted world have transformed his confused and frustrated sense of identity into peace and harmony.

Themes and Meanings

"Flying Home" is a story about racism. The main characters represent essential elements in the racial conflict in America: Jefferson is the traditional figure from the days of slavery; Todd is the young, modern black trying to escape from racial distinctions; Dabney Graves is the white landowner still governed by the bigoted assumptions of his ancestors; the white army officers, though not actually present in the story, still carry on in a nonagrarian context the old prejudices. Ellison uses the anecdotes told by Jefferson and the memories of Todd to insist on the same racial theme: Blacks are jimcrow buzzards feeding on a dead horse; they are angels who even in Heaven are ruled by a white god and subject to special restrictions; they are taught by their parents not to aim too high and are threatened by the Klan not to participate in the nation's political life. The end of the story offers no resolution to this social conflict. Todd returns to the airfield knowing that the white officers will regard his accident as a further sign of racial ineptitude. Dabney Graves would still eject any black from his land who showed signs of disrespect for the old standards. So long as the white attitude remains, the conflict will remain.

The story is not, however, primarily about racism in society; it is about racism and the effects of racism within Todd. He is experiencing an identity crisis that takes at least four forms. First, he wants to be an individual totally dissociated from his race: The burden of his every action being a partial definition of his race (a Sartrean theme in Ellison's story) is more than he wants to bear. Second, he is ashamed of his past: He wants to dissociate himself entirely from Jefferson, who fits Todd's Uncle Tom image of the black man. This is a sign that Todd has internalized the whites' perception of the black race. Third, he unconsciously wants to be white: Flying toward the sun makes him white; falling toward the earth makes him black. Fourth, he measures his own worth by another's standards. Though he has found that the judgments of the traditional black (slave) culture and of the white American authority figures are inadequate (that is, he has rejected these judgments consciously, if not unconsciously), his goal as a military pilot is to prove himself in battle so that the enemy will sanction his worthiness. While the story offers no solution to the social conflict, it does resolve the inner conflict. It is possible for the black man in American society to live at peace with himself.

The solution that Ellison finds, on the purely thematic level, is a common one in black American literature. At the root of racism and other prejudices is ignorance, not only of others but also of the self. What Jefferson teaches and what Todd learns during the experience is a way of achieving first self-knowledge and then a knowledge of others.

At the beginning of the story, Jefferson already possesses wisdom, but only on an instinctual level. It is a part of his heritage. It is present in the stories that he tells Todd. They are peculiarly appropriate to Todd's situation. They represent the state from which he needs to escape, the black man as a buzzard feeding on a dead horse, and the state that he needs to achieve, the free-flying angel who paradoxically must acknowledge human limitation and failure without denying his essential humanity. The tales initiate Todd into awareness. Todd is not free because racism has distorted his understanding of his identity, his heritage, his home—that is, his human reality. Jefferson would appear to be not fully conscious of how appropriate his anecdotes are, but they, as repositories of traditional wisdom (Todd has heard a variation of the angel "myth" as a child), speak directly to his need. Todd's initial refusal to accept the meaning of the tales is reflected in his angry reaction. He cannot accept the truth about himself. For some unstated reason, however, the truth hidden in the tales provokes repressed memories about his childhood fascination with airplanes and their associations with racial oppression. Though again unstated, what Todd seems to learn is that the airplane, instead of being a legitimate means of escape and of finding identity, represents an attempt to become white, to be what the white man is, to get his power. What Ellison does state clearly is that the airplane is for Todd an escape from the "world of men." At the end of the story, he finds in Jefferson, not the old Uncle Tom, but a human being who understands him. "A new current of communication flowed between the man and boy and himself." Nor should one leave unstated the obvious. In finally yielding himself to Jefferson and Teddy and accepting the earth as his home, he is also declaring an allegiance to American soil in spite of those who would reject him.

Todd has returned to his roots. Yet even this is not the special theme that recurs in black literature. Jefferson's tales are significant as much for their tone as for their meaning. After telling both, he laughs hilariously. He knows that they are jokes. They are his way of coping with racism, with what Todd comes to view as "an insane world of outrage and humiliation." Further, and more important, they are a sign of, and they enourage, objectivity. They allow one to get outside oneself and view the self and the world from another perspective. Jefferson is the two-headed juju man. Ellison emphasizes the crucial nature of this act of stepping outside the self several times during the story. The tales themselves offer projected presentations of Todd. Yet, more directly, before Todd's first childhood recollection, "a part of him was lying calmly behind the screen of pain." At the beginning of the second recollection, Todd, in his delirium, sees two Jeffersons, one "that shook with fits of belly-laughter while the other Jefferson looked on with detachment." By the end of the story, Todd has emitted his own "blasts of hot, hysterical laughter," while "a part of him stood behind it all, watching the surprise in Graves's red face and his own hysteria." No longer bound by his own ego, he can see himself and others in perspective and, hence, can follow a reunion with society and an inner peace.

Style and Technique

Ellison primarily uses the third-person point of view in "Flying Home," yet very early he alerts the reader that he will play some tricks with it. While in a state of semiconsciousness, Todd hears voices, not placed in quotation marks, which are both inside his head and outside. Where the voices are coming from, who is speaking, what one intends or perceives, and what biases govern thought and speech—these questions that Ellison raises involve an interrelationship between theme and point of view. When Jefferson speaks of buzzards and black angels, Todd perceives himself as the actor in those roles. When Todd enters the world of his past for the first time, Ellison almost without warning shifts to the first-person point of view and thus places the reader intimately within the mind of his protagonist. It is as though, along with Todd, the reader has difficulty distinguishing between external and inner reality. Todd's second memory is, on the other hand, clearly noted as his own thoughts. The progression in the story, in fact, is a gradual clearing of Todd's mind so that by the end he sees clearly both himself and the outer world. Both technically and thematically, point of view comes into focus.

This manipulation of point of view, however, is not nearly as interesting in itself as are its implications in another facet of Ellison's technique. Typically, Ellison likes his stories to operate on a mythical level. While maintaining a high degree of realism, including psychological realism, Ellison controls characters and events to fit into mythical patterns that universalize them. The story about a young man coming to awareness, for example, is clearly a vision of the initiation motif. His fall from the sky, like the black angel's condemnation to the hell of Alabama, follows the pattern of death and rebirth. The buzzard that feeds on death is in the final statement of the story "a bird of flaming gold," perhaps a reference to the phoenix, and certainly a reinforcement of the death-rebirth motif. The identification of Todd with Icarus and Jefferson with Daedalus is unmistakable. Flying too close to the sun Ellison interprets in his own way as part of the black man's dilemma in American society. Elements of Christian myth, Heaven and Hell, and especially the question of knowledge and how much man has a right to, and the pride of the original Fall lie behind Todd's experience. One must not forget the folk tradition that Ellison includes, Jefferson's creation and re-creation of myth. Indeed, this last is especially important because of the relation of myth in the story to theme and point of view. Myths are useless if not understood and reinterpreted in the light of immediate experience, and Todd's education is, in part, a coming to terms with his heritage.

Ellison's mythical ventures operate in the Jungian manner. The myths are not only outside Todd but also within his racial unconscious. The events in the story are his acting out the patterns that already exist in his mind. If he is not to play out the roles blindly and chaotically, he must raise them to consciousness, and choose and reinterpret those that he needs in the modern world. The story does not show Todd reaching such a level of sophistication, but it does show Ellison's own preoccupation with the task. The reader does, however, observe Todd acting out some changes in his conceptions. At the end, for example, he no longer views Heaven and Hell as whiteness and blackness, or as flying in the sky and living on the earth. Earth becomes the human community rather than Hell. Flying home is flying back to Earth.

It is also a return to the true self. A part of Carl Gustav Jung's theories about the unconscious mind suggests the presence of archetypal images of the self—persona, anima, shadow—and of various other figures, such as the wise old man. Until late in the story, however, Todd rejects the promptings of the anima, still projects the evil and prejudice in himself outwardly on such figures as Graves and the white officers, and perceives Jefferson as ignorant rather than wise. By the end of the story, his soul lives in harmony. He has internalized Jefferson's wisdom (the mythical father resides within him); he has accepted his girl's advice that he not continually prove his intelligence to the white man (that he not feed on that dead horse); he has, by accepting Jefferson as his savior, admitted a prejudice in his own psyche, and no longer blindly projects such evil on the Dabney Graveses of the world. His perspective has cleared. His inner voice is in harmony with outer voices: "Like a song within his head he heard the boy's soft humming. . . ."

Without at all denying the black heritage, Ellison insists on the presence of all cultures within the human psyche. As he says elsewhere, it is possible for a black to be a Renaissance man, one who incorporates all experiences.

Thomas Banks

FOR ESMÉ—WITH LOVE AND SQUALOR

Author: J. D. Salinger (1919-   )
Type of plot: Psychological romance
Time of plot: April, 1944, to May, 1945
Locale: Dover, England, and Gaufurt, Bavaria
First published: 1950

>*Principal characters:*
>STAFF SERGEANT X, a young American stationed in Europe in
>the last year of World War II
>ESMÉ, a thirteen-year-old English girl whom X meets in an
>English tearoom
>CLAY (CORPORAL Z), X's insensitive jeepmate during this year

The Story

The story opens in 1950, immediately after the narrator has received an invitation to Esmé's wedding. He and his "breathtakingly levelheaded" wife have decided that he cannot go, so, instead, he writes these "few revealing notes on the bride as I knew her almost six years ago."

The story proper (still in the first person) begins in April of 1944. The narrator is one of sixty enlisted men stationed in rural England, undergoing pre-Invasion Intelligence training. On the afternoon of his last day in Devon, he walks through the rain to the small town and wanders into choir rehearsal in a church. There he notices a girl with "the sweetest-sounding" voice, "an exquisite forehead, and blasé eyes." Later the girl, her five-year-old brother, Charles, and their governess come into the tearoom, where the narrator has gone to escape the rain. The girl gives him an "oddly radiant" smile and then comes over to talk with him because he looks "extremely lonely." Esmé is precious and precocious, her conversation peppered with large words and delightful misinformation about America ("I thought Americans despised tea"). The narrator learns that Esmé is titled, that both her parents are dead (she wears her father's oversized military wristwatch), and that she is being reared by an aunt. When Esmé finds out that the narrator is a writer, she asks if he would write a story for her and suggests that he "make it extremely squalid and moving." When she leaves, Esmé asks if he would like her to write to him. "It was a strangely emotional moment for me," the narrator relates. Esmé says good-bye and adds, "I hope you return from the war with all your faculties intact."

The second half of the story—"the squalid, or moving part," as the narrator says in its first line—takes place in Gaufurt, Bavaria, and is narrated in the third person. The protagonist (now "cunningly" disguised as "Staff Sergeant X") is sitting at a table in his second-floor room in an occupied German house several weeks after V-E Day (in other words, more than a year after the first scene). He has returned that day from a two-week stay in a Frankfurt hospital, where he was sent after an apparent nervous breakdown, but he does not look much improved. His hands shake, he has a facial tic, and his gums bleed at the touch of his tongue. In an attempt to hold on to something, he opens a book by Joseph Goebbels that was once owned by the thirty-eight-year-old woman who lived in this house and whom X arrested as a minor Nazi functionary. On the flyleaf, the woman has written, "Dear God, life is hell," Beneath that inscription, X now writes, "Fathers and teachers, I ponder 'What is Hell?' I maintain that it is the suffering of being unable to love," but when he finishes, he discovers that what he has written is "almost entirely illegible."

After a painful scene with his jeepmate, Clay, whose insensitivity to X's real situation keeps him from being very helpful, it is clear that X is near collapse. Suddenly, in the pile of unopened mail in front of him, he spots a package, opens it, and finds a letter from Esmé written almost a year earlier, with her father's wristwatch, sent to X "as a lucky talisman." The crystal to the watch is broken, and X does not have the courage to see if the watch still works. After holding it in his hand "for another long period," X realizes that "suddenly, almost ecstatically, he felt sleepy." The gift has somehow saved him, for, as he writes in the last line, a really sleepy man "*al*ways stands a chance of again becoming" a man with all his faculties "intact."

Themes and Meanings

"For Esmé—with Love and Squalor" is one of J. D. Salinger's most romantic and popular stories. In fact, when Salinger's first collection of short stories, *Nine Stories* (1953), was published in England, it was retitled *For Esmé—with Love and Squalor* (1953). Like so many works in the limited Salinger library, this is a story of redemption by love, and, as in most of these works—from *The Catcher in the Rye* (1951) through "A Perfect Day for Bananafish" (also in *Nine Stories*) to *Franny and Zooey* (1961)—the saving gesture is made by a child. Children are special in Salinger's work, for they alone are capable of making the sacrifice of love.

The contrast in "For Esmé—with Love and Squalor" is clear, for all the other characters want something from the narrator; only Esmé gives. The uncommunicative soldiers with whom he is first stationed in Devon talk to one another only when they want to borrow something; the letter from his mother-in-law that he reads in the tearoom asks him "to please send her some cashmere yarn." Clay wants X to make his letters to his girlfriend more interesting; a letter from X's brother asks him to send "the kids a couple of bayonets or swastikas," now that the war is over. The protagonist at the end of the story has just gone through five campaigns, he is barely holding himself together—and people are still making selfish demands on him. Only

Esmé gives—and gives the thing most precious to her, the watch from her father, who was "s-l-a-i-n in North Africa," as she spells it out in the tearoom so her younger brother will not understand. It is true that Esmé asks for something too, a story, but that is a creative offering the narrator gives gladly, for he has been saved from collapse and perhaps from death by her love.

As in other Salinger stories, there is a philosophical component to this theme. The German woman quoted Goebbels when she wrote, "Dear God, life is hell," and Sergeant X quotes Father Zossima (the elderly monk who preaches love in Fyodor Dostoevski's *The Brothers Karamazov*) when he adds that Hell "is the suffering of being unable to love." All around X are examples of this lack of love—not only in characters, but in the war itself. Esmé herself is trying to become less "cold" and training herself to be "more compassionate," as she tells the narrator in the tearoom, but her gift demonstrates that she alone is capable of pure and unselfish love. Salinger is debating the nature of life, love, and suffering through the actions and characters of his story. He posits Dostoevski against Goebbels (and ultimately Hitler), and the simple, almost childish gestures of Esmé against the selfishness of other characters and the horrors of the war. Yet what X writes on the flyleaf is "almost entirely illegible." It only becomes legible, or real, through the gift of Esmé. Only Esmé, in a word that echoes through the story, is truly "sincere."

Style and Technique

Salinger's style in this story (as in much of his work) is marked by humor, irony, and romantic lyricism.

The humor is partly one of situation, particularly in the early scene in the English tearoom. There, the narrator is confronted by Esmé's little brother, the ingenuous Charles (who asks questions such as, "Why do people in films kiss sideways?"), and by Esmé, whose poise and vocabulary are in sharp contrast to her innocence and ignorance ("when I'm thirty, I shall retire and live on a ranch in Ohio"). Even the scene with Clay, in which X is barely holding himself together in the face of his companion's crude insensitivity, holds moments of kidding.

A subtler kind of humor derives from Salinger's tone; the pervasive irony of the story (aided by irony's companion, understatement) helps to deflect its implicit sentimentality. "Are you at all acquainted with squalor?" Esmé asks about the story that the narrator has promised to write for her. "I said not exactly but that I was getting better acquainted with it, in one form or another, all the time"—which is an ironic and understated way to talk about the "squalor" of war that the protagonist is experiencing.

Finally, Salinger's style is characterized by romantic lyricism. This is, after all, a story of orphans in wartime, a sensitive hero surrounded by vulgarity, a man on the edge saved by a child. It is also a love story, even a story of thwarted love (since it opens with the announcement of Esmé's marriage to another). While with one hand Salinger muffles the romantic dimension with irony and understatement, with the other he pulls out stops on the stylistic organ, especially in the voice of Esmé. His shift from first person to third in the last half of the story is undoubtedly an attempt to gain distance from the melodramatic action, but even here Esmé's language, in her letter to Sergeant X, breaks through:

> Charles and I are both quite concerned about you; we hope you were not among those who made the first assault upon the Cotentin Peninsula. Were you? Please write as speedily as possible.

Esmé has been known to make grown readers cry.

David Peck

THE FRESHEST BOY

Author: F. Scott Fitzgerald (1896-1940)
Type of plot: Psychological realism
Time of plot: The 1920's
Locale: A train from the Midwest to St. Regis, the St. Regis school for boys in Eastchester, and New York City
First published: 1935

Principal characters:
> BASIL T. LEE, a middle-class boy in a rich boys' school who begins as a smart aleck and develops into a responsible young man
> DR. BACON, the not very tactful headmaster of St. Regis
> LEWIS CRUM, a fellow Midwesterner who attends St. Regis
> BUGS BROWN, a slightly insane classmate
> FAT GASPAR, an amiable but easily influenced classmate
> TREADWAY, Basil's short-term roommate
> MR. ROONEY, the football coach and Basil's chaperon into New York City

The Story

Basil T. Lee, the fifteen-year-old protagonist of "The Freshest Boy," is first introduced to the reader as the swashbuckling hero in the scenario of his escape into fantasy from the lonely, hostile reality of the prestigious St. Regis school for very rich boys. This scene is contrasted with an account of Basil's train ride from the Midwest to St. Regis and his anticipation of what his life at the school will be like. He has been so steeped in the tradition of attending an Eastern boys' school that "he had a glad feeling of recognition and familiarity. Indeed, it was with some sense of doing the appropriate thing, having the traditional rough-house that he had thrown Lewis' comb off the train at Milwaukee last night for no reason at all." On this trip, Lewis, a fellow student from the Midwest, reminds Basil that his reputation at his former school was that of being "a little fresh," and Basil resolves to make a new start, fantasizing about being a football hero.

At school, Basil is embarrassed that he is not from a wealthy family and writes his mother, stating, "All the boys have a bigger allowance than me. . . ." Basil feels humiliated when Dr. Bacon, the headmaster, confronts him with his poor grades and emphasizes the Lees' financial sacrifice in sending him to St. Regis. These humiliations are made more difficult to bear by the fact that Basil is aware that he is the least popular boy in school. Within the first few weeks he has gained the nickname of "Bossy" and has been involved in several fights. Consequently, it is November before the headmaster agrees to let Basil go into New York City for the weekend, and then only on the condition that he find two other boys to accompany him, which proves an impossible task. Basil sneaks off the grounds to find the only three boys who might even consider going with him. He finds Bugs Brown, who is so strange that he can associate only with "boys younger than himself, who were without the prejudices of their elders." An appointment with his psychiatrist prevents Bugs from accepting. Fat Gaspar, a generally amiable boy, gives in to peer pressure, and rather than tell Basil that he cannot go to New York City, he laughs at him and tells him that he does not want to go. Basil finally locates Treadway, his new roommate, who also rejects Basil's offer: "Like Fat Gaspar, rather than acknowledge himself eligible to such an intimate request, he preferred to cut their friendly relations short." Emphasizing Basil's isolation, Treadway packs up and moves out, leaving Basil utterly alone. In the midst of flagrant hostility, Basil again escapes into fantasy, focusing on the poster girls and identifying with Babette, crying, "Poor little Babette!" His tears are really for himself.

Mr. Rooney, the football coach, finally agrees to take Basil into New York City, not out of the goodness of his heart but because he also wants to get away from the stifling environment of the school. Mr. Rooney chides Basil, saying, "You oughtn't to get so fresh all the time," and continues by accusing him of being a coward while playing football. He lectures Basil mercilessly, but upon remembering that he going to have to trust Basil to keep quiet about his activities in New York City, he relents. When they arrive in New York City, Mr. Rooney goes off and gets drunk while Basil attends a Broadway play. Prior to the play, Basil discovers a way out of his misery by reading his mother's letter, in which she presents the opportunity for him to go to school abroad. Basil is tempted by this offer of escape and fantasizes about what he will say and how he will act toward his schoolmates, concluding that "he need no longer hate them, for they were impotent shadows in the stationary world that he was sliding away from, sliding past, waving his hand."

The play that Basil attends has a typical plot: Boy and girl meet, fall in love, face a few minor problems, resolve them, and live happily ever after. Basil imagines that life is like that and believes that he too has reached a happy ending to his school problem. Reality forces itself upon him, however, as after the play he follows the beautiful actress and her lover, the Yale football captain, and overhears their conversation. Her decision to marry her benefactor because he has done so much for her career shatters Basil's belief in easy answers in life; he realizes that "life for everybody was a struggle, sometimes magnificent from a distance, but always difficult and surprisingly simple and a little sad."

Basil finally locates Mr. Rooney, who is very drunk, and manages to get him on the train and back to school. These instances of others' problems and reactions illustrate to Basil that one cannot escape from life. "Suddenly Basil realized that he wasn't going to Europe. He could not forgo the molding of his own destiny just to alleviate a few months of pain." He starts over at St. Regis, continuing to make some errors, but the other boys sense his new attitude, his willingness to accept responsibility for his actions, and with his new maturity he gradually becomes accepted; his new status is confirmed when Brick Wales, a former enemy, assigns him a nickname (Lee-y) during a basketball game.

Themes and Meanings

Two dominant themes in Fitzgerald's works are the arrogance of the rich and the rite of passage from adolescence to adulthood. Both these themes are reflections of Fitzgerald's own experiences as a young man whose social position exposed him to the manners and expectations of the very rich without providing the means to participate directly and effectively in their way of life. Of particular importance is the positive outcome of the story. Basil, the middle-class protagonist, matures and accepts responsibility, a resolution which contrasts with Fitzgerald's stories in which the protagoinsts are reared in wealth and fail to mature. It was Fitzgerald's belief that the wealthy fail because of their sense of superiority to all others.

Basil has been indoctrinated about and had idealized life among the rich, specifically life at an elite boys' school. He knows that he is not really one of them and hence mimics their arrogance, creating a protective façade for his insecurity. Sensing his vulnerability, the other boys see that he does not really believe in his own superiority as those who have been reared in wealthy families do. They perceive him as a fraud, and with the cruelty typical of children they ridicule and ostracize him.

Basil cannot understand why there is such a contrast between his life, in which everything goes wrong, and the play and his fantasies, in which everything turns out right. This confusion reflects naïveté rather than arrogance; he is unaware, until he witnesses the scene between the actress and the football star, that everyone has problems. Once he realizes that he is not alone in his misery, he is able to become more objective, to face and analyze reality and accept responsibility. In short, he matures because of his experiences, and through his subsequent refusal to escape, he develops a self-respect that cannot be destroyed by his classmates. Once they recognize that he is no longer vulnerable, they begin to accept him. His façade of arrogance is replaced by a real strength of character that makes him actually superior to the rich boys around him.

Style and Technique

To develop the psychological realism of "The Freshest Boy," Fitzgerald employs a third-person omniscient point of view to delve into the minds of his characters, particularly focusing on the turmoil of the adolescent boy as he struggles to establish his identity in a hostile environment.

The use of fantasy elements does not remove this story from the realm of psychological realism, for Basil's fantasies are ones common to adolescence. Basil alternately sees himself as hero and victim, but the fantasies do allow him to escape, and they thereby emphasize for the reader the real trauma of Basil's life at school, where he feels that he has no control over his life.

Fitzgerald further emphasizes his theme of the difficulties of growing up by his use of Lewis as a foil to Basil. Basil's innocent idealization of life at a rich boys' school is contrasted to Lewis' more experienced and realistic view of the regimentation which actually exists.

Another contrast between the real and the idealized is developed when Basil visits New York City. The happy ending of the play represents Basil's naïve belief in easy solutions, while the real-life scene between the actress and her lover illustrates to Basil that in reality life consists of difficult and sometimes painful situations which are not easily resolved.

Fitzgerald effectively uses letters to illustrate Basil's dilemma and to forward the plot. Basil's letter to his mother provides a concise summation of his psychological state, while his mother's letter in return prompts his evaluation of his circumstances and, by offering him an alternative, makes his decision to stay at St. Regis a matter of mature choice rather than mere necessity.

Jane B. Weedman

A FRIEND OF KAFKA

Author: Isaac Bashevis Singer (1904-   )
Type of plot: Sketch
Time of plot: The early 1930's
Locale: Warsaw
First published: 1968

Principal characters:
THE NARRATOR, a fledgling writer
JACQUES (JANKEL) KOHN, a former Yiddish actor and onetime
    friend of Kafka
THE COUNTESS, a widowed aristocrat
BAMBERG, a decayed writer

The Story

Jacques Kohn repeatedly borrows money from the narrator, who willingly lends it to him because he wants Kohn's friendship. Although Kohn was once an important actor, the narrator values him more for his literary and cultural associations. Supposedly, Kohn was the first to recognize Franz Kafka's talent, and he has corresponded with other important figures: Marc Chagall, Stefan Zweig, and Martin Buber. As the narrator's cultural guide, Kohn shows him his letters and photographs, and he even arranges for him to meet Madam Tschissik, with whom Kohn performed and whom Kafka allegedly loved.

For the narrator, then, Kohn is an important link to European art and literature. For Kohn, the narrator is not only a source of money but also an audience, to whom he recounts the adventures of his younger days, such as taking Kafka to a brothel or attending an orgy with a number of writers, including the decayed writer Bamberg. As these examples indicate, Kohn's stories often are sexual, even though he is now impotent and claims that he does not find women attractive.

He does, however, have another encounter with a woman. One winter night he hears a banging at his door and the sound of a woman crying. The woman, a widowed countess, pleads with Kohn to let her hide in his apartment until morning; she has been visiting her lover in Kohn's building, but the man attempted to kill her in a fit of jealousy. Kohn points out that his apartment is unheated and that he can offer scant protection should her lover follow her and find them together.

Waving aside all objections, she insists on remaining with Kohn and even on sleeping with him. To his surprise, he is able to make love to her; the next morning, before she leaves, she kisses him and urges him to call her. Their relationship has continued, but Kohn has never tried to sleep with her again. He agrees with the Talmudic saying, "A miracle doesn't happen every day."

Themes and Meanings

Kohn does not regard this recent amatory adventure as the work of some benevolent Cupid. Instead, he views it as merely another move by the "tough angel" who is playing chess with him for his life. Kohn knows that this opponent will win finally, but Kohn seeks to prolong the game. Fate, as Kohn elsewhere names his adversary, also enjoys playing; he does not want to kill Kohn too quickly. "Break the keg, but don't let the wine run out" is the aim of Fate.

Fate tortures Kohn with poverty, sickness, despair, and cold. He brings the countess to Kohn's door not to give Kohn pleasure but to torment and threaten him: As Kohn had feared, the countess' lover does come after her. He pounds and kicks on the door, which barely holds. Kohn considers saying the prayer of the dying and is restrained only by his refusal to give his "mocking opponent" further pleasure from the situation.

Yet if man is pitted against an opponent he cannot beat, he remains a player rather than a pawn; he is not totally powerless. Thus, one bitterly cold night Kohn loses the key to his apartment. The janitor has no spare, so it appears that Kohn will have to spend the night outside. His opponent has made a shrewd move. Kohn, though, has the perfect response. If Fate wants to kill him with pneumonia, Kohn will not object. Then the game will end. Almost immediately Kohn finds his key, for his "partner wants to play a slow game."

One of the traditional proofs for the existence of God is the orderliness of the world. Singer points out that man lives in the midst of chaos. Kohn refers to *The Entropy of Reason* by a Dr. Mitzkin and suggests that the author might have written a sequel as well, *The Entropy of Passion*. Chaos, not order, is the law of nature. Yet that chaos may be a proof of God's existence. As Kohn says, if there is no God, "Who is playing all these games?"

Kohn's life is only one illustration of the entropy that rules the world, of the tendency of all things to lose their energy and disintegrate. Another is Bamberg, "a corpse refusing to rest in its grave." Even when he dances, he appears to be asleep. The orgy that Bamberg attends with Kohn disintegrates into a pseudointellectual discussion and breaks up when Bamberg becomes ill. Kafka's visit to the brothel also remains unconsummated as he, like Bamberg, gets sick. Dr. Mitzkin claims that "true wisdom can only be reached through passion," but he himself is incapable of passion.

For Singer, sex is a powerful positive force. The impotence of his characters—their inability to procreate—becomes a symbol of their inability to create and highlights the chaos in the world of the story.

Yet as this world is uncreated, it does not return to nothingness. Kohn's story remains, as does the narrator's retelling of that story. Dr. Mitzkin had predicted that in the end "man will . . . eat words, drink words, marry words, poison himself with words," yet that end is also a beginning, as Kohn observes in quoting the first words of the Gospel of John: "In the beginning was the Logos."

Whatever else man loses, he retains his language, the language that can turn "a piece of clay into a living thing," the language that can "create a world." The old writers have lost their abilities, but the numerous literary references in the story show that their medium remains powerful. Kafka has died, but his work endures and even lends importance to a faded actress. "A Friend of Kafka" suggests that in an absurd world, the word may be man's only weapon against entropy.

Style and Technique

This is another of Singer's autobiographical stories. The first-person narrator is a struggling young writer who frequents a Warsaw literary club, as Singer did before he left Poland. At the same time, Singer does alter his character for artistic ends. The narrator is shy around women, which Singer never was, because Singer wants to stress the lack of sexual energy in the story.

Singer uses the first-person narrative as a frame for a story-within-a-story, the account of Kohn's various adventures. Like Kohn's life, his account is chaotic: In four paragraphs he rambles from the countess to Kafka to Bamberg to a request for the loan of a zloty. When the narrator asks, "Did the countess ever call you?" Kohn outlines Dr. Mitzkin's philosophy before responding.

This lack of organization, this inability to focus one's efforts for creative ends, is highlighted at the conclusion of the story. Kohn is eager to introduce the narrator to Madame Tschissik—she is even waiting in the next room—yet the meeting never takes place. Instead, Kohn borrows money to go home and ends his tale with a question that has no answer. Entropy has conquered.

Joseph Rosenblum

FUNES, THE MEMORIOUS

Author: Jorge Luis Borges (1899-1986)
Type of plot: Fantasy
Time of plot: The 1880's
Locale: The eastern shore of the Uruguay River, in Uruguay
First published: "Funes el memorioso," 1944 (English translation, 1962)

> *Principal characters:*
> IRENEO FUNES, the man cursed with perfect memory
> THE NARRATOR

The Story

The history of the unfortunate Ireneo Funes is told by an unnamed narrator who, hearing of Funes' death, determines to put something into print about a very remarkable and, in one sense, disquieting man. Although he encountered Funes not more than three times, each meeting stamped itself on the narrator's memory.

The first, he tells the reader, was in February or March of 1884: He and his cousin were riding on horseback to his family's farm. As they rode along, hurrying to outpace a storm, they rode in a lane between high walls. On the top of one of the brick walls appeared an Indian boy. The narrator's cousin asked the boy what the time was, and the boy replied, "In ten minutes it will be eight o'clock." The cousin later explained, with some pride in a local curiosity, that the boy, Ireneo Funes, had the peculiar talent of always knowing the exact time without a watch.

Several times in the years that follow, the narrator asks about "the chronometer Funes," whenever he is in the area. In 1887, he hears that Funes has been thrown from a horse and crippled; unable to walk, he has become a recluse. The narrator glimpses him several times, but there is something strange about each occasion. He sees Funes behind a grilled window in the boy's house, unmoving each time, once with his eyes closed, once simply absorbed in smelling a blossom of lavender.

On a subsequent visit to the farm, the narrator brings along several books of Latin, the study of which he is beginning. During his visit, he receives a letter from Funes, asking if he might borrow one of the Latin texts and a dictionary. The narrator sends the books with some amusement that the small-town youth would think he could teach himself Latin with no more help than a dictionary. He forgets about the loan until he receives a telegram from Buenos Aires informing him that he must return immediately. He goes to the small ranch of Funes' mother to retrieve his books.

When he arrives, the woman tells him that Funes is in his room, and cautions the narrator not to be surprised to find him in the dark. Making his way to the room, the narrator overhears Funes reading—in Latin—from the book he has lent him. He enters Funes' room, and they begin a conversation that lasts until dawn.

Much to his surprise, the narrator discovers that Funes has indeed mastered even conversational Latin. They discuss the borrowed book, the Roman author Pliny's *Natural History*, which tells in one section of amazing feats of memory: Cyrus, the king of Persia, knowing each of his soldiers' names, and the like. Funes is astonished that anyone should think that such things were remarkable. He offers his own experience as an argument.

Funes says that until he was thrown from horseback, he was "blind, deaf-mute, somnambulistic, memoryless." The narrator disagrees, pointing out Funes' earlier talent with the time, but Funes' prior life now seems dreamlike to him. Now he finds that he has the ability to remember in every detail everything that he has ever experienced: every sound, every sight, every smell, as intensely and clearly as normal people do on only the most vivid of occasions. He thinks that his crippling was a small price to pay for an infallible memory. Yet there are hints that even Funes does not think of his new mental powers as a complete blessing: Although he boasts that he has in himself more memories than all men have had through history, he also compares his memory to a garbage disposal. The narrator, writing the account years later, thinks of film and the phonograph, two recording devices that did not exist when Funes lived, yet which even in their exact preserving of history are not superior to this one individual.

The mental state of Funes is almost incomprehensible to the narrator as he tries to understand what it would be like to remember every leaf on every tree, not only each time he saw it but also each time he imagined it as well. So oppressive is the power of his memory that Funes finds it hard to sleep; the darkened room, the reader comes to understand, helps him relax because it limits the amount of perception available to him.

At the climax of the story, dawn comes, and the narrator first sees Funes' face, "more ancient than Egypt," although Funes is only nineteen years old. With alarm, the narrator realizes that his every word and gesture will live indelibly in the youth's memory, and he begins to fear. What would the man's memory carry at the end of a long life? The narrator never finds out: In 1889, at the age of twenty-one, Funes dies.

Themes and Meanings

In a foreword to the publication of *Ficciones* in 1944, Borges remarked of "Funes, the Memorious" only that it was "a long metaphor for insomnia." As such, it is certainly a strikingly apt metaphor, for often when trying unsuccessfully to sleep, one's memories press insistently to the front of consciousness, and Borges did suffer from insomnia. A poem he wrote about 1936 speaks of his mind as "an incessant mirror" which multiplies the remembered details of life around him as he waits for sleep. Critics, however, have been reluctant to consider the story only a "metaphor for insomnia"; some have seen in the work a reflection of Borges' life at a particularly difficult time when his work as a writer seemed unappreciated, when he may well have considered himself a solitary observer of the world.

There is a second theme in the story, a much more general one whose irony may have appealed to Borges: the nature of thought. For all of Funes' accomplishments—he had learned English, French, Portuguese, and Latin in addition to his native Spanish—the narrator doubts that he was capable of much thought. As the narrator points out, thought depends on a paradox: The ability to generalize and to abstract requires that one forget the differences between things and concentrates on the similarities. Funes, however, never forgets. Because his memory forces details on him so violently, Funes finds it almost impossible to overlook the differences between things. His memory of the individual moment is so vivid, he is unable to generalize. The narrator states that Funes not only found it hard to understand how a word such as "dog" could represent any member of the species, but also was bothered that the same name could be used for the same dog seen from different perspectives or at different times during the day. As the narrator says, "His own face in the mirror, his own hands, surprised him on every occasion."

In a short story, it is neither possible nor desirable to present a theory of intellection, yet the theme of "Funes, the Memorious" argues that abstract thought may be hampered by a retentive memory, and that generalization, the basis of reasoning, requires that one step away from the particular and the concrete details of experience.

Style and Technique

From the very beginning of the story, the memories of the narrator and Funes are contrasted in a cleverly understated way. The narrator is using his memory of the past to write the memoir, but unlike Funes, he can only approximate forgotten details: no exact dates here—"sometime in March or February of the year '84." This was the date of their first meeting. Unlike the narrator, however, when Funes writes to borrow the Latin book, he refers to their encounter "on the seventh day of February of the year '84." A little later in the story, just before he describes the final conversation with Funes, the narrator apologizes for what is to follow: He says that he will not attempt to reproduce the exact words because almost fifty years have passed. Although he regards his summary as "remote and weak," he can only hope the readers can imagine the original sentences themselves.

Borges followed very faithfully Edgar Allan Poe's maxim that a short story must aim at a single effect, and his stories frequently build slowly to a revelation at the climax that forces the reader to reassess all that has occurred to that point. "Funes, the Memorious" is a fine example of that technique. The whole story leads to the rising of the sun and the sight of Funes' ancient face. The story illustrates also that when the climax has been adequately prepared for, the details of the revelation can speak for themselves: The narrator draws no conclusion about this astonishingly old face on a nineteen-year-old; the reader can draw his own conclusions about the burden of being unable to forget.

Walter E. Meyers

THE GARDEN OF FORKING PATHS

Author: Jorge Luis Borges (1899-1986)
Type of plot: Detective fantasy
Time of plot: 1916
Locale: Staffordshire, England
First published: "El jardín de senderos que se bifurcan," 1942 (English translation, 1946)

> *Principal characters:*
> CAPTAIN RICHARD MADDEN, a British officer
> DR. YU TSUN, an agent for German Intelligence
> DR. STEPHEN ALBERT, a missionary and sinologist

The Story

In the prologue to the original edition of *El jardín de senderos que se bifurcan* (1942), the work in which the short story of the same title was published, Jorge Luis Borges classifies the tale as "a detective story" and says that "its readers will assist at the execution, and all the preliminaries, of a crime, a crime whose purpose will not be unknown to them, but which they will not understand—it seems to me—until the last paragraph." The other pieces, he says, are all fantasies. Whether "The Garden of Forking Paths" is a detective story, a fantasy, or a combination of the two is a question that, ultimately, each reader must decide for himself.

The story begins with a reference to a history of World War I, in which it is stated that an Allied offensive planned for July 24, 1916, was postponed until July 29 because of "torrential rains." Calling the story which follows a deposition, the narrator says that it was dictated by Dr. Yu Tsun, a teacher of English, and the deposition casts light on the postponing of that attack.

The deposition begins in mid-sentence (readers are told that the first two pages are missing), with Dr. Yu Tsun, a spy for Imperial Germany although Chinese by nationality, just learning that he has been discovered. A telephone call to his confederate has been answered by a voice he recognizes, the voice of Richard Madden, a captain in the British counterintelligence service. Yu Tsun immediately concludes that his comrade is now dead and that Captain Madden knows of Yu Tsun's activity. To be discovered at this moment is especially alarming to the spy, because he has just found out the exact site in Belgium of a new concentration of British artillery. Although he knows this vital name, he has no way of getting the information to his superiors in Berlin. After some indecision, Yu Tsun acts to save himself from Captain Madden's pursuit. He takes a train to a nearby village, just ahead of the English officer.

At the village of Ashgrove, he heads for the house of Dr. Stephen Albert, an authority on Chinese culture. As he walks, Yu Tsun thinks of his great-grandfather, Ts'ui Pen, who was governor of Yunnan province. That powerful man resigned his political office to write a novel and to make a maze "in which all men would lose themselves." As he approaches the door of Albert's house, Yu Tsun reflects that the novel made no sense and the labyrinth was never found.

At the house, Yu Tsun is mistaken for a Chinese consul, and is asked by Albert if he has come to see the garden of forking paths. When Yu Tsun enters the house, their talk turns to the novel of Ts'ui Pen. Yu Tsun states that his family wishes it had never been published, calling it "a shapeless mass of contradictory rough drafts." As an example of the nonsensical nature of the work, he points out that the hero dies in chapter 3, but in chapter 4 is alive. Yet when Yu Tsun remarks on the labyrinth of Ts'ui Pen, Albert tells him that he has found it and presents a small lacquered box. To a puzzled Yu Tsun, Albert explains that the labyrinth was not a physical maze but was, in fact, the novel itself; those who looked for the maze on Ts'ui Pen's extensive estates were bound to fail. As proof, Albert produces the original manuscript of the book, where Ts'ui Pen wrote: "I leave to various future times, but not to all, my garden of forking paths."

Albert explains that he wondered for a long time how a book could be an infinite maze until he saw the manuscript. He explains that in all fiction, a character facing a decision chooses one alternative to the exclusion of all others. In Ts'ui Pen's work, however, all choices are made. In one part, an army comes to feel that life is cheap, and they therefore win a subsequent battle. In the next part, the army sees a rich banquet in progress; with the possible splendors of life in their minds, they fight hard and win the battle. Then, though, Albert's argument becomes more subtle.

Albert points out that the word "time" never occurs in the novel. Ts'ui Pen apparently believed that time was not absolute and uniform, but was rather a series of times that forked apart at some places and converged at others. That great structure includes every possible event: In most of them, Albert notes, he and Yu Tsun do not exist; in other times, one of them but not the other exists. Yu Tsun remarks that in all those possible universes, he is grateful to Albert for "the restoration of Ts'ui Pen's garden." No, Albert corrects him, not in all those many futures: In one of them, he is Yu Tsun's enemy. At that instant, Yu Tsun sees Captain Madden coming toward the house. Yu Tsun rises, fires his revolver, and kills Albert.

The final paragraph is written from Yu Tsun's prison cell. Captain Madden arrested him, and the courts tried him for Albert's murder, found him guilty, and sentenced him to hang. Yet, he says, he has triumphed: The news of the murder is in all the newspapers, newspapers which will be read in Berlin, where the name of their agent will be connected with the name of Albert—and Albert will be correctly identified as the name of the Belgian town where the English artillery is massed.

Themes and Meanings

"The Garden of Forking Paths" is a neat and clever detective story, but it also includes a theme of which Borges was very fond: the notion of multiple possibilities of an action. In science fiction, a whole subgenre of stories has been written to speculate on multiple universes arising from different choices in crucial situations: What would the present be like, for example, if the South had won the Civil War? This is the sort of story that Ts'ui Pen wrote, yet his story included not only an unexpected outcome, but also multiple possible outcomes of various actions. The idea so fascinated Borges that he wrote another short piece, "Examen de la obra de Herbert Quain" ("An Examination of the Work of Herbert Quain"); the mythical Quain wrote novels like Ts'ui Pen's. A single first chapter is followed by three second chapters, among which the reader may choose. Each of those second chapters is followed by three possible third chapters, and so on.

As Albert says in the story, people, with their attention fixed on their memory of the past and their limited perception of the future, tend to think of time as a single strand of reality, with all the unrealized events and all the unchosen alternatives only possibilities. This fascination with the theme of multiple universes marks many of Borges' works.

Style and Technique

Borges was a great admirer of the detective genre and of its leading writers, from Edgar Allan Poe to Arthur Conan Doyle and G. K. Chesterton to Graham Greene. For him, a detective story required certain characteristics: a complex plot, a small number of characters, a satisfying solution that proceeds from clues the reader has seen all along. For all these characteristics, a labyrinth is a satisfying metaphor; it is no coincidence that Yu Tsun reflects on a labyrinth, or that the idea of a maze appears in so many of Borges' works. In few of them, however, does the labyrinth figure so prominently as in "The Garden of Forking Paths."

The labyrinth—a maze of hedges, for example, in a formal garden—is a physical puzzle. Although it appears to contain many pathways, there is only one right solution. In the same way, the detective story is the literary counterpart of the labyrinth.

There are many mazes in the story, yet the conclusion provides a path through all of them: Yu Tsun's great-grandfather was killed by an unknown assassin; to many people who read about the murder of Albert, Yu Tsun is a virtually unknown assassin. Only those with the key to the mystery—the German espionage service in Berlin, waiting for a message—know why Albert has been killed. Captain Madden is tracking Yu Tsun through the labyrinth of England; Yu Tsun is entangling the unsuspecting Albert in the labyrinth of espionage; Borges is leading the reader through the labyrinth of the story. Not until the very end do readers realize why Yu Tsun, fleeing just minutes ahead of Captain Madden, should go to Albert's house and spend an hour discussing Chinese culture with him. Not until the very end do readers find their own way through the labyrinth.

Walter E. Meyers

THE GARDENER

Author: Rudyard Kipling (1865-1936)
Type of plot: Fable
Time of plot: The 1890's to 1920
Locale: Hampshire, England, and France
First published: 1926

> *Principal characters:*
> HELEN TURRELL, an English spinster
> MICHAEL TURRELL, supposedly her nephew
> GEORGE TURRELL, her late brother
> MRS. SCARSWORTH, an English visitor to military cemeteries
>   in Flanders

The Story

Helen Turrell, "thirty-five and independent," takes charge of the rearing of the supposed child of her brother, George, who dies from a fall from a horse a few weeks before the boy's birth. George, serving as a policeman in India, "had entangled himself" with the daughter of a noncommissioned officer. Helen, in the South of France because of lung trouble, has the infant brought to her and takes him home to Hampshire, England.

Helen explains all the details involving her nephew, Michael, to her friends in the village since "scandals are only increased by hushing them up." As for Michael's mother, she does not insist upon her right to the child: "Luckily, it seemed that people of that class would do almost anything for money." Since George has always sought his sister's help when he got into "scrapes," Helen feels justified in "cutting the whole non-commissioned officer connection" and rearing the boy by herself even though she is not, as "far as she knew herself," a lover of children.

When Michael is six, Helen refuses to allow him to call her "Mummy" at any time but bedtime. When he discovers that she has told her friends of this practice, he feels betrayed and swears to hurt her for her disloyalty. He promises as well to die "quite soon" and to continue hurting her after his death.

When he goes away to school at ten, Michael endures taunts for being a bastard but learns to take defiant pride in his irregular "civil status" since William the Conqueror and others born illegitimately "got on first-rate." Yet two years later, in delirium from a fever, he speaks of nothing but the disgrace of his birth.

Michael wins a scholarship to Oxford but enlists in the army instead when the Great War breaks out. After some time in France, Michael writes that "there was nothing special doing and therefore no need to worry," only to have a splinter of a shell kill him soon afterward.

After the war, Helen is notified of the location of Michael's grave in Flanders and goes to visit it. On the way to Hagenzeele, she meets an English woman making her ninth such trip. Mrs. Scarsworth claims not to have lost anyone but simply visits the graves of the loved ones of friends, sometimes taking photographs. Later, Mrs. Scarsworth reveals the truth to Helen, that she has lost someone, her lover.

At the military cemetery, with its twenty-one thousand graves, Helen does not know how to begin looking for Michael, and a man she takes to be a gardener offers his help. The gardener says, "Come with me, and I will show you where your son lies."

Themes and Meanings

Rudyard Kipling employs two autobiographical elements as the basis of "The Gardener." He grew up in England while his parents lived in India, and his only son was killed in World War I. A third inspiration is the story told in John 20:14-15 in which Mary Magdalene fails to recognize the resurrected Jesus, supposing him to be a gardener. Kipling makes the connection to this biblical story clear by writing a companion piece about it, "The Burden," a poem from which "The Gardener" takes its epigraph.

Helen's failure to recognize the gardener at Hagenzeele as the Christ is less important as a supernatural or religious occurrence than a fitting conclusion to Kipling's ironic presentation of identity, responsibility, and guilt. This irony appears in the story's opening sentence: "Every one in the village knew that Helen Turrell did her duty by all her world, and by none more honourably than by her only brother's unfortunate child." Yet if the gardener is not speaking metaphorically, and Helen is Michael's mother, she has not done her duty at all. By assuming the role of self-sacrificing, noble aunt devoted to her brother's illegitimate offspring, she has made a lie of both their lives.

Michael gets revenge on his "aunt" by dying, but she does not suffer as much as she might. Her greatest sin is her coldness. Her emotional distance from Michael, from life in general, allows her to avoid the pain that others feel when they lose someone. On the way to Hagenzeele, Helen finds repugnant the emotionalism of a woman from Lancashire who is desperate to find her son's grave. Kipling underscores Helen's insensitivity by having the woman faint on her unfeeling breast. Mrs. Scarsworth asks whether Helen thinks that the dead know anything after death and is told, "I haven't dared to think much about that sort of thing." Helen can control her grief by keeping it as abstract as possible.

She begins to recognize the truth about herself, however, when Mrs. Scarsworth confesses about her lover: "He was everything to me that he oughtn't to have been—the one real thing—the only thing that ever happened to me in all my life; and I've had to pretend he wasn't." This confession, so like the one that Helen is unable to make, almost causes Helen's impersonal façade finally to crumble. Kipling seems to be using Helen to criticize the passionless side of the English character and the almost obsessive concern with appearances and public opinion.

After Michael's death, Helen recalls his taking her to a munitions factory to see the steps in the production of a shell and realizes that with all the rituals that society expects her to observe she is like the shell: "I'm being manufactured into a bereaved next of kin." Because she is expected to play this role, she goes along with the charade, sitting on relief committees and holding "strong views—she heard herself delivering them—about the site of the proposed village War Memorial." One of several interlocking ironies is Helen's lack of awareness of how this role-playing is an outgrowth of her larger lie.

Style and Technique

"The Gardener" is notable for those elements typical of Kipling's late style: brevity, subtlety, and irony. Unfortunately, these qualities of the mature artist are occasionally interrupted by the sentimentality so characteristic of Kipling. The telegram notifying Helen that Michael is missing is delivered by the postmistress' seven-year-old daughter, who arrives weeping loudly "because Master Michael had often given her sweets."

More admirable is Kipling's economic style of storytelling as he quickly gets Michael born and killed so that he can proceed with the real story: Helen's response to this death. The ironic tone and relative subtlety of the story can be seen in Kipling's description of the event immediately following Michael's death: "The next shell uprooted and laid down over the body what had been the foundation of a barn wall, so neatly that none but an expert would have guessed that anything unpleasant had happened." Best of all is the description of the military cemetery, where order has ostensibly been imposed on death: "All she saw was a merciless sea of black crosses, bearing little strips of stamped tin at all angles across their faces. She could distinguish no order or arrangement in their mass; nothing but a waist-high wilderness as of weeds stricken dead, rushing at her." This masterly conjoining of death, war, and the chaos of Helen's emotional state helps refute H. E. Bates's claim that Kipling was not an artist but a journalist.

Michael Adams

THE GENTLEMAN FROM CRACOW

Author: Isaac Bashevis Singer (1904-   )
Type of plot: Allegory
Time of plot: Unspecified
Locale: Frampol, a fictitious village near Cracow, Poland
First published: 1957

Principal characters:
> THE GENTLEMAN FROM CRACOW, a doctor and a widower, the
> incarnation of Ketev Mriri, Chief of the Devils
> HODLE, the daughter of Lipa the Ragpicker—Lilith, a female
> demon from Talmudic legend, Adam's first wife
> RABBI OZER, a man of God whose warnings go unheeded

The Story

Singer develops his narrative carefully in five parts. Part 1 introduces the fictitious little Polish village of Frampol, whose peasants are poor and whose Jewish villagers struggle against extreme impoverishment. Frampol's only asset is its children: boys who grow tall and strong and girls who bloom handsomely. Suddenly the whole area is stricken by a devastating drought that ends in a climactic hailstorm accompanied by supernatural events: "Locusts huge as birds came in the wake of the storm; human voices were said to issue from their throats."

Then an unexpected miracle occurs. A handsome young man in his twenties, dressed in gorgeous clothes, arrives in a carriage pulled by eight horses and explains that he is a doctor and a widower from Cracow, come to Frampol to choose a new wife. He immediately provides lavish amounts of food, and the town is soon basking in its new prosperity. Only a few protest when he soon has the townspeople playing cards and gambling in violation of the accepted religious sanctions. Before long, the women and their daughters are in a frenzy of activity, all hoping to be chosen by the mysterious suitor.

In part 2, the seduction of the villagers is completed by their approval of a great ball to which all the eligible young women are to be invited. Despite protests from some of the elders that such elaborate festivities are not in keeping with Jewish tradition, the young gentleman has his way, and many lush fabrics are procured by him for the girls' ball dresses. The stranger goes on merrily eating Sabbath puddings on weekdays and playing cards, never attending prayer. Rabbi Ozer warns the villagers that they are being tricked by the Evil One, but all are possessed by their plans for the ball.

Part 3 introduces Lipa the Ragpicker and his daughter Hodle. Lipa has taken to drink after the death of his first wife and now lives with Hodle, his seventeen-year-old daughter by his second wife, a beggar who left him for nonsupport. Hodle is a village scandal. She roams the village in rags, stealing chickens and ducks and creating a legend by her lasciviousness. It is said of her that she eats cats and dogs, as well as other stray creatures who have died. She is a tall beauty, with red hair and green eyes, but when the fine fabrics are distributed, she is left with only odds and ends from which to make her gown. Her fury entertains the villagers. When all is ready for the ball, only Rabbi Ozer stays at home, locked in his study. When the dances begin, the gentleman from Cracow arrives on a white mare and watches the girls swaying to the music in the marketplace. All are dancing except Hodle.

In part 4, when the ball is in full swing, the gentleman from Cracow announces that all virgins must marry that night and that he will provide a dowry of ten thousand ducats for each. Brides and bridegrooms will be matched up by drawing lots. Despite the ritual demand that a girl must wait seven days after the announcement of her forthcoming marriage, mass excitement prevails and the only protester, an old man, is gagged. At this point, a virtual orgy breaks out, but at its peak a lightning bolt destroys the synagogue, the study house, and the ritual bath. With this event, the villagers learn the truth: The gentleman from Cracow reveals himself as a grotesque creature covered with scales, having a tail of live serpents. He is Ketev Mriri, Chief of the Devils. Hodle takes off her dress, appearing in her true identity as Lilith, the Talmudic demon who was supposed to have been Adam's first wife. She is repulsive: "Her breasts hung down to her navel and her feet were webbed. Her hair was a wilderness of worms and caterpillars."

Rabbi Ozer restores reason and order in part 5. The people have learned their lesson. An eternal light burns over Rabbi Ozer's grave, and a white pigeon often appears on the roof of the memorial chapel: "the sainted spirit of Rabbi Ozer."

Themes and Meanings

Isaac Bashevis Singer was born in a little village near Warsaw, the son of a very poor rabbi. Most of his fiction is drawn from life in Poland's Jewish communities, a life that in his childhood was rife with tales of the supernatural and mysterious. His stories often suggest a belief in a spiritual dimension to existence that science cannot explain, and his imaginative tales often exploit the folklore and superstition on which his childhood fantasies fed. All these aspects of his work are well exemplified in "The Gentleman from Cracow."

The moral of the allegory is clear: To ignore the laws and traditions is to open oneself up to calamity. Easy riches are a delusion. Nevertheless, the gentleman is so glamorous, the people so miserable in their poverty, that the temptation is hard to resist. The good Rabbi Ozer laments after the catastrophe that he should have had more foresight: "And when the shepherd is blind, the flock goes astray."

Yet there is more to the allegory than simply the story of the people's weakness, for at the end the villagers are truly regenerated. Their neighbors in the nearby town of Yanev send food, clothing, and dishes. Timber merchants send logs to rebuild the homes and public buildings. The people, including the scholars and town leaders, work diligently, so that a new town is soon created, one wiser and more truly pious. Never again do the townspeople lust for gold and fine things.

The story also expresses a political moral of a sort. Jewish communities in Eastern Europe often were threatened with extinction, and close conformity to laws and accepted practices was vital in unifying a besieged people against external pressures. When life became somewhat easier for these Jewish communities, many of the younger people would feel the pull toward assimilation, regarding the old rituals and mores as outmoded and burdensome. Then it was natural for the elders to lament the temptations of the secular Gentile life to which they saw their youths attracted, and they voiced their fears in warnings of the dangers of the Evil One. Singer must have observed this conflict as a young man in Poland, and "The Gentleman from Cracow" dramatizes not only the moral problems involved in expecting something for nothing but also the strain of conflict between two generations.

Style and Technique

Singer writes his stories in Yiddish and then watches over their translation into English. The Yiddish language is basically German, with many Hebrew words, as well as vocabulary picked up from Polish and Russian during its thousand-year history. It is therefore rich in diction and imagery that grew out of the Jews' long existence in Eastern Europe.

"The Gentleman from Cracow" opens with an exposition of the legends surrounding Frampol's history. The community house contains a parchment that chronicles Frampol's story, but the first page is missing. It is not clear at first that the story that follows is recounted in the pages of the old history, but the conclusion reveals that "the story, signed by trustworthy witnesses, can be read in the parchment chronicle." "The Gentleman from Cracow," then, is cast in a very old narrative framework: the fictitious manuscript.

The story is notable for the wealth of supernatural imagery that it presents. Part 4 opens with a gorgeous pathetic fallacy in which the setting sun stares angrily at the doings in the marketplace. The order of the natural universe has been violated by the villagers' wantonness. "Like rivers of burning sulphur, fiery clouds streamed across the heavens, assuming the shapes of elephants, lions, snakes, and monsters. They seemed to be waging a battle in the sky, devouring one another, spitting, breathing fire." This poetic evocation of God's wrath is followed by a vivid description of the behavior of the satiated humans and animals and of a weird glowing light that appears in the sky as an apparent omen.

Singer's direct style is a graceful medium for depicting his world of folk-lore, superstition, and the commonplace village life of Eastern European Jews before World War II. He is the foremost expounder of a way of life that has for the most part passed away, but that he knows intimately and re-creates compulsively.

Frank Day

THE GENTLEMAN FROM SAN FRANCISCO

Author: Ivan Bunin (1870-1953)
Type of plot: Social criticism
Time of plot: The early 1910's
Locale: Italy
First published: "Gospodin iz San Frantsisko," 1915 (English translation, 1922)

> *Principal characters:*
> THE GENTLEMAN, a businessman from San Francisco
> THE GENTLEMAN'S WIFE
> THE GENTLEMAN'S DAUGHTER

The Story

This short work has a deceptively simple plot: A rich American businessman travels with his family to Europe for a vacation and dies suddenly of a heart attack on the island of Capri. He then returns home in a coffin on the same ship on which he went to Europe. Yet over the sparse frame of this plot, Bunin weaves an elaborate narrative fabric richly textured with subtle counterpoint and evocative detail. Some critics have interpreted the tale as an indictment of Western capitalism, but such an evaluation is inadequate. Through his title character, Bunin illustrates a pervasive problem afflicting all of modern society: a fatal preoccupation with the self that leaves one coldly indifferent to other people, to nature, and to God.

Bunin's narrative exposes the shallowness and insensitivity of the gentleman's set through a variety of details. Describing the gentleman's shipboard passage to the Old World, he unveils a life-style in which everything is devoted to the passengers' comfort. Unmindful of the turbulent realm of nature outside, the passengers pursue one idle distraction after another. For them, eating is a major pastime, and the crown of their existence is dinner. Yet beneath this veneer of civility one finds a core of avarice and hypocrisy. An apparently romantic couple admired by all the passengers is revealed to have been hired by the shipping company to act out the role of being in love. Even the most basic and profound of human emotions—love—becomes a hollow travesty in this banal society.

Once in Europe, the gentleman embarks upon a numbing routine of sightseeing. The majestic churches of Italy soon become repetitious and boring, and the sightseers discover that "the same thing is found everywhere: . . . vast emptiness, silence . . . slippery gravestones under the feet and someone's *Deposition from the Cross*, invariably famous." The images of death here foreshadow the gentleman's own impending fate, but he remains as unmoved by them as he is by the religious objects themselves. Even the image of Christ's crucifixion, one of the central mysteries of Christianity, appears only as a museum piece whose fame is noted and nothing more.

The gentleman's insensitivity continues until the very moment of his death. The narrator asks rhetorically what the gentleman was thinking on the night of his heart attack. The answer is ironic: He was thinking only of his supper. He never arrives at the hotel dinner table, however; his heart attack strikes swiftly, causing consternation among the other hotel guests, who selfishly care more about their ruined evening than about the mystery of death itself. The gentleman's family now discovers the extent of the hypocrisy that runs through their social world. Before the gentleman's death, the hotel management had fawned over them. Now, though, the family is treated with cool disdain: The gentleman's body is put in the poorest room in the hotel and later conveyed to the ship in a cheap soda-water crate.

Despite the dark images dominating his portrait of the gentleman and the gentleman's milieu, Bunin does not provide an unrelievedly gloomy vision of human nature in "The Gentleman from San Francisco." In an important scene that occurs after the gentleman's death, Bunin introduces two characters who display an attitude toward the world which differs radically from that of the gentleman. These two are simple peasants descending the side of Monte Solaro. Unlike the gentleman, the peasants see the natural world around them as a resplendent realm of beauty. When they stop to pray at a statue of the Madonna perched amid the rocks, they offer "naïve and humbly joyful" praises to the Madonna, to God and to the world of nature. For these men, attuned as they are to the ineffable beauty of the universe, the realms of God and nature are one. The simplicity and humility manifest in their joyful reverence stand in sharp contrast to the indifference and selfishness apparent in the life-style and worldview of the gentleman's group.

Bunin returns to the world of the gentleman's society at the end of his narrative, depicting the ship carrying the gentleman's body back to America. Again, one notes the self-centered pursuit of idle pleasure on the ship, but now Bunin's description contains an ominous new element. In the very bowels of the ship he portrays the coffin holding the gentleman's corpse, and he concludes his tale with this image, a vivid emblem of the rank corruption lying at the core of the selfish modern world. Bunin thus suggests in "The Gentleman from San Francisco" that modern society's frantic pursuit of pleasure and satisfaction is really a macabre dance of death, leading ultimately to ruin and perdition.

Themes and Meanings

As Bunin himself commented later, this story can be read as a sober warning to a world poised on the brink of World War I. Modern society, his story implies, has fallen prey to the forces of egocentricity, arrogance, and avarice. Wealth and rank seem to be its only measure of human worth. Thus the gentleman's daughter finds herself spellbound with excitement in the presence of the crown prince of a certain Asian nation. Although the prince is described as unattractive, even corpselike, the thought that he has ancient royal blood coursing through his veins causes her heart to beat with silent ecstasy. As for the gentleman himself, he vainly believes that everyone on Capri, from the cabmen to the hotel staff, lives only to serve him. The fallacy of his perception becomes glaringly obvious after his death, when the hotel staff treats his family with undisguised disrespect. Since the source of their income has departed, they have little use for such unprofitable emotions as pity and compassion.

Although Bunin devotes the major portion of his narrative to the gentleman and his set, he does offer a modest counter to this group with the scene involving the two peasants. Their humble spirituality and their evident love both for God and for the natural world offer an alternative to the self-absorption of the gentleman's company, and in this scene the reader discovers Bunin's solution to the perils he saw threatening modern society. Individuals should not act as if the universe were centered on them, but rather they must recognize that they are only a small element in a vast and wondrous cosmos which should be approached with reverence and love, not arrogance and cynicism. Egocentric desire must yield to self-effacing acceptance of the natural order, or the result will be death, decay, and dissolution.

Style and Technique

To convey his vision of a society riddled with self-indulgence and hypocrisy, Bunin marshaled all of his gifts as a prose artist. The result is a masterpiece of expressive technique. Each word and image contributes to the work's total impact, and hardly any superfluous or insignificant detail can be identified. From the outset, Bunin creates a special narrative style whose very diction carries subtle overtones of irony to expose the folly and vanity of the gentleman's worldview. Writing of the reasons for the gentleman's trip, Bunin states: "He was firmly convinced that he was fully entitled to a rest, to pleasure, and to a journey excellent in all respects." This is not Bunin's normal style. The solemn pomposity of its formulations belongs to the gentleman himself, creating a satiric echo of his own arrogance. It is truly ironic, however, that this self-impressed character remains anonymous throughout the story. Despite his own belief in his personal significance, no one could even remember the man's name after his death.

Bunin also relies heavily on symbolic detail to evoke the shallowness of the gentleman's life-style and the dangers inherent in the narrow-minded self-absorption of his society. The relationship between the ship on which the gentleman travels and the sea through which this ship moves provides a good illustration of the writer's symbolic technique. Opposed to the power and majesty of the man-made ship is the churning realm of the gale-swept sea. Bunin's descriptions of the ship and the sea suggest that a profound struggle is being waged between the elemental forces of nature and the artificial constructs of modern civilization. This struggle even takes on spiritual or religious dimensions. Bunin notes that the ship is ruled by the captain, a mysterious figure compared to an idol or pagan god, while the Devil himself watches the struggle of ship against sea from the shoreline. It seems as though modern society has created its own gods and its own Hell, next to which the Old World devil seems almost irrelevant. Similar examples of evocative detail can be found in Bunin's descriptions of the gentleman's itinerary, clothing, and pastimes. Bunin's narrative serves as a frank mirror for the gentleman and his milieu, disclosing the severe wrinkles under his makeup and the cheap trappings in which a vain world wraps itself.

Julian W. Connolly

GHOST AND FLESH, WATER AND DIRT

Author: William Goyen (1915-1983)
Type of plot: Psychological ghost story
Time of plot: Approximately 1930-1950
Locale: A small town in East Texas
First published: 1952

> *Principal characters:*
> MARGY EMMONS, the narrator and protagonist, a resigned
> older woman
> FURSTA EVANS, a friend of Margy
> AN UNNAMED YOUNG WOMAN, to whom Margy is speaking

The Story

"Ghost and Flesh, Water and Dirt" is the story of Margy Emmons' life as told by her; it is a sad but evocative and mysterious tale which centers on her relationships with two men: Raymon Emmons, the "ghost" of the title, whom Margy "lost" to "dirt," and Nick Natowski, the "flesh," whom she "lost" to "water." Throughout the story, Margy sits in the Pass Time Club drinking beer, talking to a young woman, recalling the "fire" of her life, and sifting through the "ashes" of her memories. Margy is in her "time a tellin," and she warns her companion to "run fast if you don wanna hear what I tell, cause I'm goin ta tell." Margy speaks very briefly of the present, which for her is inextricably linked to the past and dominated by the ghost of Raymon Emmons, who comes to visit her virtually every night. She begins her story with an account of the first time she ever saw Raymon Emmons. Emmons was a thirty-year-old railroad man whom she met, fell in love with, pursued, and married when she was seventeen. Margy says almost nothing about their life together, but she talks at length about how she was devastated by his death. She did not feel that she could face life alone: "I cain't stand a life of just me and our furniture in a room, who's gonna *be* with me?" Margy went to the preacher for advice and counsel, but "he uz no earthly help." She went to her friend, Fursta Evans, but Fursta's wisdom did not satisfy her either, and so Margy dedicated herself to mourning the dead (her daughter, Chitta, died two weeks before her husband) and avoiding the life around her. She went from her house to the graveyard and back.

After a year, Margy's miserable routine was interrupted by a visit from Fursta. Fursta came knocking on her door to assail Margy for her hypocrisy and self-pity: "Why are you so glued to Raymon Emmonses memry when you never cared a hoot bout him while he was on earth . . . ?" According to Fursta, Margy's marriage was not a happy one; she was endlessly critical of Emmons and ultimately drove him to suicide by blaming him for the death of their child. Fursta argued that Margy should forget the past and begin to make the most of the days she had left: "honey, we got to *greet* life not grieve life." Margy responded that Raymon Emmons had "fastened" her to her house, but Fursta convinced her to turn her face toward the future and to give life another chance. Margy reluctantly closed up her house and boarded a train bound for California. There, she found that "the sun was out, wide . . . the world *was* still there." Margy arrived in California during World War II and promptly took a job in an airplane factory and fell in love with a sailor, Nick Natowski. After a brief period of joy during which Nick and Margy "lived like a king and queen," Natowski sailed away to war and his death, and Margy returned to Texas defeated and feeling like she had "been pastured on a rope in California."

Margy opened her house, got a job in Richardson's Shoe Shop, and re-signed herself to the life she has been living since her return to Texas: days of menial labor and nights "full of talkin" with Raymon Emmons' ghost. Margy asserts that she has gained some measure of freedom in these last years by learning to accept Raymon Emmon's power over her: "I set real still and let it all be, claimed by that ghost until he unclaims me—and then I get up and go roun, free, and that's why I'm here, settin with you here in the Pass Time Club."

Once she has told her story, Margy goes on to try to impart some of what she has learned from life to her young companion. She believes that "all life is just a sharin of ghosts and flesh," which is to say that the past and the present are intimately linked to each other, that the ghosts of lost days, of lost friends and family and lovers, are very much a part of the everyday world. Margy even goes so far as to say that she believes that the spirits of the past, the ashes of past experiences, are the dominant elements in human life: "Maybe the ghost part is the longest lastin, the fire blazes but the ashes last forever." Margy encourages her young companion to be open and recep-tive to the various realms of life and twists of fate: "I believe the real right way is to take our worlds, of ghosts or of flesh, take each one as they come and take what comes in em: . . . even run out to meet what worlds come in to our lives."

Themes and Meanings

Several of the themes which pervade William Goyen's fiction are to be found in this early story: the isolation and loneliness of human beings; the uneasy relationship between the past and the present; the melancholy quality of people's lives; and the profoundly important, poignant, and loving nature of storytelling.

Everyone in "Ghost and Flesh, Water and Dirt" is essentially alone. Raymon Emmons never attained more than a brief connection with any other human being; the isolation of Nick Natowski, the young sailor from

Chicago on his way to a cold death in the Pacific, was only briefly interrupted by his affair with Margy. Even Fursta Evans, for all her efforts, never makes a lasting connection with anyone. The listener in the bar is remote and only vaguely interested in Margy's tale; Margy lives a lonely and resigned existence, punctuated by periods of sadness so intense that she could not leave the seclusion of her house if her "life depended on it." This story and Goyen's fiction in general seem to confirm Margy's assertions that "the fire blazes but the ashes last forever," that the joys of life are fragile, evanescent, and too often unrecognized or unacknowledged ("it's true that you never miss water till the well runs dry, tiz truly true"), and that a sense of loss, of opportunities missed and promises unrealized, is an inevitable part of human life.

Margy Emmons is clearly haunted by the past, and she speaks movingly and convincingly of the interpenetration of past and present, ghost and flesh, and even of the dominance of the past. Her melancholy example and her unsettling bondage to ghosts, to failure and isolation, are, however, opposed quite forcefully by the words and actions of Fursta Evans. Fursta argues for the primacy of the present. She believes that the world is new every minute, always "as fresh as ever," and that people should forget the past and go forward "fresh and empty handed" into the future: "cause listen honey the sun comes up and the sun crosses over and *goes down*—and while the sun's up we got to get on that fence and crow. Cause night muss fall—and then thas all. Come on, les go roun." Through Fursta, Goyen creates a counterpoint to Margy, a contrary theme, not sounded so frequently or so loudly as Margy's refrain, but possessing a clear and pure chord nevertheless.

It is evident, however, in this story, as in most of Goyen's fiction, that Fursta, not Margy, is the exception, is the true eccentric. Most human beings do live like Margy, looking over their shoulders, unable to forget the past, and struggling endlessly to forge a positive link between the yesterdays and today. Most readers will accept Margy's notion that "there's a time for live things and a time for dead, for ghosts and for flesh'n bones: all life is just a sharin of ghosts and flesh." Yet Margy is in many ways an objectionable person, an unfit model, and an imperfect thinker; she is shrewish, self-pitying, unloving, and self-indulgent; her solutions to the problems of how to establish a positive relationship with the past and of how to live do not satisfy. Somehow, though, it does not matter that Margy's answers will not do for everyone; she has been redeemed through her struggle; she has been made more human, more loving, and more vulnerable through her torment and her submission to a ghost, to the spirit. Goyen's stories frequently manifest the doubleness that he saw in life: spirit and flesh in a single image; male and female in a single body; beauty and ugliness in a single instant; or, as here, past and present, failure and redemption inseparable one from another.

William Goyen's story does not provide a solution to the problems of human loneliness or of how to integrate the past and the present successfully, unless the solution is the telling of the story, the sharing of the problem, the interchange of human experience. Goyen believes that all people have stories to tell and that they should tell those stories, that the quality of life is dependent on a constant interchange of personal experience and personal knowledge. The stories always arise out of trouble and through the telling and the listening a redemption becomes possible; man is given hope and the ability to endure, to go forward in peace and with love.

Style and Technique

Goyen's style and technique are unique and highly personal. His stories typically are told by the narrator and are best understood when read aloud. They do not have plots in the conventional sense but are concerned rather with the creation of a mood or the evocation of a mysterious feeling of kinship with the teller. "Ghost and Flesh, Dirt and Water" consists entirely of a monologue by Margy Emmons with two brief italicized passages in the beginning when she speaks only to herself. Margy begins and ends with a vision of "pore Raymon Emmons," and she will no doubt tell this same story when her "time a tellin" comes again. The listener and the reader cannot help being riveted by this strange tale of lovers and ghosts and are left, if not convinced by Margy's ideas, at least moved by and sympathetic to her humanity.

The lyric quality of Goyen's prose, the recurrence of certain key phrases, and the circular movement of the story call to mind the folk ballad. Indeed, many of his stories are similar in content and quality to folk song; they come from and are about common folk, and they are told in the words of ordinary people. William Goyen is a master storyteller with a rare gift for turning everyday language into poetry.

Hal Holladay

THE GIFT

Author: John Steinbeck (1902-1968)
Type of plot: Domestic realism
Time of plot: Early twentieth century
Locale: Salinas Valley, California
First published: 1933

Principal characters:
JODY TIFLIN, a ten-year-old farm boy, the point-of-view
character
BILLY BUCK, a ranch hand
CARL TIFLIN, Jody's father

The Story

Jody Tiflin is a shy, polite, ten-year-old boy, the only child of the Tiflins, who own a small ranch in the Salinas Valley. Billy Buck, the ranch hand, is almost a part of the family and has Jody's highest respect.

One late summer day, Carl Tiflin and Billy drive six old milk cows to Salinas to the butcher. Jody would like to go along, but school has resumed. Before setting out on the mile walk to school, Jody walks up to the sagebrush line to the spring, and then to the cypress tree where pigs are butchered. On the verge of adolescence, Jody is beginning to lose his childish pleasure in smashing musk melons or killing mice. He yearns for greater excitement and responsibility.

The two men return late that evening with a gift for Jody, a red colt. Yet rather than present the gift immediately, Jody's father only tells Jody to go to bed, that he will need Jody in the morning.

After breakfast the men take Jody to the barn to show him the pony. The insensitive Carl Tiflin abhors any weakness or sentimentality and seems cross and embarrassed about giving his son the gift, but Billy Buck comprehends the boy's elation. Jody names his pony Gabilan, after the mountains next to which they live.

Jody's life now so revolves around Gabilan that he sometimes forgets his chores, but with this new responsibility, he begins to develop greater maturity. Under Billy's guidance, Jody takes good care of the pony and begins to train him. Billy seemingly knows all there is to know about horses, and in the evenings he even braids a tail-hair rope for Jody. The pony produces a strong bond between Jody and Billy.

Carl says that by Thanksgiving Gabilan will be big enough to ride, so in eager anticipation of the great day Jody begins to saddle him daily. Winter is approaching, and Jody leaves Gabilan out in the sunny corral as much as possible. On a day when Billy assures Jody that it will not rain, Jody leaves the pony out in the corral when he goes to school. It does rain, however, and when Jody gets home, Gabilan has taken cold.

For the first time, Billy has failed Jody. Yet he assures the boy that Gabilan will get well, and he nurses the pony skillfully. The next day, however, Gabilan is worse, and by the second day Billy admits that Gabilan has "strangles" and is a very sick pony. Billy and Jody take turns sleeping in the barn and nursing Gabilan, but the pony does not get better. Billy lances the pony's throat to drain the pus, and for a few hours the pony is more spirited. Yet congestion returns, and later Billy must open a hole in Gabilan's windpipe so he can breathe. Gabilan seems better again, but while Jody naps in the hay that night, the barn door blows open and the red pony runs out into the winter wind.

By the next morning, hope has faded. Jody is sent to breakfast, but instead goes to the dark cypress tree—a place associated in his mind with death—to think. He returns to the barn and waits all day with Gabilan, but while he sleeps that night, the barn door again blows open. When he awakes at dawn Gabilan is gone. Jody rushes from the barn and follows the pony's tracks up the ridge; in the sky he sees buzzards beginning to circle. He runs up the hill into the brush, and in a clearing he finds his pony in the throes of death, buzzards awaiting their moment.

Just as the first buzzard alights on the pony's head and sinks its beak into Gabilan's eye, Jody plunges into the circle of birds and grabs the buzzard by the throat. With a rock he smashes the bird's head; he is still beating the bloody bird when Carl and Billy come over the hill. Jody's father is cool and distant as always, reminding Jody that the buzzard did not kill Gabilan. Billy Buck, however, lifts Jody into his arms to carry him home. Only Billy understands how Jody feels.

Themes and Meanings

"The Gift" is about a young boy's passage from innocence to experience. The "gift" is more than a pony; it is also maturity. Jody grows up through taking responsibility, through facing death, and through accepting the fallibility of his hero.

Harsh father that he is, Carl Tiflin does help his son grow up by the way in which he gives Jody gifts. He gives Jody a rifle, but no bullets, because he knows that the boy is not ready for the power to kill until he comprehends the meaning of death. Similarly, the pony is given on the condition that Jody take full responsibility for its care.

Steinbeck sends Jody to the spring or to the cypress tree, places that Jody vaguely associates with life and death, respectively, when he needs to think things out. It is from the cypress tree that Jody first sees buzzards circling; he hates them because they eat carrion and are associated with death, but he recognizes that they are a necessary part of the natural cycle. His irrational but understandable attack on the buzzard at the end of the story purges his rage, and Billy understands that this cathartic attack on "death" is not necessarily a childish reaction.

Perhaps most important to Jody's maturation is his recognition, and then acceptance, of Billy's fallibility. He is angry at Billy for being wrong about the rain, and Jody's faith in his hero is shaken by Billy's failure to save Gabilan. Yet his final acceptance of Billy's love and his knowledge that, though he failed, Billy gave his best, are adult attitudes.

Especially in the 1930's Steinbeck's stories celebrated the interrelatedness of love and work. In almost every story, one figure of wisdom, authority, and love seems to represent the author's point of view. Invariably, this character is a person of compassion and sensitivity and is also a worker who is skilled and competent, but unpresumptuous and sharing. In "The Gift," this character is Billy Buck; it is he who guides Jody through the traumatic transition to manhood.

Style and Technique

"The Gift" was the first of three stories published in 1937 as the novella *The Red Pony*. (The other two stories are "The Great Mountains" and "The Promise"; a fourth story, "The Leader of the People," involves the same characters.)

It was in the 1930's, the decade when Steinbeck's fiction grew out of what he knew best—the paisanos of Monterey, the inhabitants, such as the Tiflins, of the small towns and rural valleys of California, and the dispossessed migrant farm laborers of *In Dubious Battle* (1936) and *The Grapes of Wrath* (1939)—that Steinbeck produced his greatest work. He mastered the colloquial language of the people about whom he wrote, and his broad experience among the townsmen, farmers, and farm workers enabled him to describe these people, their lives and their work, authentically and with intricate detail. Not especially innovative in style and technique, Steinbeck wrote "The Gift," like most of his fiction, in the third person and from the omniscient point of view. The plot is straightforward and readily comprehensible. What is masterful about Steinbeck's style is his rendition of detail.

Having worked as a horse trainer for the United States Army, Steinbeck, like his character Billy Buck, knew horses. From Billy the reader learns that horses are "afraid for their feet," that a horse which puts its whole nose and mouth in the water to drink is spirited, and that the moods of horses are expressed by their ears. Steinbeck was an equally keen observer of human action and motivation. When Carl and Billy come in for breakfast, Jody habitually listens to their steps to hear if they are wearing flat shoes or boots, since boots mean that they will be riding somewhere. Though the sounds are implanted in his memory, he always looks under the table anyway, to make sure. In the glow of first possession of the red pony, Jody tortures himself by imagining that the pony has disappeared, or that rats have gnawed holes in the saddle; in his good fortune, the possibility of loss seems so threatening that the possibility must be entertained to soften the loss should it occur. As such passages suggest, Steinbeck's "gift" to the reader is a sensitive, moving depiction of the end of childhood.

Jerry W. Wilson

THE GIFT OF THE MAGI

Author: O. Henry (William Sydney Porter, 1862-1910)
Type of plot: Dramatic irony
Time of plot: 1902
Locale: New York City
First published: 1905

Principal characters:
DELLA, a young married woman
JIM, her husband

The Story

Della Young is a devoted young married woman. Christmas Eve finds her in possession of a meager one dollar and eighty-seven cents, the sum total of her savings, with which she wants to buy an appropriate gift for her husband, Jim. A recent cut in the family income, from an ample thirty dollars a week to a stingy twenty dollars a week, has turned Della's frugality into parsimony. Although she lives in an eight-dollar-a-week flat and her general surroundings, even by the greatest stretch of the imagination, do not meet the standards of genteel poverty, Della determines that she cannot live through Christmas without giving Jim a tangible reminder of the season.

Distraught, she clutches the one dollar and eighty-seven cents in her hand as she moves discontentedly about her tiny home. Suddenly, catching a glance of herself in the cheap pier glass mirror, a maneuver possible only for the slender and agile viewer, the perfect solution suggests itself. Whirling about with happiness, she lets down her long, beautiful hair. It is like brown sable and falls in caressing folds to below her knees. After a moment's self-admiration, and another half-moment's reservation, during which time a tear streaks down her face, she resolutely puts on her old hat and jacket and leaves the flat.

Della's quick steps take her to the shop of Madame Sofronie, an establishment which trades in hair goods of all kinds. Entering quickly, lest her nerve desert her, she offers to sell her hair. Madame Sofronie surveys the luxuriant tresses, unceremoniously slices them off, and hands Della twenty dollars. For the next two hours Della feels herself in paradise, temporarily luxuriating in the knowledge that she can buy anything she wants. She decides on a watch fob for Jim's beautiful old watch. If there are two treasures in the world of which James and Della Dillingham Young are inordinately and justly proud, they are her hair (lately and gladly sacrificed) and Jim's revered gold watch, handed down to him by his grandfather.

She finally sees exactly what she wants, a platinum watch fob that costs twenty-one dollars. She excitedly anticipates Jim's reaction when he sees a proper chain for his watch. Until now, he has been using an old leather strap which, despite the watch's elegance, has forced him to look at the time surreptitiously.

Arriving back at the flat, breathless but triumphant, Della remembers her newly bobbed appearance. She reaches for the curling irons and soon a mass of close-cropped curls adorns her shorn head. She stares at herself anxiously in the mirror, hoping that her husband will still love her. As is her usual custom, she prepares dinner for the always punctual Jim and sits down to await his arrival. The precious gift is tightly clutched in her hand. She mutters an imprecation to God so that Jim will think she is still pretty.

At precisely seven o'clock, she hears Jim's familiar step on the stairs, his key in the door. He is a careworn young man, only twenty-two and already burdened with many responsibilities. He opens the door, sees Della, and an indiscernible look, neither sorrow nor surprise, overtakes him. His face can only be described as bearing a mask of melancholy disbelief. Even though Della rushes to assure him that her hair grows fast and that she will soon be back to normal, Jim cannot seem to be persuaded that her beautiful hair is really gone. Della implores him to understand that she simply could not have lived through Christmas without buying him a gift; she begs him, for her sake, as well as the season's, to be happy.

Jim, as if waking from a trance, embraces her and readily tells her that there is nothing a shampoo or haircut could do to Della that would alter his love for her. In the excitement he has forgotten to give her her gift, and now he offers her a paper-wrapped package. Tearing at it eagerly, Della finds a set of combs, tortoise shell, bejewelled combs that she has so often admired in a shop on Broadway, combs whose color combines perfectly with her own vanished tresses. Her immense joy turns to tears, but quickly returns when she remembers just how fast her hair grows.

Jim has not yet seen his beautiful present. She holds it out to him and the precious metal catches all the nuances of light in the room. It is indeed a beautiful specimen of a watch chain, and Della insists on attaching it to Jim's watch. Jim looks at her with infinite love and patience and suggests that they both put away their presents—for a while. Jim has sold his watch in order to buy the combs for Della even as she has sold her hair to buy the watch chain for Jim.

Like the Magi, those Wise Men who invented the tradition of Christmas giving, both Della and Jim have unwisely sacrificed the greatest treasures of their house for each other. Yet of all those who give gifts, these two are inevitably the wisest.

Themes and Meanings

O. Henry often chose to translate tragedy or misfortune into an emphasized regard and tenderness for the unlucky or the underdog. He never cared for the so-called higher classes, but preferred to cull his characters, and his sympathies, from watching ordinary people on the streets and in the shops and cafés. This perspective on the world around him is highly visible in "The Gift of the Magi," where, to enforce his quasi-religious message, he counterpoints the elements of love and caring with those of poverty and sacrifice.

The extreme devotion manifested on the part of the young married couple becomes almost incongruous when contrasted against the dreariness and bleakness of their material surroundings. Each arrives at the conclusion that it is impossible to live through Christmas without granting the other's supreme wish. It is not "selfish magnanimity"—a desire to revel in the sacrifice of giving—which motivates them. They truly embrace the noble sentiment of selflessness.

Thus, despite the specter of poverty, the story is animated by an unexpressed hope for the future. (This is a variation on the old theme that love conquers all, particularly material setbacks.) By setting the story at Christmastime, the author suggests that simple, unselfish human love is the basis of such hope for mankind.

Style and Technique

O. Henry's humor and imagination conquer any journalistic tendencies he may have transferred to fiction. His penchant for dramatic irony, a trademark in many of his short stories, gives his style its distinctive flavor. Gentle and ingenious, his writing is pervaded by that eminently salable quality known as "human interest." This quality is best exemplified in his quest for sincerity: his desire to write about real people in real situations.

Della and Jim are not the products of an overly sentimental imagination. The author strives to create circumstances as well as physical surroundings that ring true to life. Both the protagonists accept life as they find it without giving in to the negative emotions of hopelessness or despair. Della's only moment of doubt still revolves around her husband's well-being, when she seeks divine intervention so that she may remain pretty in Jim's eyes. Jim covers his fear of Della's disappointment with an almost affected nonchalance when he requests that they merely put their Christmas gifts away and keep them for an unspecified future. Only then does he reveal that he has sacrificed his treasure to secure Della's desire. His certainty that they will both use these items in the future provides the unspoken thought that life is bound to improve for them.

The protagonists do not react to each other out of saintliness, duty, or love of self-imposed sacrifice: They simply embody the twin spirits of love and Christmas. For the less-than-devout O. Henry, these essences are one and the same. The author suggests that sentiment does not have to be sacrificed to the cause of realism.

Rhona E. Zaid

GIMPEL THE FOOL

Author: Isaac Bashevis Singer (1904-   )
Type of plot: Fable
Time of plot: Early twentieth century
Locale: Frampol, Poland
First published: "Gimpel Tam," 1945 (English translation, 1953)

> *Principal characters:*
> GIMPEL, the narrator and protagonist, who questions whether
> he is a fool
> ELKA, his promiscuous wife
> THE SPIRIT OF EVIL, who tempts Gimpel

The Story

Gimpel, who has had the reputation of being a fool since his school days, is the narrator of his own story. He relates how the other children used to tease and play tricks on him, and how, because he did not want to endure their taunts when he expressed disbelief in what they said, he made the decision to believe them—in the hope, as he says, that it would do them some good.

An orphan, Gimpel was apprenticed to a baker, and all of his customers continued to tease him by telling him outlandish things that had supposedly happened. Gimpel says that he knew the unlikelihood of these tales, but again, rather than argue with his customers, he took the attitude that anything is possible and was again taunted for his gullibility. When Gimpel asked the rabbi's advice, the rabbi told him that the others were the fools, not he, and that it is better to act like a fool for all of one's life than to be evil for a single hour.

Gimpel next describes an event that takes place when he is an adult. Everyone plays matchmaker in his marriage to Elka, a promiscuous girl who has already borne one child out of wedlock. Elka, contrary to tradition, demands a dowry from Gimpel, and he acquiesces and reluctantly goes through with the marriage. She refuses to let Gimpel sleep with her, yet when she has a child in four months, she insists that the child is his. Gimpel does not believe her, but all the townspeople argue him "dumb," as he says. He soon discovers that he loves the child and that the child loves him, so he goes along with Elka's unlikely tale. Although Elka swears and curses at him, he finds that he loves her, too.

One night when an oven bursts and almost starts a fire at the bakery, where Elka makes him sleep, Gimpel returns home unexpectedly and finds Elka in bed with another man. When Gimpel brings charges against her to the rabbi, she boldly denies everything. The rabbi advises Gimpel to divorce her, but as he lies awake at night, Gimpel discovers that he longs for her and the child and that he cannot be angry, so he rationalizes his change of heart: He may have had a hallucination; he tells the rabbi that he was mistaken. The rabbi advises Gimpel to stay away from his wife until the matter is adjudicated.

Nine months later, Elka gives birth to another child, and this time Gimpel decides no good will come from doubting, so he resolves to believe everything that he is told. In the next twenty years, Gimpel becomes a successful baker while Elka bears four daughters and two sons. He says that many things happened which he "neither saw nor heard"; he simply believed. Finally, Elka becomes ill, and on her deathbed she confesses to Gimpel that she has deceived him all those years and that not one of the children is his. Gimpel admits to being shocked at her confession.

After the proper period of mourning, Gimpel is visited by the Spirit of Evil, who advises him to urinate in the bread dough to revenge himself on the community, and he does so. Yet, in a dream he sees his deceased wife in a shroud, her face black. She berates him, saying that she had deceived only herself, and that she is now paying for her transgressions. Feeling that his immortal soul is in jeopardy, Gimpel buries the dough in the frozen ground, divides his possessions among his children, and goes wandering through the world telling tales to children and depending on the goodness of people for his sustenance.

As an old, respected man, Gimpel says that he has learned that there are no lies, that if something does not really happen, it is dreamed at night. In his dreams Gimpel sees Elka, who now looks as radiant as a saint to him. She tells him that the time is near when he shall be with her again. Gimpel ends his tale by saying that the world is imaginary and that when his death comes he will go joyfully, for the afterlife will be real and he will not be deceived there.

Themes and Meanings

Isaac Bashevis Singer is known for stories that re-create the lost world of Jewish life in the Polish ghetto. This is the setting of "Gimpel the Fool," but the story also presents a gently humorous psychological study as well as a thematic analysis of the nature of reality. From the very beginning, Gimpel the narrator cannot quite understand why he is treated as a fool. That he is narrating his own story makes it unlikely that one should consider him foolish in the ordinary sense. He is only partially a naïve narrator; although he is constantly tricked and deceived by others, Gimpel does show an awareness of what they are doing. His apparent "foolishness" consists in his taking the line of least resistance to avoid their teasing: He simply decides that it is easier to believe what he is told than to make an issue of it. In addition, his faith in God makes him believe that many things are possible, so he convinces himself of the improbable. In a sense, his simplicity and naïveté protect him from harm; his narration shows him to be largely oblivious of the viciousness of others' pranks, and this apparent gullibility leads to relative contentment in his life.

The rabbi's comment to Gimpel that the others are the real fools, combined with Gimpel's epiphany on hearing Elka's words in the dream, show that he may not be the complete fool that others have made him out to be. After his temptation by the Spirit of Evil and Elka's advice to him, his decision to go out into the world as a beggar, depending on God to provide for him, shows that he has emerged from his temptation with greater faith. His final comments on the illusory nature of life, that it is "only once removed from the true world," sound profound rather than foolish.

Throughout the story, the narrator shows some understanding of what others are doing to him. Although he does not always realize exactly how terrible things are or might be for him, his attitude of acceptance makes his life bearable. In the final analysis, Gimpel himself has made the decision to believe what he is told, and this decision has led to a life of peace and contentment. The story thus presents an insight into the reality of life, as Gimpel realizes that life is what the individual makes of it.

Style and Technique

By having the protagonist narrate his own story, Singer achieves a mixture of humor, realism, and fantasy; what Gimpel narrates is unquestionably happening, but the interpretation of the events is that of a simple, naïve commentator (although Gimpel is not really very naïve when he tells the story, because it may be assumed he is speaking after the events, with his newfound wisdom and understanding). From Gimpel's own words, the reader comes to understand the kind of person that Gimpel is, as well as the events in his life, in a way that the narrator himself does not completely comprehend. The reader is able to infer that Gimpel is not as intelligent as others; as Gimpel says, "they argued me dumb." His realization of what others are doing to him is apparent as he comments, "I realized I was going to be rooked," and "To tell the plain truth, I didn't believe her." His eventual compromise—"But then, who really knows how such things are?"—is a mixture of his attempt to avoid strenuous intellectual debating and his simple faith.

The strong faith, the essential goodness, of the narrator is childlike in its simplicity: He is like a child who does not know how to interpret the incomprehensible things that are told to him by adults. Singer maintains this tone of childlike simplicity by his choice of words and by the unaffected language with which Gimpel expresses his perception of reality.

Roger Geimer

THE GIRLS IN THEIR SUMMER DRESSES

Author: Irwin Shaw (1913-1984)
Type of plot: Psychological realism
Time of plot: The 1930's
Locale: New York City
First published: 1939

> *Principal characters:*
> MICHAEL LOOMIS, a man approaching middle age
> FRANCES LOOMIS, his wife

The Story

"The Girls in their Summer Dresses" chronicles the origin and conclusion of a married couple's quarrel as they walk through lower Manhattan on a Sunday morning in November. Michael and Frances Loomis have left their apartment and are proceeding along Fifth Avenue toward Washington Square. As they are walking along the crowded thoroughfare, Frances observes that Michael has turned to look at a pretty girl and remarks good-humoredly about it. Michael, who seems unaware that she has previously noticed his habitual girl-watching, also makes light of the incident. He explains that the girl's complexion drew his attention to her, a country girl's complexion seldom seen in New York.

The conversation, sprinkled with jokes and patter, suggests that so far they have had an enjoyable weekend. Frances expresses a need for more time with Michael and urges that they call off a previously planned country outing with friends so that the two of them can spend the day in the city together. After Michael readily agrees, she begins making plans aloud for his approval, while they continue their walk. They will attend a Giants' football game, have a steak dinner at a famous restaurant, and go to a film.

As Frances is making her plans, selecting the activities that she knows her husband will enjoy, Michael's eyes stray to another attractive girl, and this time Frances is unable to conceal her frustration and dismay. She intimates that, since he is so interested in the girls, he might prefer to spend the day walking along the avenue. Michael's point of view is that he takes only an occasional glance. Further, he tells Frances, there are few really attractive girls to be seen in the city. Frances dismisses this conclusion, making it clear that she considers Michael's behavior habitual and ingrained. Indeed, she can describe not only the frequency of his girl-watching but also his manner of looking and the time he spends on each. The effect of the episodes on Frances is to increase her insecurity, and, as the story progresses, she reveals deepening anxiety and resentment. She takes no comfort from his insistence that he is happily married, for she believes that he looks at every woman who passes with the kind of look he once gave her. In reality, Michael takes pride in his wife but enjoys watching other women. To Frances this seems both contradictory and threatening.

Sensing the beginning of a quarrel that will ruin their day, Michael suggests that they have a drink, even though it is not much past breakfast. Frances rejects the idea and changes the subject temporarily. When they reach Washington Square Park, they decide to walk among the people there, but soon Frances' insecure mood returns and she begins talking about Michael's annoying habit. In an effort to reassure her, he claims that his habit is harmless and that he has always been faithful, but Frances remains troubled and gloomy. After a brief time, she agrees that they should go for a drink.

At a bar on Eighth Street they order brandy from a Japanese waiter, having decided that brandy is the proper drink to have after breakfast. As they drink, the conversation returns to the troublesome subject, and Michael now admits that he enjoys girl-watching. After ordering a second brandy, he becomes expansive and loses all restraint. He talks of the countless beautiful girls in New York, classifying them as to places they are found, professional types, racial and national types, and girls who belong to different seasons, among them, "the girls in their summer dresses." Frances believes that he wants the women, and Michael, now no longer caring, acknowledges that he does. When she pathetically declares that she too is attractive, he agrees that it is true. When she suggests that he would like to be free, he hesitates and then admits that at times he would. Now weeping, she presses him further, believing that someday he will "make a move," and Michael replies, after further hesitation, that he will. Regaining some of her composure, Frances asks that he not talk to her about the attractiveness of other women and Michael acquiesces.

They call the waiter and, to his astonishment, order a third round of drinks. No longer intent upon spending the day alone with her husband, Frances suggests that they telephone their friends, who will take them for a drive into the country. After Michael agrees, she walks to the telephone, and he watches her, thinking, "What a pretty girl, what nice legs."

Themes and Meanings

The story employs a dramatic point of view that emphasizes the fragility of human relationships. It shows understanding and agreements to be temporary and tentative, likely to decay under a threat of differences and opposition, to be reestablished only with difficulty. An anatomy of a marriage quarrel, the story centers upon Michael's compulsive girl-watching. Michael is visually oriented and essentially superficial; to him women are primarily sex objects.

Frances grasps the underlying problem when she says that his habit is that of a boy. Michael has an eye for other details as well. As he leads Frances to the bar on Eighth Street, the narrator explains, he is "looking thoughtfully at his neatly shined heavy brown shoes." A careful observer himself, he does not suspect that his wife notices his attention to the girls. At first, he tries to be evasive and indirect with Frances; he then tries to minimize the importance of his pastime. In response to her goading, however, he turns to exaggeration and masculine bravado. When his admission finally occurs and he acknowledges his feelings, the reader does not know whether to take him seriously—whether he really means what he is saying or is caddish enough to think that Frances should share his fantasies.

Despite her own attractiveness, Frances is basically insecure, and this leads her to moodiness and a kind of nagging repetition. She apparently has no other role, identity, or interest in life than being Mrs. Michael Loomis. She desperately wants his attention, approval, and reassurance. Her anguish and his ungentlemanliness arise from their superficial characters.

As with other stories by Irwin Shaw, this one touches upon the theme of lost or disappearing youth. Both Michael and Frances feel the approach of middle age and seek to fend it off. The title emphasizes this theme. Although the plot occurs in November, Michael recalls, among many other groups, "the girls in their summer dresses" who represent freshness, youth, and vitality as he himself is losing these qualities without being fully aware of what is happening. Frances appears to have no defense against the ravages of time except her marriage, and she finds the prospect of losing this security difficult to bear.

Style and Technique

The narrative achieves compression within a tightly unified framework. The story works through subtle shifts of mood and tone in the dialogue; the narrative is presented primarily from a dramatic point of view which creates tension and suspense, for the reader can never be sure of each character's actual mental state or interior thoughts. The author allows the story to develop through their conversation. The authorial voice intervenes to describe the characters' reactions, tone of voice, and emotional states as these change during the conversations. The dialogue achieves a realistic colloquial tone and reflects the economy one finds in dramatic dialogue.

The characters themselves are too commonplace to be very interesting. Their interests and conversation are shallow, the remarks on mundane topics sprinkled with joking and exaggerations. They have forsaken their roots in the Midwest and appear to have no ties with the past. They live in Manhattan, in comfort if not affluence; yet their main interests appear to be partying, drinking Scotch, attending films and football games, and, with Michael, girl-watching. Although Frances reveals some emotional depth and intensity, she shares her husband's essentially superficial pleasures. Nothing they say or do indicates that they possess even a casual acquaintance with their environment's cultural wealth—its libraries, concerts, art galleries, or live theater.

Intimacy and distance between the two characters are marked by recurring motifs of hands and touching, a skillful imagistic technique used by Shaw. Michael holds Frances' arm as they walk along Fifth Avenue, and she pats his after the encounter with the first girl. He presses her arm as he is trying to reassure her following the second incident with a girl, but shortly thereafter she withdraws her hand as she complains about his habit. They join hands to go to Washington Square Park. At the bar, Michael puts out his hand to her after she has poignantly reminded him how good a wife she has been. She withdraws her hand to press him with additional questions, arising from her state of insecurity. By this time, the opportunity for understanding and intimacy has vanished.

As with other Shaw stories, the conclusion circles back to the beginning. Early in the story, Frances mentions their planned outing with their friends, the Stevensons. Preferring to spend the day with Michael, she begins making other plans, only to return to their original purpose after she has been upset by his insensitive behavior. As the narrative concludes, she is walking to the telephone to call the Stevensons and accept their invitation.

Stanley Archer

GLADIUS DEI

Author: Thomas Mann (1875-1955)
Type of plot: Allegory
Time of plot: Late nineteenth or early twentieth century
Locale: Munich, Germany
First published: 1902 (English translation, 1936)

> *Principal characters:*
> HIERONYMUS, a disturbed young man
> M. BLUTHENZWEIG, an art dealer

The Story

Munich is alive and radiant with life and art, energy, and enthusiasm. Young and old, Germans and foreigners, all feel at home in the city. Indolence and leisure—the basis of all culture and civilization—are the characteristics of the life-style of the citizens of Munich, especially in the streets of the northern quarter. Handsome men and beautiful women saunter by; both the rich and the poor patronize art and literature.

This pleasant atmosphere is nowhere more evident than on the Odeonsplatz, in front of the large windows and glass showcases of the big art shop owned by Herr Bluthenzweig. There are antiques, modern art, art books, bronze nudes, original paintings, and especially reproductions of masterpieces on display. One large picture, a fine sepia photograph of a sensuous Madonna in a wide old-gold frame, displayed in the first window, is the center of attraction to the art lovers of Munich; the original of this picture was the sensation of the year's great international exhibition, an event well advertised all over town by means of effective and artistic posters.

A young man with hollowed cheeks, wrapped in his own thoughts, covered in a black cloak, with the hood drawn over his head, walks hurriedly. Oblivious of the sun-drenched, fun-loving city, he arrives at a dark church, which is empty except for an old woman on crutches. After genuflecting, the frail young man looks straight at the crucifix on the high altar. He seems to be seeking answers, strength, and reassurance from his God.

After praying and meditating for a little while, the young man leaves the church to go to the Odeonsplatz. Studying the faces of the people staring at the pictures displayed in the showcases in the windows of Herr Bluthenzweig, he concentrates his gaze on the picture of the Madonna. He can hear two university students admiring the sensuous beauty both of the photograph and of the model. Though offended and scandalized, Hieronymus stands staring at the picture for a quarter of an hour, fascination and repulsion revealed in his distraught face.

In fear and trembling, Hieronymus leaves the spot. He cannot understand why the picture of the sensuous Madonna goes wherever he goes. His soul is outraged; no amount of prayer and fasting can exorcise it.

On the third night after his visit to the art shop, Hieronymus receives a command from Heaven: Speak out against frivolity, blasphemy, and the arrogance of beauty that flaunts itself naked; sacrifice yourself amid the jeers of your foes; you are My martyr and prophet; be not fainthearted; I am giving you the gift of tongues.

Obedient to the unshakable will of God, Hieronymus retraces his steps to the art shop and demands to see Herr Bluthenzweig. No one pays any attention to the poor young man as all the shop attendants are busy waiting on their wealthy clientele. Finally, as Herr Bluthenzweig approaches Hieronymus, the young man demands that the photograph of the Madonna be removed from the showcase in the window and never be displayed again. The picture is a scandal—it ridicules the doctrine of the Immaculate Conception. The world, Hieronymus says, is a valley of tears, corrupt and contemptible, sinful and miserable. This real world cannot and should not be camouflaged by the unreality of art and passing beauty. Art that extols the temporal mocks the eternal God. Genuine art does not lead man to sin; genuine art teaches man to hate the world and love God. Hieronymus charges the dealer to burn the picture and throw the ashes to the four winds. His voice reaches the crescendo of a scream: Burn, burn, burn everything—all these antiques, statues, busts, and volumes of erotic verse; these are remnants of accursed paganism.

Herr Bluthenzweig loses his patience. When he asks Hieronymus to leave, the young man does not budge; peremptorily, Bluthenzweig orders his servant Krauthuber, a big, burly human hulk, to throw Hieronymus out.

The next minute, Hieronymus finds himself in the street—exhausted, weak, and powerless. He does not see the jeering, amused people around him. He sees in the mosaic square in front of him the vision of an auto-da-fé—vases, busts, erotic books, pictures of famous beauties, and nude statues, all heaped in a pyramid and going up in flames as a result of his burning words and to the exultation of his followers. He sees the sword of God (*gladius Dei*) rising in splendor, quick and fast (*cito et velociter*), above the doomed city. In peace and serenity, Hieronymus lowers his eyes and covers his head.

Themes and Meanings

"Gladius Dei" dramatizes the perennial tension between Christ and Apollo, the sacred and the secular, Christianity and paganism, God and the world, the city of God and the city of man. It is another echo of the famous rhetorical question of the Christian apologist Tertullian in the second century—What has Athens to do with Jerusalem?—and of the question of Alcuin in the eighth century—Is there anything in common between Ingeld and Christ?

For the radical believer, art and religion are antithetical unless art is employed explicitly in the service of religion: One cannot serve two masters. In contrast, the ordinary believer does not see an absolute dichotomy: For him, art and religion are two complementary realities; there is no necessary opposition between the two, and he believes that he can have the best of both worlds.

Thomas Mann dwells on this dialectical nature of the subject of art in a number of works, especially in his play *Fiorenza* (1906), his most important work of the years 1904-1907. "Gladius Dei" is an offshoot of *Fiorenza*, and Hieronymus is a descendant of Brother Girolamo.

Style and Technique

The principal characters in "Gladius Dei" are not well-rounded, nor are they intended to be; instead, they are clearly identifiable types. Hieronymus represents the extreme view that art which is not unequivocally in the service of religion is an affront to God. Bluthenzweig, the spokesman for the common man's liberal faith, manages to win this battle, but the war between Christ ·and Apollo goes on forever. Indeed, even in defeat, Hieronymus thinks that he has triumphed: It is a personal victory to stand up for one's beliefs.

The meaning of the story and the character of Hieronymus are evocative of the famous dream of Saint Jerome (Hieronymus, in Latin), in which the classicist writer Jerome is confronted by the Supreme Judge Jesus Christ, who accuses him: "You are a Ciceronian, not a Christian." Interestingly, though Jerome promised his Master and Judge to give up classical studies and avoid pagan ideals in his writing, he continued to use pagan myths and classical images in his Christian writings. Like Jerome's dream, "Gladius Dei" exposes the dialectical elements found in the nature of art and in the life of the artist.

Zacharias P. Thundy

THE GLEANER

Author: H. E. Bates (1905-1974)
Type of plot: Lyric realism
Time of plot: Probably the early 1930's
Locale: Probably rural England
First published: 1934

Principal character:
THE GLEANER, an old woman

The Story

An old woman toils slowly up a hill from her village to the harvested field where she will glean scraps of stalks and rubble after the plowing, which has been a right traditionally reserved for the rural poor for many centuries in England. She reaches the gate of the field, passes through, and, sack in hand, bends to her gleaning. It is noon on an early autumn day, and the sun beats down mercilessly on the gleaner. She works quickly and anxiously; it is a race against time because her occupation is confined to the daylight hours, and she fears the arrival of other gleaners, competitors for these leavings which are essential to her survival.

As she labors alone in the center of the field, memories return of her childhood many years before, in an earlier century. Then, as a little girl, she did exactly the same work, made the same gestures as she does now, taught originally and prodded on by her mother, in a long generational line of gleaners. The old woman is the last survivor of this ancient calling.

It is late in the afternoon. The gleaner continues to work, but more slowly now, bowed down by fatigue and by the success of her endeavor, the half-filled, heavy sack. A thistle wounds her hand, drawing blood. She continues her gathering, oblivious of the multicolored flowers through which she makes her way, but deeply content in her vocation.

Now she can do no more; it is dusk. The sack is almost completely filled and very heavy. She has reached the climax of her task: She must somehow get the burdensome prize, for which she has toiled so long, up on to her shoulder. She makes one great hoisting effort—but it fails, and the sack falls to the ground nearly upended. Righting the sack, she tries again, and with a last, stupendous attempt, brings her winnings up on to her shoulder, and tears of pain and weariness to her eyes. Slowly she turns, moves out of the field and down the road on which she came, disdaining to wipe her tear-stained face. As she moves homeward, the evening breezes dry her tears.

Themes and Meanings

In this story and in many others, H. E. Bates attempts to communicate his love and reverence for the rural working people among whom he grew up in the Midlands of England. The solitary character in "The Gleaner" is simultaneously a literal, clearly visualized, individual person and a mythic heroine whose trip up and back from the hill is a quest for both survival and meaning. Bates depicts it as a successful, triumphant quest; ranged against the gleaner are various elements of nature, as well as the weakness of her sex and advanced age. She works against time, the heat of the sun, and the denuded land, which does not yield up its substance without her strenuous effort, wounding her in the process. Yet the gleaner never questions her role or her function in life. Working almost by reflex, she is part of nature even as she opposes nature and it opposes her efforts. A tiny figure as she bends in the center of the vast field, she nevertheless dominates her world as the only human presence in it.

Four cycles are interwoven in the story. The individual cycle of the gleaner's life is limned from childhood memory to present old age; the cycle of her vocation, many generations of gleaners, spans the centuries, although with the present avatar's death, this race will become extinct. Part of Bates's sorrowful early life experience was to see the countryside that he loved increasingly ravaged by the factory-slum complex of the Industrial Revolution. In this story, however, nature is unchallenged; the gleaner moves through portions of two nature cycles: the daily one, from noon to dusk, superimposed on the seasonal shift from summer to autumn. Perhaps the most basic meaning of the story is its insistence on conflict and harmony in almost perfect balance in the natural world. The sun causes the old woman her deepest suffering through the heat of its rays, yet the light of the sun is absolutely necessary for the successful completion of her task.

Style and Technique

One of the central meanings of Bates's story is his assertion of the close, organic connection between the gleaner and her natural environment; throughout the narrative, striking metaphors urge this connection. At the very beginning of the story, she is introduced in terms of plant imagery, as a very ancient, bare branch of a gnarled, little tree. Her face is the hue and texture of wood that has been etched and planed down by the centuries. Her gestures as well as her appearance link her to the animal kingdom. She is compared to a bird, relentlessly foraging for each minute speck of grain. Separate aspects of the gleaner take on a life of their own; at times, Bates creates the illusion that she is an army of allied organisms, not simply one frail person: Thus, her hands move almost independently over the rough ground, like a pair of scouring mice, as she gleans. Her fingers are similarly animated, like the young ends of ancient trees.

From these and other examples, it can be seen that Bates is a very visual writer, and dynamically so: From beginning to end, the gleaner is presented in action, confronting her environment rather than a passive victim of it. This incessant activity contributes to the image of a heroic, mythic figure who transcends time and place. Some of the images, therefore, emphasize her great age; others, paradoxically, describe her as a very young person. As the gleaner's day wears on, her accumulating fatigue slows down her movements to the pace of a little girl who has been playing in the sun too long. By not specifically naming his heroine or her locale, Bates emphasizes her timeless, mythic dimension. The archetypal aspect of this woman is made explicit in a passage near the end of the story in which she is referred to as an Earth Mother, whose origin merges with that of the grain she bears.

Bates writes in the tradition of the modern, streamlined story of Sherwood Anderson and Ernest Hemingway, in which, more often than not, plot is subordinated to character. "The Gleaner," however, is by no means a plotless story; in it, the earth-figure protagonist undertakes and completes a mythic journey that is both trial and quest. This journey is framed by the gleaner's trip up the hill to the field at noon, followed by her return down to the village at dusk. The trial is of her skill and resourcefulness—almost no speck of grain eludes her by the end of the day—as well as of her strength and endurance. In her trial she is aided, not by individual helpers, but by her own instinctive, unconscious nature. Complementing passages in the story which metaphorically link the gleaner to aspects of her environment are others personifying often gigantic figures which heighten her trial and obstruct her quest, such as the great trees rimming the field which throw out balls of shadow on it in the waning day.

The elixir, the object of great value which shapes the journey as quest, is literally the filled bag of gleanings, perhaps the central symbol of this story. There are two aspects to the meaning of this symbol: life as process (the bag as the gleaner fills it during the course of the narrative) and life as attained goal (the heavy, brimful burden, which she successfully hoists over her shoulder in the climax of the journey).

Bates was a dynamically visual writer, and here his handling of point of view is similar to that of a modern filmmaker, who follows his subject with a variety of panoramic, angled, and close-up shots. For contrast, the print medium enables Bates to move inside his heroine's consciousness for brief, flashlike moments of memory and perception. Perhaps no single aspect of short-story technique is more difficult to bring off successfully than the ending; here, Bates's visual technique triumphs. The gleaner recedes down the hill on her way home. The tears of exertion and earlier frustration have now been dried by the evening air, leaving salt, which she can taste on her lips— her own salt, which the author, in his last line, urges the reader to see as merging with the salt of the earth she treads: Character and setting, kept separate though organically linked from the beginning, finally become one.

Sanford Radner

GLIMPSE INTO ANOTHER COUNTRY

Author: Wright Morris (1910-　　)
Type of plot: Whimsical comedy
Time of plot: 1983
Locale: San Francisco and New York
First published: 1983

> *Principal characters:*
> HAZLITT, an elderly San Francisco academic
> MRS. HAZLITT, his wife
> MRS. THAYER, a visitor to New York
> DR. THAYER, her husband

The Story

Hazlitt, an elderly San Francisco academic, goes to New York to see a specialist about a matter of "life assurance." On the plane, he is bemused by the behavior of the woman seated next to him as she completely ignores him. Hazlitt is not offended, since he is "guarded even with his colleagues at the university," and he is attracted by the woman's intelligent profile and "appealing intactness."

Hazlitt considers it rude, however, when she does not share *The New York Times* with him and is "flabbergasted" when he observes her beginning to read D. M. Thomas' *The White Hotel* (1981) on its last page and continuing to read the final chapter in reverse. Shifting to a news magazine, she finally speaks to Hazlitt, declaiming about the dangers of travel. The ice broken, he finds himself telling her that he knows the author of *The White Hotel* (in fact, they have never met), who "would consider it a personal favor if you read his book as it was printed, from the front to the back."

Shocked, the woman complains about this apparent madman to her husband, whom Hazlitt deduces is a fellow academic. Hazlitt apologizes, and Dr. Thayer introduces himself. The neurotic Mrs. Thayer responds by thrusting the "filthy book" at Hazlitt: "Read it any way you like!" She then returns to maintaining "to the last his nonexistence."

Arriving in New York and checking into the Plaza, Hazlitt remembers his wife's caution to carry a hundred dollars in twenties "so that when the muggers looked for money they would find it." He takes a horse-drawn carriage to Bloomingdale's and on his arrival is surprised to find Mrs. Thayer purchasing something from a street peddler, so surprised that he topples out of the carriage and into the peddler's arms. The peddler is amused and gives Hazlitt "the smile of a collaborator."

In Bloomingdale's, Hazlitt impulsively buys what he considers expensive bracelets for his wife, but while the clerk takes his driver's license away to have his check approved, the store is suddenly closed because of a bomb scare. He calls his wife to tell her about his day but leaves out the bomb scare, since it would disturb her, and "for some reason," he does not mention Mrs. Thayer either.

The next day Hazlitt receives the assurance he wants from the specialist and feels that he is now "free of a nameless burden." He returns to Bloomingdale's to regain his driver's licence, and with his new sense of freedom, he impulsively exchanges the bracelets for an expensive strand of pearls. He cannot afford them, but "writing the numbers, spelling the sum out gave him a tingling sense of exhilaration." He imagines his wife's "wide-eyed astonishment, her look of disbelief."

Hazlitt proceeds to the Metropolitan Museum of Art, where he, as a graduate student, had enjoyed watching people contemplate the works of art. In the gift shop, he sees another browser, the omnipresent Mrs. Thayer, read the last in a collection of Vincent Van Gogh's letters, then the next-to-last, then the next. He goes to the Fountain Court lunchroom, which he remembers so fondly from his youth, but it has been renovated, eliminating the dusky pool and sculptured figures he recalls so vividly.

In the basement rest room, he finds a group of boys, apparently under the influence of drugs, making a toilet overflow to flood the room and smearing themselves with shaving cream. They demand that he give them something but knock the handful of coins he offers into the water. He gives them the pearls and leaves them fighting over their booty.

He returns to the gift shop to buy an Etruscan pin "that he felt his wife would consider a sensible value." Outside, he passes a bus and hears tapping on a window. Mrs. Thayer waves to him, her eyes giving him "all the assurance he needed."

Themes and Meanings

Hazlitt is one in a long line of elderly or aging characters in Wright Morris' fiction who feel somewhat displaced in the modern world. They encounter change, however, with more confusion than bitterness. Hazlitt, who does not fly very often, has the stewardess explain how to pull the dining tray from the seat in front of him and pry the lid from his salad dressing, but he recognizes such new—to him—things as inevitable, as is the change in the Fountain Court. Instead of experiencing nostalgia, Hazlitt simply makes connections between the present and the past, as when street sounds remind him of radio plays of the 1940's. Still, things are not as they should be, as the bomb scare indicates. The porter at the Plaza explains that the bathroom faucets turn opposite the usual directions: "A sign of the times, Hazlitt thought."

Other dilemmas facing modern man are touched upon in "Glimpse into Another Country." Hazlitt has difficulty communicating with the Thayers on the plane and does not understand why he criticizes her reading the novel backward. When Dr. Thayer explains that, though "there is something in what you say," his wife is free to read as she pleases, Hazlitt is nonplussed: "It was usually he who was the cool one, the voice of reason in the tempest, the low-keyed soother of the savage breast. Worse yet, this fellow was about half his age." In the taxi from the airport, Hazlitt wants "to chat a bit with the driver, but the Plexiglas barrier between them seemed intimidating."

Yet Morris' world is not one of stereotypes, clichés, and simplistic alienation. When Hazlitt becomes separated from his driver's license, he has not lost his identity but gained a peculiar sense of freedom, "an obscure elation." His wife fears for him in New York, but the porter at the Plaza, the street peddler, and the clerks at Bloomingdale's go out of their way to be friendly and helpful. Hazlitt almost brings the rest room incident upon himself by refusing to recognize a potential danger.

Like many Morris characters, Hazlitt journeys through life with an amused detachment, never taking anything truly seriously since there are plenty of others—such as his wife and Mrs. Thayer—willing to assume that burden for him. For Hazlitt, past and present, the strange and the everyday seem to merge; he moves about as in a dream. In Bloomingdale's, he watches a television picture of a milling crowd in India indifferently passing by dead or sleeping bodies: "The film gave Hazlitt a glimpse into a strange country where the quick and the dormant were accustomed to mingle. Perhaps . . . it was not the walkers but the sleepers who would range the farthest in their travels." Since everything becomes part of the inexplicable interrelatedness of life, Hazlitt is not surprised at finding Mrs. Thayer everywhere he goes.

Style and Technique

Morris mixes whimsical and poetic fictional styles to reflect the alternately matter-of-fact and bewildered points of view of his characters. Appropriately for a dreamlike story, "Glimpse into Another Country" uses water imagery for poetic effect; Hazlitt observes events as if they were beyond the limitations of normal time and space, as if they were happening underwater.

The most significant use of water imagery occurs in the museum scenes. Hazlitt expects to encounter water at the Fountain Court; instead, he finds a pool in the rest room. When the boys fight over the pearls, "They thrashed about violently at Hazlitt's feet like one writhing, many-limbed monster." It is as if he has returned the pearls to the sea, where they belong. When he leaves the museum in the rain, he sees Mrs. Thayer's face "only dimly through the rain-streaked window" of the bus. Their relationship, as always, is out of focus, as in a dream, as if underwater: "What appeared to be tears might have been drops of water."

Sensory imagery is used to reinforce Hazlitt's sensitivity, because of his awareness of mortality, to the nuances of everything around him. Hazlitt is particularly alert to sounds. When he calls his wife, he asks if she can hear the car horns in the street below his hotel window, and he imagines the sights and sounds of their kitchen: "Hazlitt knew so exactly just how it all was that he could hear the sound of the wall clock—stuffed with a towel to mute the ticking." After visiting the specialist, freed of anxiety about the approaching muting of his own ticking, he walks through the lobby of the Waldorf-Astoria "for the pleasure of its carpet and the creak of expensive Texas luggage"— yet more assurance, the sound of life.

Michael Adams

GOBSECK

Author: Honoré de Balzac (1799-1850)
Type of plot: Psychological realism and social realism
Time of plot: Early nineteenth century
Locale: Paris
First published: 1830, revised 1835 (English translation, 1896)

> *Principal characters:*
> JEAN-ESTHER VAN GOBSECK, a powerful moneylender
> COUNTESS ANASTASIE DE RESTAUD, a faithless wife
> COUNT ERNEST DE RESTAUD, Anastasie's husband
> COUNT MAXIME DE TRAILLES, Anastasie's lover
> ERNEST DE RESTAUD, Anastasie's only legitimate child
> MR. DERVILLE, the narrator of the story and one of its
> agonists

The Story

"At one o'clock one morning, during the winter of 1829-1830, two persons not members of the Vicomtesse de Grandlieu's family were still in her salon. A handsome young man left the room as he heard the clock strike." Thus casually begins a story in which another story will be told—a detailed recounting of social and moral evils.

Madame de Grandlieu, the viscountess, has noticed in her daughter Camille a romantic inclination toward the young Count Ernest de Restaud, who has just left, and warns the seventeen-year-old girl that he has a mother capable of squandering away millions; as long as the mother lives, no family would approve the marriage of a young daughter with Ernest de Restaud. The other visitor that night, Mr. Derville, a lawyer and friend of the family, overhears Madame de Grandlieu's words to Camille and announces a story that will modify the viscountess' opinion about Ernest de Restaud's fortunes.

More than a decade earlier, relates Derville, he sublet a room from a usurer, then a man in his late seventies. The moneylender occupied another room in the same damp and dark building. The only person with whom the miser had any neighborly communication was the narrator, at the time a law student of very limited means. There follows a description of the gaunt, strong old man, a striking personality notwithstanding his negative traits. Jean-Esther Van Gobseck was born about 1740 in the city of Anvers (Antwerp), of a Dutch father and a Jewish mother. When he was ten years old, his mother sent him away to the Dutch colonies in the East Indies. During the ensuing half-century, he knew the feeling of life imperiled and then saved, of fortune lost and found again; he did business with historic figures in remote lands; he became acquainted with all the particulars of the American

Revolution. His religion was uncertain.

The old man spent most of his time either sitting in his dark room by a fireplace with more ashes than embers, or running about Paris hounding his debtors. He expressed his philosophy to Derville: "You believe in everything; I believe in nothing. Keep your illusions if you can," and "Gold represents all the human forces." Gobseck related his encounters with two persons exemplifying extremes of behavior: a young working woman striving against all odds to support herself and a countess living in luxury but unable to satisfy a note signed to pay for the gambling losses of her lover. Gobseck boasted: He was rich enough to purchase the consciences of those who pulled the strings within the government; was that not power? He could have the loveliest women's caresses; was that not pleasure? Did not power and pleasure sum up the whole social order? In the eyes of Derville, the gaunt, little old man grew into a grotesque figure personifying the power of money; life, especially mankind, horrified the young man. There is a ray of light in this spectacle of vice: The narrator, now the successful lawyer Derville, lets Madame de Grandlieu know that his wife is that same humble working girl long ago mentioned by Gobseck.

The narration returns to the point where Derville finishes his studies and is able to acquire an independent office owing to a significant sum of money that Gobseck lends him at a high though not usurious rate of interest. A year later, Derville is present at a visit from Count Maxime de Trailles to the already octogenarian Gobseck; this count is the same well-known dandy—a supremely elegant, high-class gambler, and an unprincipled adventurer and exploiter of women—who several years before had played a role in the episode of the spendthrift countess. The beautiful noblewoman, Anastasie, appears at the moneylender's quarters and shows him her diamonds—really those of her family—the value of which amounts to a fortune. Derville instructs the parties with his unfailing honesty while trying to hold out a hand to the distraught woman: It is not likely that the diamonds could be validly pawned without the consent of the countess' husband. Gobseck reacts at once: He will only buy the diamonds. Derville still whispers in the woman's ear that she ought to appeal to her husband's mercy rather than sacrifice a fortune belonging to her family. Yet the money evidently is needed for her lover, who then uses emotional coercion, and Anastasie accepts the usurer's low offer of eighty thousand francs. Now Gobseck gives the screw another turn: He delivers fifty thousand francs to the countess and, completing the price, some notes signed by Maxime de Trailles and already due and protested, which Gobseck has discounted far below their face value from his fellow moneylenders. The young Trailles roars an insult; the old man coldly produces a pair of pistols and observes that, being the insulted party, he will fire first. Trailles stammers an apology. Anastasie bows and disappears, undoubtedly terrified, and Trailles follows her. The act unravels with the excited appearance of Anastasie's husband. Derville intervenes in the resulting dispute, advising Gobseck and the count to compromise, and a document is signed allowing the latter to recover his diamonds at a sacrifice.

Some days later the count walks into Derville's office. A conversation follows in which new light is thrown on the moneylender's personality. Derville reveals that he is convinced that aside from Gobseck's financial doings and cynical observations about human nature, he can be the most scrupulous and upright of men. There are two men in him, a miser and a philosopher; should Derville die leaving children behind, Gobseck would be their guardian. The count has health problems and is afraid of what may happen to his properties in case of his death; therefore, he asks Derville to prepare documents transferring his properties to Gobseck, as well as a defeasance to be signed by Gobseck and kept by Derville, by virtue of which his principal estates are left to his only legitimate child and heir to his title.

At this point in the narration, sleepy Camille goes to bed; consequently the viscountess indicates that Derville can call the count by his name, Restaud—the reader recalls the family name of the young visitor who attracted Camille's attentions. The story is resumed and climaxes in a series of highly dramatic scenes. The count is taken to his bed gravely ill and, unable to send the defeasance to Derville, hides it from his wife, who, accompanied by her children, keeps a permanent vigil in the adjoining room. Derville tries in vain to convince the countess that it is also in her interest that he should see her husband. When the count finally dies, Derville and Gobseck arrive and force their way into the death chamber only to find the count's body lying on the floor like another piece of litter, and the Countess Anastasie, disheveled and bewildered, who in her blind distrust of her husband and Derville has just found and burned the defeasance.

Gobseck, faithful to his nature and ideas, keeps Restaud's estates as long as he lives, taking very good care of everything; the principal heir and very young count will benefit from growing up in adversity, the greatest teacher. Derville ends his narration with the news of Gobseck's recent death at the age of eighty-nine, in a revolting scene of ruinous hoarding and miserliness. Now Ernest de Restaud, already a young man of good character, will come into possession of his estates and be able to marry Camille. The story concludes with Madame de Grandlieu still voicing some reservations, which can be surmounted.

Themes and Meanings

The succession of versions, titles, and labelings of this novella, or rather long short story, reveals a shifting of thematic focus. In the definitive text, the figure of the moneylender has reached its fully rounded size and is central as the portrayal of a remarkable individual as well as a social phenomenon, while the conflict between the Comtesse de Restaud and her ill-treated husband—or the consequences of misconduct—remains as an important secondary theme.

Balzac's art grew in parallel with the growth of "Gobseck," in which its salient topics and motifs are already found in full bloom: the interplay of polar principles—a moral polarization also working within the characters' psyches—the dramatic situations and outspoken, confrontational dialogues, the characters grandiloquently describing and justifying themselves with regard to the opposing characters and society—not only the usurer Gobseck but also the dandy Count Maxime de Trailles. There is also the keen attention directed both toward moral conflicts deep in the individual consciousness and toward the conflicting forces and affairs observed in society.

In trying to transport the Parisian milieu of 1830 to his own distinct social conditions and mentality, the American reader may find correspondences between some of Balzac's incidents and, for example, those in the popular soap opera "Dallas." Balzac was accused of succeeding better in the portrayal of evil than in the presentation of virtue. Repeatedly and from several angles he answered this charge. Commenting on Samuel Richardson's *Clarissa* (1747-1748), he replied to one of the editors of *La Semaine*: "Do you think that such work would be readable if it were necessary to have the decent people whose lives lack drama occupy in it the extent of space they occupy in social reality?"

Style and Technique

Balzac's style is easily translatable; in other words, the reader of a good translation does not miss much of the enjoyment that the original text ought to produce. It should be remembered that many of the very greatest novelists—Stendhal, Herman Melville, Fyodor Dostoevski, Leo Tolstoy, and Italo Svevo—although vigorous and also stylistically effective in rendering their fictional worlds, have not excelled in poetic expression or beautiful language; to this assertion in all its parts Balzac is no exception.

The important characters of this story appear again, sometimes with leading roles, in many of Balzac's novels, beginning with *Le Père Goriot* (1835; *Père Goriot*, 1860). Considering chronologically the development of "Gobseck" and the gestation of *Père Goriot*—whose protagonist, Anastasie's father, is also mentioned in "Gobseck"—it is plausible that the strong types of Gobseck and Maxime de Trailles as well as the social state of affairs represented by Goriot's daughters and their aristocratic husbands and lovers inspired Balzac's vision of a great cycle of novels to be entitled *La Comédie humaine* (1829-1848; *The Human Comedy*, 1885-1893) in an analogy with Dante's *The Divine Comedy*. In this aspect as well as in those pointed out in the previous section, "Gobseck" occupies a central position in Balzac's oeuvre.

A. M. Vázquez-Bigi

GOGOL'S WIFE

Author: Tommaso Landolfi (1908-1979)
Type of plot: Surrealistic parody
Time of plot: Mid-nineteenth century
Locale: Unspecified
First published: "La moglie di Gogol," 1954 (English translation, 1963)

> *Principal characters:*
> NIKOLAI VASSILEVITCH GOGOL, a Russian writer
> CARACAS, Gogol's "wife," a balloon doll
> FOMA PASKALOVITCH, the narrator, Nikolai Gogol's
> biographer

The Story

The story is purportedly a chapter of a biography of the great nineteenth century Russian writer, Nikolai Vassilevitch Gogol. The supposed biographer, Foma Paskalovitch, begins suspensefully by pointing out that he is about to relate something about Gogol's wife that is so scandalous as to cause him to hesitate revealing it. After this suspenseful beginning, the narrator reveals that Gogol's "wife" was actually a life-size balloon in the form of a woman. The plot's exposition consists of a description of the inflatable doll and two incidents in which the biographer, who was apparently close to Gogol, observed the "wife."

What distinguishes the inflatable doll is that with each inflation it takes on a different form, depending upon the amount of air pressure that is filling out its anatomy. It can never be made to look the same way again once it is deflated. To give even greater variety to the appearances of the doll, Gogol has a number of different wigs and shades of makeup with which he ornaments it. Thus, the doll can be made to conform, more or less, to the desires and tastes of Gogol with each inflation. From time to time, when the doll has taken on a form especially pleasing to Gogol, he falls in love with that form "exclusively," and maintains it in that form until he falls out of love. After a few years of living with the doll, Gogol bestows a name upon it, Caracas.

It is to demonstrate the relationship between Gogol and his balloon woman, and the decline of that relationship, that the biographer recounts two incidents in which he observed Gogol and Caracas together in Gogol's home. In the first incident, Paskalovitch hears Caracas speak. He is sitting with Gogol in the room where Caracas is always kept—a room where no one is normally allowed to enter—and the two writers are discussing a Russian novel. Caracas is sitting on a pile of cushions against a wall and is made up as a beautiful blonde. Suddenly, and surprisingly, she utters in a husky voice, "I want to go poo poo." Gogol, horrified, jumps at the doll and, ramming two fingers down its throat where an air valve is located, he deflates it. He makes apologies to Paskalovitch and attempts to resume their talk, but it is impossible. Gogol explains that he loved that form of Caracas, and now he feels despondent having lost her. It is impossible to reconstruct that exact form.

Before relating the next incident, Paskalovitch comments on a specific tension that developed between Gogol and Caracas. He notes that over time the doll seemed to acquire a distinct personality that unified all its various manifestations. Through all its changes—from blonde to redhead to brunette, from plump to slim—some unnamable quality seemed to pervade that gave Caracas a sort of identity, something that gave it distinction as an individual independent of Gogol's control. Moreover, to Gogol this identity appears hostile. What expresses this hostility most dramatically for Gogol is his contraction of syphilis. Gogol claims to have had no contact with any woman other than his balloon-wife, yet he contracts the disease and undergoes the painful treatment of it. He says to Paskalovitch, "You see what lay at the heart of Caracas; it was the spirit of syphilis."

The second incident makes up the plot's climax, recounting the tragic end of Gogol's "marriage" to Caracas. Gogol, tortured by feelings of "aversion and attachment" to Caracas, has begun to speak more fantastically about her, complaining that she is aging, that she pursues pleasures he forbids, even that she has betrayed him. On the night of the silver anniversary of their "wedding," Paskalovitch is with Gogol and Caracas in their home. Gogol's behavior is inconsistent, vacillating between affection for Caracas and repugnance. At one point, he exclaims, "That's enough! We can't have any more of this. This is an unheard of thing. How can such a thing be happening to me? How can a man be expected to put up with *this*?" Gogol then grabs his air pump, inserts it in the tube at the doll's anus, and inflates her persistently, weeping and shouting all the while, "Oh, how I love her . . . my poor, poor darling! . . . most pitiable of God's creatures. But die she must!" The doll swells to distorted proportions, her face running through various expressions, of amazement, supplication, disdain. Finally it bursts violently, scattering small fragments of rubber around the room. Gogol gathers these pieces and puts them in the fire, crossing himself with his left hand. With Gogol's wife thus "murdered," Gogol surprises Paskalovitch with yet another dramatic act. Charging Paskalovitch to hide his face against a wall and not to look, Gogol rushes to another room. He reenters bearing a small bundle which he also hurls into the fire. Paskalovitch has peeked, and he perceives that the bundle is a baby—a rubber doll that might, by its appearance, be regarded as Caracas' son.

The denouement of the story consists of Paskalovitch looking ahead to the next chapters of the biography of Nikolai Vassilevitch Gogol, and his reflections on the purpose of this chapter treating Gogol's wife. He has at least, as he puts it, "given the lie to the insensate accusation that he ill-treated or even beat his wife, as well as other like absurdities."

Themes and Meanings

"Gogol's Wife" contains many qualities typical of Landolfi's writing, including criticism of intolerance, especially intolerance of any disinclination to accept the extraordinary. Here, Landolfi dramatizes this in a story that is Kafkaesque in its representation of a monstrosity that does not yield itself easily to reason. In its sensational combination of the prosaic (as a biography of a famous writer) and the absurd (Gogol's regarding his inflatable doll as his wife) the story is surrealistic: Otherwise mundane, everyday elements become monstrously distorted.

Within this surreal framework, themes are developed regarding identity and the struggle between reality and fantasy. The question of identity arises in Landolfi's treatment of Gogol's balloon-wife. The first qualities of Caracas that are described are her mutability: Gogol can change her at will into vastly different forms of woman; in fact, he has no choice, since the doll can never be made the same way twice. Diversity, change, mutability, are all elementary characteristics of Caracas. Yet, as the story unfolds, Gogol and Paskalovitch become increasingly more aware of unifying traits in the doll, which are apparently not so much the result of physical similarities from one manifestation to another as they are the result of a developing personality. Gogol refers to the doll's acting out independently, first in relatively trivial ways, as when it embarrasses him with its utterance, "I want to go poo poo." Gogol explains at this point that "she only does it for a joke, or to annoy me, because as a matter of fact she does not have such needs." As Paskalovitch suggests at one point, Gogol likely bestowed a name upon the doll because of such indications of individuality. Ultimately, however, this independence manifests itself more cruelly with Gogol's contraction of syphilis, which he attributes to his contact with Caracas, and finally to behavior in the doll that causes him to accuse it of betraying him. The specific behavior that leads to this and other complaints of Gogol is never revealed. The important question is, what is it that Gogol loves? What attracts him in this love-hate relationship? If, on the one hand, the meticulous description of the doll underscores its unreality (as a "wife," in any case) and instability (never being the same twice), on the other hand, Gogol's devotion to the doll as Caracas and his emotional involvement, which is emphasized rather than diminished by his destroying it, attest the existence of something very real. Furthermore, Gogol's and Paskalovitch's perception of the unifying traits of the doll cannot be denied. This treatment of identity, then, is paradoxical: Caracas is at once unreal and real, both created by Gogol and creating him, inasmuch as she alters his behavior.

This enigmatic treatment of the evasiveness and rich ambiguity of identity serves to point out the coexistence of reality and fantasy. In Landolfi's story these do not cancel each other, but work to re-create each other. In a rather distasteful pun, Paskalovitch suggests that the unifying attributes of Caracas are "no less than the creative afflatus of Nikolai Vassilevitch himself." Caracas is, by this interpretation, Gogol's "inspiration," in a literal as well as a figurative sense, the product both of his air and of his imagination. Caracas is in this sense no less real than Gogol's body of literature that supported him and made him famous.

Gogol's destruction of Caracas and the doll baby expresses his acknowledgment that he no longer has control of his creation, which presents him mysteriously with unwanted results: embarrassment, anxiety, syphilis, and a doll son.

Style and Technique

While giving serious treatment to the relationship between reality and fantasy, "Gogol's Wife" also bitterly parodies literary biography. Through use of the first-person point of view, in the persona of Foma Paskalovitch, the biographer of Nikolai Gogol, Landolfi mimics and exaggerates what he regarded as the sensationalism inherent in biographical studies. From the outset, Paskalovitch dons an exaggerated fastidiousness that interferes with more than it assists in the "biography." There is the regular intrusion of such phrases as "I should specify," "perhaps I should say at once," "let us not mince matters," and "as my readers will already have understood." With this fastidiousness is also suggested a fawning admiration of his subject, expressed by means of ill-timed references to Gogol's genius, usually juxtaposed with lurid or sensational details about the balloon-wife.

The biographer's interest in the lurid details of the balloon-wife maintain the atmosphere of sensationalism at a high pitch. Thus, much detail is offered in the treatment of the doll's genitalia, in the valves at the back of its throat and anal sphincter, in Caracas' private room, with its Oriental decor. When the biographer notes that he was eyewitness to the dramatic end of the affair, he is quick to exclaim, "Would that I had not been!"

Landolfi pokes fun at the sensationalism most pointedly, however, through the biographer's use of suspense. In the opening sentence the biographer states that he hesitates to relate the story about Gogol's wife. He indicates then that what he is about to disclose will probably be offensive to many, and that in fact he himself recoils at the thought of it. Arguing the responsibility of a biographer to tell the whole truth, he then promises a detailed account of the affair. This hesitation and then determination to be truthful bring up a serious question about biographies, and especially those literary biographies that have revealed damning details of their subjects' lives. Landolfi himself, in his own time, refused interviews and discouraged curiosity about his personal life, denying the value of such details for use in literary studies. The serious question is here mocked, however, for Paskalovitch's hesitations, drawn out over several pages and renewed before every new sensational revelation, only create suspense and arouse prurient interest. When he states, after a string of disclaimers and hesitations, that he will continue "without more ado," he only draws attention to the unnecessary ado he has already squandered; and when he curbs himself with "but let us not anticipate," he only emphasizes how much has already been anticipated, and encourages more premature guesswork about Gogol's relations with his wife.

In a final tone of mockery and as an indictment perhaps of literary biography in general, Landolfi ends with the acerbic irony,

And what else can be the goal of a humble biographer such as the present writer but to serve the memory of that lofty genius who is the object of his study?

Dennis C. Chowenhill

GOING HOME

Author: William Trevor (William Trevor Cox, 1928-   )
Type of plot: Domestic realism
Time of plot: Probably the 1960's
Locale: The South of England
First published: 1972

> *Principal characters:*
> CARRUTHERS, a thirteen-year-old boy who attends boarding
>   school
> MISS FANSHAWE, a thirty-eight-year-old undermatron at the
>   school
> ATKINS, a waiter in the dining car of a train

The Story

At the end of each term, Carruthers and Miss Fanshawe travel together by train from the Ashleigh Court school to their separate destinations. The journey has become a ritual, and in this no-man's-land on the train an unusual relationship has developed. While Miss Fanshawe has a certain supervisory responsibility for Carruthers, he seems to have taken advantage of the freedom on the train to act out his aggression, and she appears to indulge more than restrain him. He smokes, drinks alcohol, lies, and embarrasses her with outspoken comments and questions. The verbal aggression is directed against her and the waiter, but it is evident that his mother and the headmaster of the school are his real targets, and Miss Fanshawe's indulgence is the result of her tacit approval of his anger.

In the first part of the story, they are alone in the dining car, and since the story is almost all dialogue, the reader must slowly piece together the information about the characters. The waiter has a part only insofar as he becomes the butt of Carruther's aggression; since the waiter is new, the boy forces him to listen to his story. His father and mother divorced when he was three, and he spends his summers with his mother, mostly at fashionable Continental resorts. His mother "has men all over the place. . . . She snaps her fingers and people come to comfort her with lust." Adolescent disgust heightens this account, and it is clear that he likes to invent salacious fantasies about other people's lives, but what is most evident is that Carruthers does not feel that he is going to a real home. School is an equally loveless and unpleasant place, where he has joined in the communal games of sadism and victimization.

His conversation explains his aggressive behavior, but on this occasion, he is especially vindictive and seems to exceed the rules of the ritual. He tells the waiter about Miss Fanshawe's life of service at the school, where she is

constantly put upon and unappreciated. In general, he sketches Miss Fanshawe as a purposeless person who is "watching her life go by," and he demands to know whether it is fair that his mother, "the female," should have
so many lovers and Miss Fanshawe none at all. In a frenzy, Carruthers tears
the waiter's sleeve, and the furious waiter shouts, "That child is a raving
lunatic."

When they return to their compartment, Carruthers reveals to Miss
Fanshawe that this is their last time together because he has been expelled
for attempting to steal from the headmaster's office. He apologizes to her
and confesses that when she comforted him once, he had been crying
because he had "thought [the school] would be heaven, a place without Mrs.
Carruthers"—in other words, that school would provide him with a real
home. Now he seems to break down, admitting that Miss Fanshawe was the
only one there who was kind to him and that he does not know why he acts
so aggressively.

Suddenly, the quiet Miss Fanshawe begins to tell him about her home life,
prompted by her recognition that she has been drawn to him because of his
need for care and love. She tells him about her concealed despair and her
desperate craving for love, "to be desired, to be desired in any way at all."
She tells of her unhappy and dull life with her aging parents, who treat her as
a failure and have "sucked everything out of her." She begins to implore him
to understand when he tells her that he does not, and her frenzied account of
her dream that she could take him and provide him with a real home life ter-
rifies him. When he tries to cut short her account of her life, she refuses to
stop and, finally, withdrawing from the role in which she has placed him, he
tells her that she "doesn't make any sense." She is forced to admit to him that
she may be mad "beneath the surface . . . out of loneliness and locked up
love."

By the end of the story, the boy is overwhelmed by the intensity of her revelations, resentful of her confession, and sick of alcohol. At his journey's
end, he walks away from her onto the railway platform, and she watches him
meet his mother.

Themes and Meanings

This story challenges the reader with a question: How much honesty can
human relationships bear? Beginning with the rather clichéd situation of the
English schoolboy in revolt against the restraints of middle-class codes of
behavior, the story quickly deepens to explore what may be revealed in a
situation of total honesty. What the boy sees as hypocrisy and dishonesty are
"appearances" that ought to be dropped while they are in the no-man's-land
of the train, but the anarchy of individual impulse which replaces the
accepted rules is so frightening to others that it is labeled "lunatic" and
"criminal." More important, perhaps, the fragile relationship that has existed

between him and Miss Fanshawe cannot sustain total self-revelation; Carruthers fails to "understand" Miss Fanshawe and wishes for the train journey to end as usual so that he can escape from her confession.

In an ironic twist, the title takes on another meaning: These characters are striking home to the core of each other, and when they get there, they seem to discover that there is a limit to the degree of confession and aggression that other people can tolerate. When everything about another person, all the dirty linen, is revealed in public, the story seems to ask, what then? Which is preferable, the later phase, in which everything that Miss Fanshawe has felt ashamed to express is put into words, or the earlier phase, when Miss Fanshawe and the waiter practiced the technique of indulgence ("Take no notice"; "He couldn't help himself") and restraint ("Lies like that, she explained, could get a waiter into trouble"; "She didn't answer")?

The story reveals a conflict that is without resolution because of the unchangeable nature of certain elements of individual experience. For example, Carruthers and Miss Fanshawe have a similar wish for a different home, but children do not choose their parents, any more than Miss Fanshawe can undo the fate of being "untouched by beauty." Carruthers responds to emotional deprivation with a fearless form of self-assertion, which may be a criminal impulse, whereas Miss Fanshawe's response is to withdraw into passivity and fantasy. There may be a suggestion here of a gender difference. In addition, there is a wide age difference, but, most of all, there is the fact that love is what one needs, and yet love cannot simply be given when requested. What is learned from total honesty, then, is the basic unfairness of life, which assigns advantages and opportunities to individuals by some perverse logic. Total honesty does not change this recognition or the facts of life by making them more explicit.

Since the story does not include any suggestion that either Miss Fanshawe or Carruthers has been changed by this episode, the setting on the train and the time frame should be considered. Their relationship is destined to end anyway, so it is fitting, perhaps, to see this kind of self-revelation as a safety valve. A no-man's-land of this kind provides the necessary opportunity for self-expression, which is therapeutic because it is occasional and outside the characters' ordinary routine.

Style and Technique

"Going Home" engages the reader in the tensions which are central to the meaning of the story, "the longing to speak, the longing above all things in the world to fill the compartment with the words that had begun." First conceived as a radio play, it has very little narrative comment. Indeed, the story resembles the plays of Harold Pinter, the bizarre tensions in the dialogue paralleling the conflicting desires of the characters, who both yearn to be intimate and are frightened of intimacy. At first, the reader has to work hard to piece together from implications in the dialogue the factual basis of the relationship, and then, perhaps, compassion for the characters grows, but the reader is finally alienated by the rawness and the hopelessness of these revelations.

Because the characters are so enclosed spatially, and because they become so intimately involved in private matters, the reader is put in the situation of a voyeur. The atmosphere of the story is one of impending violence and scandal. Simple expressions bear such an extraordinary cargo of implied violence and pain that the story borders on the horrific; it almost becomes a bad dream. At first the boy's voice dominates, but when the dam bursts and Miss Fanshawe begins to talk, her simple narrative is shocking in its pain and explicitness.

Denis Sampson

GOING TO MEET THE MAN

Author: James Baldwin (1924-   )
Type of plot: Psychological realism
Time of plot: The early 1960's
Locale: A town in the American South
First published: 1965

> *Principal characters:*
> JESSE, a white deputy sheriff
> GRACE, his wife
> JESSE'S FATHER and MOTHER, who teach him to be a racist
> A BLACK CIVIL RIGHTS LEADER, who challenges racism in the
> South

The Story

"Going to Meet the Man" divides clearly and purposefully into two parts. In the first half, the main character, Jesse, a white deputy sheriff in a Southern town, lies in bed with his wife, Grace, for the first time in memory suffering from insomnia and impotence. James Baldwin catches Jesse on this night at a moment of crisis, which he shares with other white males: The Old South is now history, the blacks are protesting *en masse* by registering to vote, and a new South that Jesse cannot conceive is about to be born. That he cannot accept what is happening is clear from hints about what he, as deputy sheriff, will be doing the next day to break up the registration. Yet his resistance is much more evident in his paranoid reflections about blacks; what he would like to do is escape from the black world altogether.

He describes to Grace (who is, however, probably sleeping) an incident that took place that day at the courthouse. In order to stop the blacks from singing, the sheriff arrested "the ring-leader" and began to beat him senseless. Jesse continued the brutality at the jail, but, before falling unconscious, the young black man reminded him of an incident in their past when he, as a little boy, had defied this white man for showing disrespect toward his grandmother. The memory raises Jesse's antagonism to an even higher pitch; he wishes to exterminate the race. He and his fellow whites in the South are "soldiers," "out-numbered, fighting to save the civilized world." Yet, as Baldwin comments, they cannot succeed in organizing because they are, in fact, "accomplices in a crime." This note of guilt, which actually lies behind Jesse's paranoia, ushers in the second half of the story.

One of the black spirituals, like those that have haunted him all day, comes "flying up at him" from "out of the darkness . . . out of nowhere." It brings with it both fear and pleasure, and a memory out of his childhood. This flashback, which continues until the last paragraph of the story, is the pivotal event in Jesse's life. It begins on another evening when he is unable to sleep. A black man accused of raping a white woman is fleeing the vengeance of the white community and by morning has been caught. The child has no awareness of the situation; he only senses the excitement. His parents tell him that they are going on a picnic. What he actually witnesses is the castration, burning, and mutilation of the captured black man. As Jesse observes the festive occasion, the sensual fascination, and the strange beauty on his mother's face, he himself experiences the greatest joy of his life and an uncommon love for this father who had "carried him through a mighty test, had revealed to him a great secret which would be the key to his life forever."

Indeed, it is. His psychic life is henceforth warped. The sadistic memory transforms him, as well as his wife: "the moonlight covered her like glory," and "his nature again returned to him." His sexual potency, his identity as a man, is inextricably linked to brutality, to the projection of his own guilt on the black man as a scapegoat. Yet curiously, and symbolically, he becomes the "nigger" raping his own wife. The last sounds that he hears as the story ends, the cock, the dogs, and "tires on the gravel road," only suggest that he may at last realize his guilt and inevitable suffering.

Themes and Meanings

Baldwin's story operates, to be sure, on a political level. The setting in the American South during the early 1960's, and the depiction of events that were probably taking place at the very time that Baldwin was writing (voter registration among the blacks began in earnest in 1964; the story was published in 1965) suggest composition in the heat of the moment, unlike Baldwin's more youthful works, which tend to be reflective, balanced, and objective. It is even, perhaps, a political satire, the protagonist being its object—a warped white mentality in the South that contentedly and periodically sacrifices a black to the gods as a deterrent against the eruption of savagery. Still, the main interest in the story is not political, and Baldwin's exposé of the white mentality is hardly a simple projection of evil onto the enemy. Instead, what one gets is a psychological and spiritual study that argues against such projections: There is a cautionary identification of the white protagonist with the human race, a call for empathy and introspection that raises the experience above a moment in history.

The story traces the experience of a man in torment. At first he does not even know that he, like the society to which he belongs, is on the verge of a crisis. He is a man damned by his inheritance, by his past, and in need of salvation. As he lies in bed, he senses that something is wrong, but his sleeplessness and impotence are merely the tangible signs of his malaise. He would like to turn to his wife for relief, but he thinks that she cannot give it because she is too pure. He cannot ask her to perform sexual acts that would cure his impotence, and hence his insomnia. At this stage, Jesse's only solution is sexual release. That his wife's name is "Grace" and that he regards her as a "sanctuary" suggest to the reader, but not to Jesse, that the real solution is on a spiritual rather than a physical level.

His recollections of the day's events offer a second avenue of escape for Jesse, the projection of his own guilt onto someone else, for it is guilt, after all, that is causing his crisis. As he beats the black civil rights leader, he begins to shake even more violently than his victim—beating is an exorcism misdirected. The experience does, however, begin to work on his memory. He recalls an earlier experience with that black man as a boy. The solution to his present crisis, the reader begins to discover, is in the past, in memory, but Jesse does not reach the crucial experience until the flashback.

The story is a journey backward in time. Each memory brings him closer to the truth and at the same time elicits rationalizations to protect his moral being. Against his will, however, a song out of the past forces the crucial memory upon him; "the key to his life" was the lesson that the community had taught him. It had demonstrated vividly the way to purification, projection of guilt onto the black race. He had wished then to be the man holding the knife that castrated the "rapist." The experience justified his subsequent behavior, emasculating the black male and substituting himself in his place: He shouts at the black man in jail, "You lucky we *pump* some white blood into you every once in a while—your women!" This repressed event out of Jesse's past has continued to operate on an unconscious level. It inextricably connected his instinctual sexual life with society's racial bigotry. The memory of the black's genitals he could not separate from his own. Sexual potency became an obsession. Now that this memory has become conscious, Jesse, at the end of the story, says aloud to his wife that he is the "nigger" performing the sexual act. Through this empathetic ritual, instead of projecting his guilt, Jesse becomes the guilty man. This is a violation of the code, a betrayal of the tacit conspiracy among whites.

This Freudian accounting for racial bigotry in Jesse would suggest that he is on the way of being cured of his illness. All one knows for sure, however, is that Baldwin leaves him as a vulnerable man, defenseless because he has lost his mask, alone because he has betrayed his race, and susceptible to the fear of castration. The sound of cars on the gravel road is now a threat to him rather than to a black victim. A recurring theme in Baldwin is once again clear: Color is deceit, reality is within. If freedom is an escape from one's inheritance, the story offers no assurance that such escape is possible.

Style and Technique

What makes the story effective is a tension between the naturalism of the subject and much of the language, and the artistry that so clearly controls them. Baldwin is hardly prudish about the details or the realities of man's animalism, yet he responds to them with a refined sensibility. The artistic intelligence is evident even in the density of the text. As he explores Jesse's typical white attitudes, Baldwin is able to include every conceivable motif in the history of racial conflict in America: the sexual provocativeness of the black race to the white mind; the instinctive fear of reprisal by the repressed race; the aesthetic provincialism in whites toward black features; typical assumptions about black inferiority; bafflement before the Uncle Tom image; naïve reactions to black music; use of the Bible to sanction prejudice against the accursed race; whites as protectors and guardians not only of these primitive peoples but also of the civilized world. The list could continue. Baldwin makes Jesse's story a microcosm of the white man's role in the racial struggle. Jesse's mental journey, his memory, is not only personal but also racial.

Yet Baldwin's artistry lies not merely in the density of the text, in its universalizing effect. What is even more fascinating to watch is the multitude of parallels that Baldwin works into the fabric. In order to emphasize the effect of the past, Baldwin presents both Jesse and the civil rights leader as boy and man; he also sets up the little black boy, Otis, against the black "rapist." He divides the story neatly into halves to show present and past; in both parts the man and the boy begin their experiences in bed. In the past the boy wishes he had held the knife; in the present he actually holds a cattle prod and strikes the black man in the genitals. While in bed, Jesse is touching himself, protecting himself, as he remembers the castration scene. The act of recollection, in fact, is a castration ritual as Jesse deprives himself of his identity as a man. Baldwin carefully works in the sound of gravel three times during the story: at the beginning, when Jesse fears the arrival of black avengers; in the middle, as cars leave for the castration ritual; and at the end, as Jesse once again awaits the avengers. What all these parallels have in common is the suggested identification of Jesse with the black man who is his enemy. This is especially evident in the empathetic identification at crucial moments in the story; not only does Jesse await violation as the two black males in the story had, but he also shudders along with his victim in the jail and becomes the "nigger" in raping his wife. While the presence of such artistry in a naturalistic story may seen too self-conscious and illogical, the parallels themselves are perfectly appropriate to a theme that announces the essential identity of all human beings.

The most fascinating parallel of all, however, places the racial struggle in the American South in a larger context. In this case the parallel is ironic. The several Christian symbols in the story suggest that Baldwin's choice of his protagonist's name was not arbitrary. Jesse believes that he is a Christian man, living according to the Bible. For him the black race is of the tribe of Ham. It is accursed. The sacrifices of the "rapist" and the civil rights leader are repetitions of the Crucifixion—though Jesse is blind to the parallel. The cock that crows at the end identifies Jesse with Peter, yet Jesse is hardly one to found a church. Nor is Jesse able to fulfill the role of his namesake, the father of David, the ancestor of Jesus. Baldwin's Jesse will have no such place in history. The only branch that will grow from his root will be his own phallus, or a knife, or a cattle prod. He has not, like David or Jesus, created a world where "the wolf shall dwell with the lamb," nor does he "decide with equity for the meek of the earth" or possess "the spirit of wisdom and understanding." Jesse's children shall not inherit the earth; he is childless—unless Baldwin's irony turns back on itself, as is often the case in the works of Baldwin and other black writers who understand the ironies of life. The tragic truth is that Jesse is all of us, human beings trapped by a past from which there may be no escape. Baldwin himself had to leave his father's home, and even America, to find freedom from a Puritan consciousness; the haunting past appears as much like Original Sin as like Freudian repression. The artistry in Baldwin's story is not, after all, inconsistent with the naturalistic theme; though the past has its inevitable hold, the conscious mind makes its effort to give order and to transcend. The tension is in Baldwin, and in his story; it may be in Jesse once he raises his past to consciousness. The effect of the story is to leave the tension in the reader.

Thomas Banks

GOLD COAST

Author: James Alan McPherson (1943-   )
Type of plot: Social realism
Time of plot: The late 1960's
Locale: Cambridge, Massachusetts
First published: 1968

> *Principal characters:*
> ROBERT, a young black man, an aspiring writer working as a
>   janitor
> JAMES SULLIVAN, Robert's supervisor and friend
> MEG SULLIVAN, his wife
> JEAN, Robert's rich, white girlfriend
> MISS O'HARA, a tenant in Robert's building and Sullivan's
>   enemy

The Story

Robert, a young, black aspiring writer, supports himself by working as a janitor in a Cambridge, Massachusetts, apartment building. In "the days of the Gold Coast," the old building near Harvard Square had been a haven for the rich; later, poet-novelist Conrad Aiken lived there; now, it is rather run-down. Even seedier is Robert's predecessor, James Sullivan, an elderly Irishman who has been forced to retire. Sullivan lives in the building with Meg, his half-mad wife, and their smelly, barking dog. He is technically Robert's supervisor, and most of the story concerns their relationship.

Robert likes being a janitor because he is confident of a bright future as a writer, and he also enjoys making the white liberals he meets at parties uncomfortable by talking enthusiastically about his duties, which include, he insists, being able "to spot Jews and Negroes who are passing." His youth and confidence make him pity Sullivan: "He had been in that building thirty years and had its whole history recorded in the little folds of his mind, as his own life was recorded in the wrinkles of his face." Sullivan acts the role of an all-knowing mentor forever dispensing advice to his young "assistant." Excessively proud of his Irish heritage, he repeats stories of sitting in bars with James Michael Curley, the longtime boss of Democratic politics in Boston, and of knowing Frank O'Connor when the Irish writer taught at Harvard.

Robert considers one of the pleasures of his job the opportunity to find material, assuming "that behind each of the fifty or so doors in our building lived a story which could, if I chose to grace it with the magic of my pen, become immortal." Yet the tenants prove too ordinary to supply what he needs; even going through their garbage reveals little of interest. Sullivan tries to help by surveying the evidence but can conclude only that "Jews are the biggest eaters in the world." Robert thinks that Sullivan does not really hate Jews but simply resents "anyone better off than himself." Ironically, Sullivan's antagonist is Irish. Miss O'Hara hates the Sullivans for reasons Robert never discovers. She accuses the former janitor of never being sober and has been trying to get him fired for twenty-five years. She also conducts a campaign to have the couple's dog removed from the building.

In addition to his writing, Robert's main interest is his relationship with Jean, "a very lovely girl who was not first of all a black." He likes being with her because she does not expect him to play a role, as so many in the turmoil of the late 1960's are doing. She wants him only to be himself and to write: "Like many of the artistically inclined rich, she wanted to own in someone else what she could not own in herself. But this I did not mind, and I forgave her for it because she forgave me moods and the constant smell of garbage and a great deal of latent hostility." She resents, however, his wasting his time with Sullivan, who, chased by Meg to a filthy sofa in the basement, calls Robert at two o'clock in the morning to drink with him. Robert admires Sullivan for being well-read and able to spew out his diatribes against hippies and the medical profession in well-constructed sentences.

Chaos enters the lives of Robert and Sullivan at about the same time. When Robert's affair with Jean ends, he writes little and no longer enjoys his other work, because he is "really a janitor for the first time." When Miss O'Hara finally succeeds in having the Sullivans' dog taken away, Meg's madness and her husband's sad loneliness increase. To appease Meg, Robert writes a letter from a New Hampshire farmer telling the Sullivans how happy their dog is living with him. After carrying it about for days searching for someone with New Hampshire license plates to ask to mail the letter, Sullivan tears it up.

Deciding that he can no longer be a janitor "because there is no job more demeaning," Robert moves out. He later sees Sullivan in a crowd in Harvard Square but decides not to speak to him. This episode in his life is over.

Themes and Meanings

The main themes of "Gold Coast" deal with racial and age differences and with loneliness. McPherson captures many of the surface details of American life in the late 1960's with hippies, drug dealers, and lonely middle-aged men driven wild by young women wearing miniskirts. More important, Robert's confidence about his writing career reflects the growing optimism of many American blacks resulting from the decade's progress in civil rights. The relationship of Robert and Jean is a testing of the generally more liberal social atmosphere but fails the test. Sullivan is uneasy about their affair, since "it is in the nature of things that liberal people will tolerate two interracial hippies more than they will an intelligent, serious-minded mixed couple." The latter poses a more substantial threat to the prevailing social order. Their seriousness makes them feel estranged from both white and black worlds, as when they ride in the subway and find themselves in a car with whites on one side, blacks on the other, tension and hatred all around. With no room on either side for both to sit, they stand, holding a steel post, in the middle, "feeling all the eyes, [trapped] between the two sides of the car and the two sides of the world." Leaving the subway, "we looked at each other... and there was nothing left to say."

The age difference, more than the racial difference, creates tension in Robert and Sullivan's friendship. While the old man enjoys talking to Robert because he thinks his "assistant" needs the wisdom he imparts to get along in the world, the young black man understands the complexities of their changing society much better. Sullivan's Boston, with its colorful Irish politicos, is no more. The Sullivans' being out of step with their times is emphasized when a hippie insults them in Harvard Square: "Don't break any track records, Mr. and Mrs. Speedy Molasses."

Robert respects Sullivan but occasionally has difficulty doing so. When Jean is around, Robert, perceiving the old man through her eyes, sees him as dirty and uncomfortable. Robert hates passing the Sullivans' apartment because of the "smell of dogs and cats and age and death about their door." He does not want to be confronted by James Sullivan's mortality, because he does not want to think about his own. Sullivan reminds Robert that "nothing really matters except not being old and being alive and having potential to dream about, and not being alone." Listening to one of Sullivan's drunken late-night harangues, Robert is distracted by the laugh of a girl on the street outside, by the sound of youth and the promise of the future, and he resents Sullivan, hating himself for doing so: "I was young and now I did not want to be bothered." This barrier of age, tinged with the contrast between the failure of one and the potential success of the other, is what keeps Robert from speaking to the old man at the end of the story. The demons of loneliness and rejection plague characters of all ages and races throughout McPherson's short stories.

Style and Technique

As with many writers of his generation, McPherson employs brand names and the titles of songs and television programs to establish time and place and to reveal character. Robert draws conclusions about a married couple in his building based on their garbage: S. S. Pierce cans, Chivas Regal bottles, back issues of *Evergreen* and *The Realist*.

Close attention to detail defines McPherson's style throughout "Gold Coast." Because Meg Sullivan loves animals more than people, she keeps "little pans of meat posted at strategic points about the building." McPherson uses many such details to establish Meg's character: "She was never really clean, her teeth were bad, and the first most pathetic thing in the world was to see her sitting on the steps in the morning watching the world pass, in a stained smock and a fresh summer blue hat she kept just to wear downstairs, with no place in the world to go." Miss O'Hara is fanatical about cleanliness and puts out "her little bit of garbage wrapped very neatly in yesterday's *Christian Science Monitor* and tied in a bow with a fresh piece of string." Robert wonders where she gets the string and imagines "her at night picking meat-market locks with a hairpin and hobbling off with yards and yards of white cord concealed under the gray sweater she always wore." This use of details to create both pathos and humor while maintaining a skillful balance between the two keeps "Gold Coast" from being annoyingly sentimental.

Michael Adams

THE GOLD-BUG

Author: Edgar Allan Poe (1809-1849)
Type of plot: Mystery
Time of plot: The 1800's
Locale: Sullivan's Island, South Carolina
First published: 1843

Principal characters:
WILLIAM LEGRAND, a recluse
THE NARRATOR, a physician and friend

The Story

Many years before the story's present, the unnamed narrator of "The Gold-Bug" made friends with William Legrand, a descendant of an old Huguenot family of New Orleans, who now lives in a hut on Sullivan's Island, nine miles from Charleston, South Carolina. Once wealthy, Legrand lost his fortune and now lives a simple life with his Newfoundland dog and one servant, an old black man named Jupiter, a former slave. Well educated, misanthropic, subject to mood swings between enthusiasm and melancholy, Legrand spends his time fishing, exploring the island, and collecting shells and entomological specimens, of which he has many.

One unusually cold day in October, the narrator visits Legrand after an absence of several weeks. As the narrator warms himself by the fire, Legrand enthusiastically tells him about a strange bug he has found, one of a brilliant gold color with three black spots and long antennae. Because he has lent the bug to a soldier from nearby Fort Moultrie, Legrand cannot show the insect itself; instead, he draws a picture of it upon a piece of paper he takes from his pocket. As the narrator holds the paper, the dog jumps on him, causing his hand to move close to the fire. When he looks at the drawing, he sees a representation of a skull rather than a bug. Legrand is visibly upset by his friend's reaction, examines the drawing by candle, and then locks it in his desk, saying nothing more. The narrator thinks it prudent not to upset Legrand further and takes his leave.

About a month later, Jupiter delivers a note from Legrand to the narrator in Charleston begging him to come at once. The urgent tone of the note, and Jupiter's comments that Legrand is acting strangely and must be ill, alarm the narrator. Jupiter insists that Legrand has been bitten by the bug. The narrator fears that his friend's mind has become unhinged, especially when he sees the spades and scythe that Jupiter has been told to buy. Upon returning to Legrand, the narrator is even more fearful. Legrand says that the bug will make his fortune, as though the insect were real gold. He promises that the narrator will understand his excitement if the narrator will accompany him and Jupiter to the mainland on an all-night expedition. The narrator's assistance is needed and he is the only person in whom Legrand can confide. The narrator fears that Legrand has indeed gone mad, but he agrees to Legrand's request.

The party is led by Legrand to an area of densely wooded hills and crags. Using the scythe, Jupiter clears a path as directed to a tall tulip tree. Legrand instructs him to climb the tree, taking the gold-bug with him. The narrator is now convinced that Legrand has lost his mind. Jupiter, however, follows instructions, climbs out on the seventh limb, and there finds a skull. Legrand directs him to drop the bug (which is unusually heavy) through the left eye socket of the skull. After Legrand makes calculations on the ground, the party begins digging, but finds nothing. Remembering Jupiter's confusion concerning left and right, Legrand rightly concludes that Jupiter made a mistake. The error is corrected, and digging proceeds in another spot. By now the narrator is beginning to guess that there is method in Legrand's apparent madness. The digging uncovers some human bones and a large chest; inside is a wealth of gold and jewels. After some difficulty in removing the treasure to Legrand's hut, the men examine their wealth, estimating it to be worth a million and a half dollars, an estimate which the narrator says later proved to be much too low.

Once the men's excitement has subsided, Legrand explains how he was able to solve the riddles that led to finding the treasure. The paper on which Legrand had drawn the bug proved to be parchment and therefore nearly indestructible; it was found half-buried near the wreck of a longboat and near the place where the bug was captured. Legrand had wrapped the bug in the parchment in order to carry it home and had put the parchment in his pocket when he lent the bug to the soldier. When the narrator held the parchment near the fire, the heat made visible the drawing of a skull. By using heat, Legrand uncovered additional markings, including the picture of a kid, which he took to stand for the pirate Captain Kidd. Knowing the persistent rumors in the area concerning Kidd's buried treasure, he was sure he was on to something. Further heating revealed lines of numerals and other notations, forming a cipher. Legrand describes in detail how he broke the code, enabling him to locate the tulip tree and measure to the correct spot for digging. At the end, Legrand admits that dropping the bug through the skull, instead of dropping a bullet as the code directed, was designed to mystify the narrator further. Legrand had been annoyed that his friend doubted his sanity and enjoyed puzzling him. The skeletons found with the treasure, Legrand speculates, were those of Kidd's helpers, whom he did not want to live to tell the secret of the burial place. Thus, by the end of the story, Legrand has explained all the mysteries attending the discovery of the treasure.

Themes and Meanings

A mystery story need not necessarily involve an intellectual theme in the ordinary sense of the term. The gradual unraveling of the mystery and the suspense created are usually sufficient to hold the reader's interest. The reader receives pleasure from matching his wits with the character attempting to solve the mystery and/or the character who created the mystery. In Poe's detective and mystery stories such as "The Purloined Letter" and "The Gold-Bug," the main characters themselves, such as Dupin and Legrand, receive this kind of pleasure, as well as expectations of monetary reward. At the same time, in their explanations of their procedures they often make comments on human nature which serve as themes.

One such theme is expressed by Legrand as he tells the narrator how he decoded Kidd's cipher. Legrand has the skills in logic and the past experiences with such codes to succeed at the task. Yet more fundamentally, he bases his attempt upon the conviction, he says, that any mystery which one human intelligence can construct, another human can solve if he applies his intellect properly and persistently. Thus armed, Legrand cracks the code with little difficulty, to the amazement of the narrator.

The experience of the narrator in trying to understand what motivates Legrand early in the story supplies a second theme. Because of Legrand's reputation for being mentally unbalanced, at least at times, the narrator jumps to conclusions about his friend's condition, despite the fact that the narrator is a physician. Some of Legrand's actions are puzzling, and he takes no one into his confidence until after the discovery of the treasure. At times he seems to mystify the narrator purposely, as though he were playing a game. As a result, the narrator throughout the first half of the story has growing doubts about Legrand's sanity. Not until the treasure is virtually in their hands does the narrator realize that Legrand has had rational purposes all along. The narrator then comments on the narrow line between sanity and insanity and how easily one can misjudge a person's mental condition.

Style and Technique

Legrand, the hero, is similar to other Poe characters; he is well educated, possessed of excellent reasoning powers, somewhat reclusive, formerly wealthy, and known for his mental instability. Like Dupin, the hero of Poe's later detective stories, Legrand's actions puzzle other characters, especially the narrator friend, with whom the reader tends to identify. Combining two such characters with a puzzling situation became a formula for Poe in creating suspenseful stories.

The structuring of "The Gold-Bug" in two parts is also typical of Poe. Suspense builds in the first part because neither the narrator nor the reader understands Legrand's actions. The quotation used as a headnote implies that Legrand may indeed be mad. When his actions lead to the discovery of the treasure, one mystery is solved. A major question remains: How did Legrand know where to look? In the second half of the story, Legrand explains the reasoning that led to such success. Again, suspense builds as he gives his detailed explanation, which by the end of the story ties up all loose ends. Regardless of whether he guesses the answers, the reader is treated to mystery and suspense in a well-wrought tale in which the hero accomplishes his goal.

In addition to suspense, "The Gold-Bug" includes a touch of humor, principally achieved by the incongruity between the elevated language (used by many Poe characters) of Legrand and the narrator and the dialect of Jupiter. Blacks in Poe's tales are often comic stereotypes; their powers of understanding and intellect are limited, and their language contrasts sharply with that of other characters. In Jupiter's case, Poe gives him the black dialect of Virginia rather than that of South Carolina, no doubt because Poe was more familiar with Virginia blacks.

"The Gold-Bug" immediately became popular after winning the *Dollar Newspaper* story contest (and a prize of one hundred dollars) in 1843; it has also inspired much critical comment. It has been praised for its original plot and for the realism of the description of Sullivan's Island. (The story is one of a relatively small number in which Poe used a real place as a setting.) In many incidental details it reflects Poe's experiences during his tour of army duty at Fort Moultrie, between 1827 and 1828.

Whatever the source of the popularity of "The Gold-Bug," it remains one of Poe's best-known stories. It appeals to readers who love a mystery, a cryptograph, and sustained suspense, and who enjoy a happy ending with well-deserved rewards.

Louise S. Bailey

THE GOLDEN HONEYMOON

Author: Ring Lardner (1885-1933)
Type of plot: Realistic satire
Time of plot: 1920
Locale: St. Petersburg, Florida
First published: 1922

> *Principal characters:*
> CHARLEY, the narrator and protagonist, the insensitive,
> garrulous, and naïve husband of Lucy
> LUCY, Charley's tolerant wife of fifty years
> FRANK HARTSELL, an old suitor of Lucy, now a veterinarian
> and married to a female version of Charley
> MRS. HARTSELL, a talkative and boring woman

The Story

At first glance, the title simply reveals the occasion for the story's events, the celebration of a marriage that has endured for fifty years. It is only after reading the story that the readers understand the irony in the celebration of a union more brass than gold. Charley, the ingenuous first-person narrator, recounts his adventures in St. Petersburg, but in doing so reveals himself as shallow, insensitive, and boring. As the plot unravels, so does Charley, yet he remains blissfully unaware of and not bored by a life composed of unrelenting trivia.

The structure of the story is the recollection in detail of a trip to St. Petersburg, Florida. The story begins with the most important word and person in Charley's life, "Mother," as he calls his wife, Lucy. His refrain, "You can't get ahead of Mother," is evidence of his pride in all things connected with himself, whether it be the state of New Jersey or his prosperous son-in-law, John H. Kramer, a real-estate man and member of the Rotary Club, an important status symbol in Charley's eyes. After a tedious and typical explanation of how and why he and Lucy went to Florida for their "golden honeymoon," including prices, detailing to the penny the differences between a sleeper and a compartment on a train and a complete timetable for all stops made between Trenton and St. Petersburg, Charley is ready to begin his real story.

The real story, however, is actually the revelation of Charley's character and his marriage to Lucy, both of which are tested by the vicissitudes of travel and encounters with new and old acquaintances. On the train, Charley unconsciously reveals that appearance and status are extremely important values for him. He notes and admires anyone he meets who is a Rotarian, rides backward on the train, facing his wife, and insists on sleeping in the top berth to protect his image, even though neither he nor his wife sleeps well when he is in that precarious position. During the trip, Charley is nearly left behind in Washington, D.C., an occurrence which entails the admission that it is Mother who manages and carries the money.

It is, however, in describing St. Petersburg and the people that they encounter there that Charley reaches the peak of his powers. Ungrammatical, inelegant, clichéd details concerning the "Tin-Can Tourists," their new president, the "Royal Tin-Can Opener," and their official song, which Charley does not remember exactly, are followed by a complete account of their first night at the meeting of the New York–New Jersey society. No tidbit is too trivial for Charley to recite. After Mother's birthday celebration, marred because the Poinsettia Hotel charged seventy-five cents for a small, tough sirloin steak, Charley and Lucy plunge into social activities at the park: band concerts, checkers, chess, horseshoes, dominoes, and roque. Charley quickly establishes himself as a champion checker player, while Lucy enjoys the concerts.

While listening to a concert, Lucy makes the acquaintance of a Mrs. Hartsell, the woman who married Lucy's cast-off fiancé, Frank. Lucy tells Mrs. Hartsell only that she and Frank had been good friends before he moved to Michigan and became a veterinarian. To Charley's chagrin, the Hartsells join them at every opportunity; they dine together, attend the Michigan Society meeting, which Charley finds far inferior to the New York–New Jersey meeting, and play cards. Although Lucy and Frank enjoy renewing their old friendship, Charley cannot abide Mrs. Hartsell. Since she is presented through Charley's eyes with many of the same characteristics noted in Charley, the feeling is mutual. Threatened, Charley disparages Frank's beard, his former occupation, and his checker-playing ability. Although he easily defeats Frank at checkers, the card games are another matter. Frank and Lucy continually trounce Charley and Mrs. Hartsell, a phenomenon that Charley attributes solely to the constant talking, inattention, and poor skills of Mrs. Hartsell.

To his delight, Mrs. Hartsell receives her comeuppance while playing roque with Lucy. After Lucy withdraws, claiming an inability to play longer because of a lame back, Mrs. Hartsell makes a wild long shot and drops her teeth on the court. Charley laughs long and heartily at both women. The unspoken competition between the two couples intensifies when Frank challenges Charley to a game of horseshoes, a game that Charlie claims not to have played in twenty years. From the beginning, it is obvious that Frank Hartsell is the better player, but he cannot beat Charley when it comes to making excuses. Charley complains of a lack of practice, old horseshoes with points that immediately make his thumb raw and sore, and finally Frank's awkward style and unbeatable luck. Facing certain defeat, Charley quits, but his anger continues.

That night while playing cards and, as usual, being defeated, he blurts out the truth about Lucy's former relationship with Frank. This results not only in an uncomfortable split with the Hartsells but also in a quarrel between Lucy and Charley. In a fit of pique, Lucy says that she wishes she had married Frank Hartsell instead of Charley, and Charley retaliates by agreeing with her. The result of this spat is two days of silence from Lucy. Finally she relents, for the sake of their "Golden Honeymoon," and they kiss and make up. The Hartsells depart in a huff for Orlando, leaving Mother and Charley to enjoy the remaining days of their vacation.

The remainder of the story recounts their departure from St. Petersburg and their return home; Charley concludes with the observation, "Here comes Mother, so I guess I better shut up."

Themes and Meanings

The meaning in this story is not in what happens but in how it happens and to whom it happens. The revelation is of character, not plot. Insight is granted to the reader, not to the characters: Charley learns very little, if anything, about himself or about human nature; he and Lucy remain blissfully unaware of their prejudices, their narrowness, their sentimentality, and the banality of their lives. Although this story has been read as a condemnation of middle-class values and marriage, Lardner does not totally condemn Charley and his "golden honeymoon." The meaning of the story lies in the reader's understanding of Charley; perhaps to understand all is indeed to forgive all. Certainly both Lardner and the reader see Charley clearly, much more clearly than he sees himself.

Style and Technique

Lardner's ear for American dialect and his ability to reproduce its syntax, grammar, and cadence are as important in this story as characterization and plot. The character of Charley is revealed not only through what he says but also through the way he says it. His ungrammatical sentences, awkward diction, and malapropisms are essential to understanding his worldview. In addition, the first-person point of view is a perfect vehicle for a character such as Charley, a naïve narrator who reveals considerably more about himself than he intends.

Thus, the irony promised in the title continues throughout the story. Charley says what he does not mean; he reveals what he himself does not know. This irony softens the story's condemnation of middle-class complacency; through humor, Lardner suggests that although "The Golden Honeymoon" may not be solid gold, it is neither futile nor bitter.

Linda Humphrey

THE GONZAGA MANUSCRIPTS

Author: Saul Bellow (1915-   )
Type of plot: Comic realism
Time of plot: c. 1950
Locale: Madrid
First published: 1954

> *Principal characters:*
> CLARENCE FEILER, a young scholar, unemployed but with a
> small income, who comes to Madrid looking for the
> Gonzaga manuscripts
> FAITH UNGAR, an art student in Madrid who befriends Feiler
> GÚZMAN DEL NIDO, Gonzaga's friend and literary executor,
> who Feiler thinks has the manuscripts

The Story

For the purposes of this story, Saul Bellow invents a famous modern Spanish poet, Manuel Gonzaga, whose elusive manuscripts set the plot in motion. Clarence Feiler is a naïve young man from California who hears from a Spanish Republican refugee that there are more than one hundred poems by Gonzaga somewhere in Madrid. Feiler wrote his graduate thesis on Gonzaga's *Los Huesos Secos*, an experience which, he felt, put him "in touch with a poet who could show me how to go on, and what attitude to take toward life." Feiler has been leading an aimless life; he realizes that he is "becoming an eccentric" and is "too timid to say he believed in God," and so his quest for the Gonzaga manuscripts evolves into a quest for his own identity. Finding the manuscripts and presenting them to the world matters to him, and "what mattered might save him."

Feiler's first act upon arriving in Madrid is to find Miss Faith Ungar, an art student whose fiancé is an airline pilot regularly engaged in bringing in black-market pesetas from Tangiers. Miss Ungar is sympathetic to his ambitions, but he frets that "the kind of woman who became engaged to an airline pilot might look down on him." Her friendship with Feiler does seem sincere, though, and perhaps would have developed into something deeper had he had the courage to pursue it. At one time he even reflects, "*He* should have a woman like that. It passed dimly over his mind that a live woman would make a better quest than a dead poet." The moment passes, however, leaving a faint aftersense of an opportunity wasted.

Feiler takes a room at a pension and immediately involves himself in a verbal exchange with a Miss Walsh, a querulous Englishwoman who baits him about his country's testing of atomic bombs. When she calls him "some sort of fanatic," Feiler responds by identifying her as "a nasty old bag." His discomfiture as an American in Europe thus begins soon and unexpectedly.

The baiting of Feiler the American naïf continues when he visits Gúzman del Nido, the friend and literary executor of Manuel Gonzaga. Caught in a terrible rainstorm on his way to Gúzman's home, Feiler arrives sodden and at a considerable disadvantage among the other guests—an Italian monsignor, an Egyptian woman from New York, and a German insurance executive. When Feiler tells a humorous story, he is mortified by the blank response, and he soon realizes that he is being patronized by Gúzman. Feiler discusses Gonzaga's poetry with Gúzman, who seems to think that he cannot appreciate the Spaniard's sensibility, and his frustration is complete when Gúzman tells him that he gave the poems to a Countess del Camino, now dead. Gúzman thinks the poems may have passed on to the countess' secretary, also dead, but whose nephews may know something of the whereabouts of the poems. To conclude his exasperating day, when Feiler returns to his pension he is sure—for no apparent reason—that the police have searched his room.

He resolves to track down the nephews in Alcalá de Henares, but when he finds them they can only taunt him with silly anti-American jokes about "La bomba atómica" and send him on another quest to Segovia to see Pedro Alvarez-Polvo, who had been a great friend of the countess. Alvarez-Polvo gives Feiler a pompous lecture on Segovian architecture, and in a comedy of misunderstandings reveals that he thinks Feiler is interested in the rights to a pitchblende mine formerly owned by the countess' secretary. The uranium content of pitchblende brings Feiler face-to-face once more with the motif of "la bomba atómica," and he finally cries out in fury, "What do I care about atom bombs! To hell with atom bombs!"

So much for the quest for the poems and for Feiler's sense of his mission in life. Upon his return to his hotel room in Segovia, he is convinced that his valise has been searched. When he berates the manager in a great rage, a man in the lobby mistakes Feiler for an Englishman and harangues him for criticizing Spain: "The whole world knows you have a huge jail in Liverpool, filled with Masons. Five thousands Masons are *encarcelados* in Liverpool alone." Feiler packs up and heads back to Madrid, defeated in spirit and dreading the next meal with Miss Walsh.

Themes and Meanings

The misadventures of Americans in Europe make up an old theme in American literature. Usually, as best illustrated in the many treatments of the topic by Henry James, the Americans are ingenuous and in danger of coming to grief at the hands of the more worldly Europeans who are eager to exploit them. The story of Clarence Feiler becomes, then, a special version of the initiation rite of the young naïf: the innocent abroad and all that happens to him. The naïveté of his desire to "bring the testimony of a great man before the world" appears comic in the light of what befalls Feiler, but there is no real evidence at the story's end that he is yet aware of how ludicrous he must have appeared to the Spaniards. His obvious bitterness, as well as the fact that on the train ride back to Madrid "he sat numb and motionless," suggest, however, that self-knowledge may not be far off for Feiler.

A special aspect of the theme is the hostility toward Americans that shows up in the motif of "la bomba atómica." Miss Walsh picks up this theme first, when in a lament about the excessive rain she grumbles to Feiler that "You people may be to blame for that." Feiler is astonished to find himself a member of any group suspected of subverting the average mean rainfall in Spain, and his ensuing dialogue with Miss Walsh is truly comic. He can only protest "I am not all Americans. You are not all the English. . . . You are not Winston Churchill, I am not the Pentagon." At this point they exchange contemptuous epithets and Feiler stalks out in rage.

Equally comic is Feiler's visit to the nephews of the countess' dead secretary. They prove to be "a family of laughers." One of them had lived in England for a few months many years before, and the family rejoices in addressing him as "My Lord." Upon Feiler's arrival, "My Lord" is encouraged to speak English, and he responds with "Jolly country, eh?" and "Charing Cross," signing off with "Piccadilly. And that's all I can remember."

Dealing with these madcaps and eccentrics unhinges Feiler's nervous system and certainly contributes to the paranoia he exhibits in his conviction that his room and luggage have been searched. His distaste for the people he meets, his disabling frustration in his quest, and the mild sense of rue he retains from his brief friendship with Miss Faith Ungar—all these elements make Feiler a wiser man and give him a kind of self-knowledge that he had not anticipated.

Style and Technique

Bellow attempts no razzle-dazzle effects, but tells his story in a conventional alternation of dialogue with passages of description and summary from the third-person omniscient point of view. He is economical but effective with figurative language (for example, "The gaunt horselike Spanish locomotives screamed off their steam" and "Trolley sparks scratched green within the locust trees"). Bellow catches in a few lines the misery of Miss Walsh, whose admitted commitment to life's satisfactions contrasts so effectively with Feiler's aimlessness and timidity. Bellow says of her, "she thought she was a person of charm, and she did have a certain charm, but her eyes were burning." Later, Feiler notes her "busted-up face" and he feels sorry for her "and yet lucky to have met her." She hints at a life wasted for passion when she admits, "You see, I used to read widely once. I was a cultivated person. But the reason for it was sex, and that went." She is a minor character, but a memorable one, created by a few quick lines of description.

One of Bellow's most effective narrative devices is his use of descriptions of the weather. It is the relentless rain that precipitates Miss Walsh's tirade against the American scientists' meddling with the laws of nature, and it is the rain that soaks and humiliates the egregious Feiler even before he has to stand up against the condescension of the smirking Gúzman. Finally, when Feiler leaves Segovia to return to Madrid and the bitter Miss Walsh at his pension's dinner table, it is the rain that participates in a grand pathetic fallacy to mock the hapless Feiler: "As the train left the mountains, the heavens seemed to split; the rain began to fall, heavy and sodden, boiling on the wide plain."

Frank Day

GOOD COUNTRY PEOPLE

Author: Flannery O'Connor (1925-1964)
Type of plot: Comic realism
Time of plot: The late 1950's
Locale: A small Southern town
First published: 1955

> *Principal characters:*
> MRS. HOPEWELL, a farm owner and the scandalized mother of
> Hulga
> HULGA HOPEWELL, a lonely, sullen young woman with a
> Ph.D. in philosophy
> MANLEY POINTER, an itinerant Bible salesman who calls on
> the Hopewells
> MRS. FREEMAN, a tenant farmer hired by Mrs. Hopewell

The Story

Mrs. Hopewell, a widowed farm owner, is in the practice of hiring tenant farm families to assist her in maintaining the farm. Her current helpers, the Freemans, are busybodies and quite nosy, but they are reliable and serve her better than the previous tenants. Mrs. Hopewell regards Mrs. Freeman and her family as "good country people" and is fond of uttering homespun maxims such as "Nothing is perfect" or "That is life!" and being reassured by Mrs. Freeman's frequent rejoinder, "I always said so myself."

The backward, unsophisticated ways of the Freemans, however, only perturb Mrs. Hopewell's daughter, Hulga, who changed her name from Joy when she left home to attend college. Having earned a Ph.D. in philosophy, Hulga is a troubled, introverted young woman; she lost her leg in a childhood hunting accident and has not been "normal" since. She is a source of embarrassment to her mother, who "was at a complete loss" in explaining her daughter's ambitions. One could say "my daughter is a nurse or a school teacher or a chemical engineer," but she could not say "my daughter is a philosopher." That was something that "ended with the Greeks and Romans." With an artificial leg and a heart condition, Hulga seems destined for a quiet life spent in irritating her mother and the workers surrounding her.

One afternoon, however, something upsets the ecology of the household. Manley Pointer, who announces himself as an itinerant Bible salesman interested in "Chrustian" (*sic*) service, arrives at the door and engages Mrs. Hopewell in a discussion of salvation and Bible truth. At first merely polite to the young man, Mrs. Hopewell is quickly charmed by his "salt of the earth," simple country ways, and invites him for supper. Hulga is appalled by Pointer, but sees his visit as an opportunity to enlighten a woefully naïve country boy about the ways of the world. After supper he walks her to the front gate and convinces her to meet him for a walk at ten o'clock the next morning.

Hulga lies awake the night before imagining that she will seduce this innocent, redeeming him from both his religious convictions and his moral inhibitions. When she sneaks off to meet him the next day, she is startled by his unusually aggressive temperament when he asks how her wooden leg is joined to the rest of her torso. Initially disturbed but strangely attracted to Pointer's naïveté, she allows him to kiss her. She suggests that they head toward the barn, imagining herself as the aggressor and seducer. Here she turns their conversation to her philosophical opinions about life and eternal destinies, announcing that she is one of those people who have "taken off their blindfolds and see that there is nothing to see."

After a series of passionate kisses, Pointer begs Hulga to tell him that she loves him. At first she balks, with an elaborate discussion of what she means by the word "love," but finally relents. He asks her to prove her love by letting him remove her wooden leg. Suddenly aware that she is not with the naïve, unsophisticated rube she imagined, she is fearful, crying out "aren't you just good country people?" Opening the briefcase that he had been carrying through their escapade, he reveals an assortment of odd objects, including a flask of whiskey, a deck of cards with pornographic pictures, and a prophylactic. Placing her wooden leg in the briefcase, Pointer declares to Hulga, "One time I got a woman's glass eye this way. . . . You ain't so smart. I been believing in nothing ever since I was born!"

The story ends with the helpless Hulga watching the serpentine figure of Pointer "struggling over the green speckled lake"; Mrs. Hopewell, watching the same scene with Mrs. Freeman and remarking on the sincerity of the young man, muses "I guess the world would be better off if we were all that simple." "Some can't be that simple," Mrs. Freeman replies, "I know I never could."

Themes and Meanings

O'Connor clearly designed "Good Country People" as a shockingly ironic story. Hulga is the prototypical O'Connor character whose pride and selfishness come to her only in the midst of a violent or shocking revelation. Hulga regards herself as aloof from the "good country people" among whom she lives; imbibing of philosophy and its contemplation of "deeper questions," Hulga sees herself as liberating people from their illusions, believing she has none of her own.

Manley Pointer serves as the agent for her self-discovery. Pointer at first appears to be a crude, otherworldly Fundamentalist and Hulga's mission is to strip away his Christian principles by seducing him in the hayloft. She is, however, completely fooled by his impersonation; it is she who is "taken in" and in the end, it is she who wants to be reassured that Pointer is "just good country people." Instead, Pointer reveals himself as a country existentialist, living for the moment, unaffected by the pretensions which govern Hulga's private illusions.

Meanwhile, Mrs. Freeman stands out as the only character in the story who "sees through" the illusions of the Hopewell household. She knows her place in the economy of the household and hers is the final comment in the story. When she says "some can't be as simple" as Pointer, she means that she herself could never fall prey to the flimflam antics to which Mrs. Hopewell and Hulga have succumbed.

Style and Technique

O'Connor was well-known for her use of the grotesque and the bizarre to rivet a reader to her tales. Here the sudden revelation of Manley Pointer's malevolence is both dramatic and shocking, but a fitting climax to a story whose protagonist, Hulga, made a profession of dispelling illusions. The reader expects the confrontation between Hulga and Pointer to occur but is surprised by the role each ends up playing.

O'Connor had an unmatched ability to capture the cadences of country speech and the banalities of everyday conversation. Her depiction of Mrs. Hopewell and Mrs. Freeman's frequent kitchen conversations helps to underscore the role-playing and insincerity lurking behind the Southern landscapes that served as the setting of most of her stories. In like manner, O'Connor uses two minor characters in the story, Mrs. Freeman's daughters, Glynese and Carramae, as effective foils for the character of Hulga. Neither Glynese nor Carramae has any illusions about her lot in life, and the homey details of their lives which O'Connor presents—Carramae's bout with morning sickness, for example—serve as a vivid contrast to the airy, philosophical notions with which Hulga has insulated herself.

Bruce L. Edwards, Jr.

A GOOD MAN IS HARD TO FIND

Author: Flannery O'Connor (1925-1964)
Type of plot: Horror
Time of plot: The 1950's
Locale: Georgia
First published: 1953

> *Principal characters:*
> THE GRANDMOTHER, Bailey's mother and the protagonist
> BAILEY, her son
> BAILEY'S WIFE
> JUNE STAR, Bailey's daughter
> JOHN WESLEY, Bailey's son
> RED SAMMY, owner and proprietor of a roadside eatery
> THE MISFIT, a psychopathic killer

The Story

This grotesque tale of sudden violence in the rural South opens quietly, with a family planning a vacation. The husband, Bailey, his wife, and their children, John Wesley and June Star, all want to go to Florida. The grandmother, Bailey's mother, however, wants to go to east Tennessee, where she has relatives, and she determinedly attempts to persuade them to go there instead. Unable to convince them that the trip to Tennessee will be novel and broadening for the children, the grandmother offers as a final argument a newspaper article which states that a psychopathic killer who calls himself The Misfit is heading toward Florida.

Ignoring the grandmother's wishes and warnings, the family sets out the next morning for Florida. The grandmother settles herself in the car ahead of the others so that her son will not know that she has brought along her cat, Pitty Sing, hidden in a basket under her seat. As the trip proceeds, she chatters away, pointing out interesting details of scenery, admonishing her son not to drive too fast, telling stories to the children. Throughout the drive, the children squabble, the baby cries, the father grows irritable. In short, the trip is both awful and ordinary, filled with the trivia, boredom, and petty rancors of daily life, from which the family cannot escape, even on vacation.

At lunchtime, they stop at Red Sammy's, a barbecue eatery, where the grandmother laments that "people are certainly not nice like they used to be," and Red Sammy agrees: "A good man is hard to find." In this conversation, the grandmother, narrow-minded and opinionated, repeatedly assures herself that she is a lady, a good Christian, and a good judge of character: She maintains that Red Sammy, a bossy loudmouth, is a "good man" and that Europe "was entirely to blame for the way things were now."

After they leave the roadhouse, the grandmother manipulates her son into making a detour to see an old plantation she once visited as a girl. Suddenly, she remembers that the plantation is not in Georgia but in Tennessee. She is so upset at this realization that she jumps up and upsets her valise, whereupon the cat jumps out onto her son's shoulder, her son loses control of the car, the car overturns, and they all land in a ditch.

As they emerge, an old, "hearse-like" automobile comes over the hill and stops for them. Three men step out, one of whom the grandmother instantly identifies as The Misfit. The grandmother, realizing that he intends to kill them, tries to talk him out of it by appealing to his chivalry, urging him not to shoot a lady. Then she tries flattery, asserting that she can tell that he is a "good man." She tries to tempt him by suggesting that he stop being an outlaw and settle down to a comfortable life. She urges him to pray to Jesus for help and forgiveness. Finally she tries to bribe him with money. All these tactics fail. As she talks with him, he has his henchmen take the other members of the family to the woods and shoot them.

Although The Misfit rejects all the grandmother's arguments, he listens to them closely; he pays particular attention when the grandmother refers to Jesus. Indeed, The Misfit declares, "Jesus was the only One that ever raised the dead. . . . He thrown everything off balance. If He did what He said, then it's nothing for you to do but throw away everything and follow him." In his intense pride, however, The Misfit maintains that he is unable to believe without having been a witness; therefore, "it's nothing for you to do but enjoy the few minutes you got left the best way you can—by killing somebody or burning down his house or doing some other meanness to him. No pleasure but meanness."

When the grandmother is at last alone with The Misfit, she abandons all of her tactics. Her head clears for an instant, in which she sees the murderer as thin, frail, and pathetic. Declaring "Why you're one of my babies. You're one of my own children!" she reaches out and touches him. He recoils in revulsion and shoots her. Having been witness to the grandmother's moment of grace, The Misfit admits that "meanness" has lost its kick: "It's no real pleasure in life."

Themes and Meanings

This intensely ironic story investigates with horrifying effect what happens when one of the worst anxieties of modern life, the threat of sudden violence at the hands of an unknown assailant, becomes a reality. Because such occurrences are relatively rare, the characters and the reader are lulled into a false security that such a thing will never happen to them. In addition, by voicing anxiety about encountering a psychopathic killer, the grandmother makes such an encounter seem all the more unlikely.

From O'Connor's point of view, the grandmother's encounter with The

Misfit presents her with the supreme test and the supreme opportunity that every human being must face: the moment of death. Her death, moreover, comes through the agency of an apparently gratuitous and incomprehensible evil. Her ability to accept such a death is therefore the supreme test of her faith. That the grandmother at the moment of death truly embraces the Christian mystery is her great triumph. Although, in Christian terms, such a moment is always a gift, it is one for which the recipient has prepared throughout her life. The grandmother's most essential attribute is therefore not her meddlesomeness or her smugness, of which there has been considerable evidence throughout the story, but her maternal compassion and concern, and it is through this maternal love that she has her moment of revelation. As O'Connor once described it, "she realizes . . . that she is responsible for the man before her and joined to him by ties of kinship which have their roots deep in the mystery she has been merely prattling about so far."

The action of grace is not confined altogether to the grandmother but begins to undermine The Misfit's own egotism and sadism. Insisting on the possibility of redemption for even this most evil of her characters, O'Connor expressed the hope that "the old lady's gesture, like the mustard-seed, will grow to be a great crow-filled tree in the Misfit's heart, and will be enough of a pain to him there to turn him into the prophet he was meant to become." In O'Connor's own words, this story, like all of her fiction, "takes its character from a reasonable use of the unreasonable, though the reasonableness of my use of it may not always be apparent. . . . Belief, in my own case anyway, is the engine that makes perception operate."

Style and Technique

In remarks prefatory to a public reading of this story, Flannery O'Connor stated that "what makes a story work . . . is probably some action, some gesture of a character that is unlike any other in the story, one which indicates where the real heart of the story lies." This action, which is "both totally right and totally unexpected," must operate "on the anagogical level, that is, the level which has to do with the Divine life and our participation in it." O'Connor, anticipating a non-Catholic audience essentially hostile to her religious and philosophical position, manages to dramatize her views within the story: She shows a human being change and creates an effective scene in which God's grace intervenes in the natural world. Thus, O'Connor makes it possible for the reader to focus on what she sees as crucial: "In this story you should be on the lookout for such things as the action of grace in the Grandmother's soul, and not for the dead bodies."

A balance for the seriousness, even sublimity, of this moment of grace is the black humor of the dialogue between The Misfit and the grandmother, which precedes the grandmother's gesture. Much of this humor derives from the regional particularities of Southern speech, which O'Connor's sharp ear accurately registers. When the grandmother urges The Misfit to seek God's help, he replies, "I don't want no hep, I'm doing all right by myself." Another source of humor is the bizarre logic of The Misfit's outlook on the world: "I call myself The Misfit . . . because I can't make what all I done wrong fit what all I gone through in punishment." Finally, there is the sardonic understatement of The Misfit himself, who declines the grandmother's offer of money, noting, "Lady, . . . there never was a body that give the undertaker a tip."

A brilliant mixture of horror and humor, compassion and tough-mindedness, this story epitomizes O'Connor's greatest powers as a writer. Her bedrock of belief in the Roman Catholic faith made it possible for O'Connor to view that most horrifying representative of humankind, the serial killer, with sympathy and hope. Her tough, critical intelligence made her sensitive to the petty hypocrisy and smugness that sometimes accompany religious faith, but she was also able to see that these are at worst venial sins. It was this clear perspective that enabled O'Connor to note "that the old lady lacked comprehension, but that she had a good heart." Thus, the reader may observe about O'Connor what O'Connor observed about the Southerner: She "is usually tolerant of those weaknesses that proceed from innocence, and . . . knows that a taste for self-preservation can be readily combined with the missionary spirit."

Carola M. Kaplan

GOODBYE, MY BROTHER

Author: John Cheever (1912-1982)
Type of plot: Realism
Time of plot: The late 1940's
Locale: An island off Massachusetts
First published: 1951

Principal characters:
POMMEROY, the narrator
HELEN, his wife
LAWRENCE (TIFTY) POMMEROY, his brother
RUTH, his wife
CHADDY POMMEROY, another brother
ODETTE, his wife
DIANA POMMEROY, a sister
MRS. POMMEROY, mother to the three boys and their sister

The Story

The narrator begins the story by announcing that he is a Pommeroy, that his father drowned when he was quite young, and that his mother told her children that their family relationships had a kind of permanence they would not likely find in life again. The Pommeroys enjoy the illusion that they are unique. The narrator then introduces the four children, their places of residence, and their spouses. The narrator relates that, as a family, the Pommeroys used to spend summers on Laud's Head, an island off the Massachusetts coast, where, during the 1920's, their father replaced the family cottage with a big house. It is the narrator's favorite place in the world.

One afternoon late in the summer, all the family members have assembled on Laud's Head, except Lawrence and his wife and children, who finally cross over from the mainland on the four o'clock boat. Although brother Chaddy and the narrator welcome Lawrence, the narrator remarks that family dislikes are deeply ingrained, and he remembers that twenty-five years before he hit Lawrence on the head with a rock. During the cocktail time after the new arrivals have settled in, it becomes obvious that Lawrence is not like the others, as he is critical of his sister, indifferent to what he drinks, and quarrelsome about being called "Tifty," a nickname dating from his youth when his slippers used to make a "tifty, tifty" sound as he walked. His father coined the name. Lawrence has something of the Puritan cleric in his makeup, the narrator remarks, a nature reminiscent of the family's pre-colonial ancestry. After dinner, the mother becomes drunk and quarrels with Lawrence about the repairs to the old house, which he insists is sliding slowly into the sea and is a waste of money to maintain. The narrator recalls the time when Lawrence, away at boarding school, decided to separate himself from his mother by not returning home for the Christmas holidays. The mother remarks, as she goes off to bed, that in her afterlife she is going to have a very different kind of family, one with "fabulously rich, witty, and enchanting children."

The next morning, the narrator awakes to the sound of someone rolling the tennis court. He meets Lawrence's simpering children downstairs and asks Lawrence for a game, but is turned down. Later in the morning, he finds his brother examining the house's shingles; Lawrence observes that, though the house is relatively new, their father installed the two-hundred-year-old shingles to make it look venerable. The narrator remembers how in the past Lawrence upbraided the family for their refusal to join the modern world and for their retreat into what they supposed was a calmer and happier time, implying that such an attitude was a measure of an irremediable failure. The appearance of Mrs. Pommeroy, their mother, demonstrates to the narrator that there is little hope of any rapport between the matriarch and the changeling: Their mother suggests that they all go swimming, have martinis on the beach, and "have a *fabulous* morning."

Lawrence's rebukes to the family force them into a more strenuous physical regime and they swim more often. His comment to the Polish cook that she is sad and ought to get paid more angers her, and she tells the narrator to keep Lawrence out of her kitchen. One evening while playing backgammon after dinner, Lawrence becomes angered by his sister-in-law Odette's flirting with the narrator. Lawrence reads significance and finality into every game; he "felt that in watching our backgammon he was observing the progress of a mordant tragedy in which the money we won and lost served as a symbol for more vital forfeits," says the narrator. Chaddy and the narrator play each other, their mother plays Chaddy, and Lawrence, as usual, gets in the parting shot by remarking that he thinks they would all "go crazy cooped up with one another . . . night after night"; he goes to bed.

That night the narrator dreams about Lawrence and remarks that he should not let him upset the restful vacation that he needs after working so hard during the year. The family prepares to go to a costume ball at a local club during which they are told to come as they wish they were. The narrator and his wife go as a bride and a football player, and the narrator notes that, with the transition wrought by the costumes, they feel as they had in the years before the war. They discover that many people have come to the dance as brides and football players. Lawrence and his wife arrive, but are not in costume, and he refuses to dance with her and is appalled in general by the party and the behavior of its guests. The family does not get home until morning.

The next day Mrs. Pommeroy, the narrator's wife, Helen, and Odette all enter their work in the flower show. Ruth, Lawrence's wife, stays home and does her laundry. The narrator observes that Ruth "seems to scrub . . . with a penitential fervor"; he wonders what she thinks she has done wrong. Alone on the beach, he encounters Lawrence and notes his gloomy expression; he reassures him that it is only a summer day. Lawrence responds by confessing that he does not like it on the island, that he wants to sell his equity in the house, that he came back only to say good-bye. Yet Lawrence has been saying good-bye to the family and to life as long as the narrator can remember. The narrator suggests that Lawrence fails to grasp the realities of life; Lawrence snaps back that the realities of life are that their mother is an alcoholic, Diana and Odette are promiscuous women, Chaddy is dishonest, and the narrator is a fool. As Lawrence walks away, his brother swings a water-sodden root from behind and hits him in the head. With the sudden strength of two men, the narrator rescues Lawrence from the undertow which was dragging the dazed man down. The narrator returns to the house and joins the others, back from the flower show. Lawrence shows up with a bloody bandage in his hand and confronts the family with the evil deed of his brother. He announces, "I don't have any more time to waste here . . . I have *important* things to do," and goes upstairs to pack.

The next morning, as Lawrence and Ruth leave for the mainland, only the mother gets up to say good-bye. The matriarch and the changeling look at each other "with a dismay that would seem like the powers of love reversed." As the ferry blows its whistle in the distance, the narrator muses on the beautiful day and laments his brother's fearsome outlook. "Oh, what can you do with a man like that?" he asks, one who will think only of the dark bottom of the sea where their father lies, rather than of the iridescent beauty of the surface, "the harsh surface beauty of life." Later, on the beach, he sees his wife and sister, Helen and Diana, emerge "naked, unshy, beautiful, and full of grace," from out of the sea.

Themes and Meanings

Like other examples of Cheever's fiction, this story contains a mixture of sadness and joy. The Pommeroys are a family given over at times to the illusions of their uniqueness, and they do avoid the hard realities of life, as Lawrence suggests. As the narrator cautions at the story's end, however, such illusions are necessary, because they are human, and they provide at least a temporary stay against the "full fathom five" where they all will eventually lie with their father. Helen dyes her hair to hide the years, Odette flirts to restore her youth, Chaddy wins at games, the mother drinks to forget, the narrator overworks and is, perhaps, a fool, but their failures endear them to the reader in ways that Lawrence's harshness, for all of its truth, does not. Cheever does not let the reader off the hook, though, and he forces the narrator to confess his desire to kill his brother and presumably his brother's ability to get at the hard truth. The narrator chooses to observe the harsh beauty of the surface of life and not to plunge to the icy depths below.

Besides the theme of illusion and reality, which he treats with unresolved ambiguity, Cheever also struggles through an examination of the family and its past, to reintegrate his fallen or expelled protagonists into the world as they find it. The narrator is trying to restore the family's sense of identity through description of a nourishing past and using his love to distort truths, and yet to permit the occasional insight which goes beyond the powers of Lawrence, whose omission of love makes existence unendurable. Unable to accept his brother's vision of doom when Lawrence announces that the house will fall into the sea and, by extension, prophesies the downfall of the family, the narrator ends the story with a life-sustaining image which depicts the sea not as a destructor, but as life-giving. The names of the two women, Helen and Diana, rich with mythic associations, add a dimension of tradition to his vision and reinforce Cheever's need to explore the past, even into antiquity.

Style and Technique

The most characteristic element of style in this story is the presence of the unnamed narrator, who characteristically reflects Cheever's comments on the events of the narrative in the wry, compassionate, and detached way of a sympathetic observer; much of the appeal of Cheever's stories derives from his perceived relationship with his readers, available through such a fictional presence.

The story is divided between the rather flat, dour pronouncements delivered by Lawrence and the rich, sensuous counterpassages of the narrator. As Lawrence, for example, calls Odette a promiscuous woman, the narrator describes her in sensual detail, noting the roundness of her shoulders and the whiteness of her skin. Similarly, at the conclusion of the costume party, the guests rescue the floating white balloons from the sea while Lawrence laments the partygoers' foolishness. The lushness of the prose that Cheever employs when describing the smells, the sounds, and the contentment of the narrator's life among his family strikingly contrasts not only with Lawrence's gloom but also with his matter-of-fact language. The sense of possibility of the former overshadows the finality of the latter.

Charles L. P. Silet

GOOSEBERRIES

Author: Anton Chekhov (1860-1904)
Type of plot: Parody
Time of plot: The 1890's
Locale: The countryside in provincial Russia
First published: "Kryzhovnik," 1898 (English translation, 1916)

Principal characters:
IVAN IVANICH CHIMSHA-HIMALAISKY, a veterinary surgeon
NIKOLAI IVANICH CHIMSHA-HIMALAISKY, Ivan's brother, a
    retired landowner
BURKIN, a high school teacher
PAVEL KONSTANTINOVICH ALEKHIN, a landowner

The Story

Ivan Ivanich Chimsha-Himalaisky and Burkin are hunting in the countryside when a heavy rain begins; they decide to seek shelter at the home of a local landowner, Pavel Konstantinovich Alekhin. Alekhin is young, unmarried, and a hard worker; he is also inclined to neglect his appearance in the absence of guests. In preparation for dinner and an evening of conversation, Alekhin and his guests bathe in the river; the guests notice that the water around their host turns brown as the dirt cascades off his body. The narrator, who is presumably the author, looks upon Alekhin with favor, however, as he accentuates the young landowner's love of hard work and energetic interest in everything around him.

After their ablutions, the three gentlemen settle down with tea as Ivan Ivanich tells Burkin and Alekhin the curious story of his brother's life. Nikolai Ivanich Chimsha-Himalaisky went to work as a clerk in a large city at the age of nineteen. Both of the brothers grew up in the countryside, but their family estate was sold to settle debts. Nikolai Ivanich has never reconciled himself to life in the city and makes plans to acquire enough money to buy a small estate where he can grow gooseberries, which become a symbol in his mind of gracious living in the countryside. He spends his days dreaming of the future estate: where the main building will be located, ducks swimming in a pond, how he will eat soup made from cabbages which he has grown himself, and where the gooseberry bushes will be planted. Ivan Ivanich does not sympathize with his brother's dream, viewing it as an escape from reality and an unnecessary limitation upon one's field of action. Instead of retreating to a country estate, a person should see the world and be active in society, he thinks.

After this aside, Ivan Ivanich returns to his story. Nikolai Ivanich becomes very stingy as he pinches pennies in order to buy his estate. In his forties, he marries an ugly, elderly, but rich widow in order to acquire more money for his estate. This poor woman, who was accustomed to good living with her former husband, loses control of her finances and is put on a Spartan regimen by Nikolai Ivanich. Within three years she dies; Nikolai Ivanich buys three hundred acres, and he sets about making his dream come true. There are a few drawbacks, however; there is neither a pond nor gooseberry bushes. There is a river, but it is polluted by a factory on one side and a kiln on the other, making the water coffee-brown. Undaunted, Nikolai Ivanich plants gooseberry bushes and settles into the life of a country squire.

Ivan Ivanich decides to pay his brother a visit in order to see how he is doing. The estate is cluttered with ditches, fences, and hedges, with the resulting impression of complete disorder. A dog which looks like a pig barks at the visitor, bringing out a barefoot cook who also looks like a pig. The cook directs Ivan Ivanich to his brother, who has grown stout and also resembles a pig. The reader realizes how removed this estate is from the dream which Nikolai Ivanich had envisioned as a youth.

Ivan Ivanich now describes Nikolai Ivanich's life as a landed proprietor. The formerly timid clerk now pontificates on all sorts of issues and demands to be addressed with respect by the peasants, whom he alternately treats with severity and generosity, as the mood becomes him. He opines that education is necessary for the masses, but that they are not yet ready for it; corporal punishment is evil, but in certain cases still necessary for the peasants, and so forth.

One evening, the two brothers are drinking tea as the cook brings in a full plate of gooseberries grown by Nikolai Ivanich, the first fruits of his bushes. After five minutes of silent contemplation, Nikolai Ivanich puts one in his mouth and pronounces it to be very tasty. In fact, Ivan Ivanich tells Burkin and Alekhin, the gooseberries were sour and hard. A terrible depression overcomes Ivan Ivanich as he realizes how deluded his brother is and how happy he is with so little.

At this point the story of Nikolai ends as Ivan Ivanich begins a monologue condemning the way of life which his brother is leading. His main complaint is that such a life shuts the person off from the sufferings of people around him as he pursues the goal of personal happiness and leads that person even to espouse opinions, such as Nikolai Ivanich's concerning education and corporal punishment, that prolong the suffering of other people. In an impassioned outburst Ivan Ivanich implores Alekhin never to become such a landowner and not to seek his own happiness as much as to seek to do good.

Burkin and Alekhin are somewhat disappointed at this story, hoping to hear something a bit more exciting and adventurous. They keep their opinions to themselves, however, and go to bed, exhausted. On this note the story concludes, the reader perhaps as perplexed as Burkin and Alekhin.

Themes and Meanings

"Gooseberries" is one of a number of stories in which Anton Chekhov views the human penchant for voluntarily limiting one's life. In some cases the reason is fear, in others an inclination toward laziness. The author contrasts the two landowners, Alekhin and Nikolai Ivanich; the former is energetic, while the latter is almost inert. While it is presumed that Alekhin labors to improve his estate, Nikolai Ivanich is content to leave things as they are and pretend that he has found the ideal for his youthful dreams. In a sense, life has become static for Nikolai Ivanich, who apparently sees no need for change in his life or in the lives of others. He is satisfied, but he has not fulfilled his potential and the reader comes to view Nikolai Ivanich's happiness as pathetic.

Nikolai Ivanich's brother, Ivan Ivanich, is particularly incensed at his insensitivity as Nikolai pursues his own level of happiness and cares naught about the happiness of others. This story is one of the very few occasions on which Chekhov takes a stand on social questions of the time, such as education of the peasants and the brutality of the upper classes toward the lower. Chekhov was criticized for his lack of social consciousness and, in this story, six years before his death, he declares himself to be on the liberal side of issues, at least within a Russian context.

In the early 1890's, Chekhov came under the influence of Leo Tolstoy, the famed Russian novelist and religious thinker. Tolstoy advocated retreating from corrupt society to the healthy atmosphere of a simple life in the country. Tolstoy's theory proposed that individuals should perfect themselves, not worry about society, and that through these people finding happiness and peace, society would gradually improve. When Chekhov wrote this story, he had come to the conclusion that Tolstoy's theories were unrealistic. In "Gooseberries," the author satirizes what some people consider their happiness; Nikolai Ivanich's happiness certainly does not lead to the betterment of society. In place of Tolstoy's emphasis on "being good," Chekhov prefers the person who "does good," a much more active approach to social change.

A minor theme in this story is the power of obsession. Nikolai Ivanich's dream so overpowers him that he no longer sees reality and believes that the sour and hard gooseberries are delicious. As a physician, Chekhov saw the benefits of moderation not only in matters of physical health, but also in matters of the spirit; obsession will lead the individual to ruin. In this story, it causes Nikolai Ivanich to delude himself, lose contact with reality, and, in Chekhov's view, resign from an active role in the human process.

Style and Technique

Chekhov is renowned for his economy of words and ability to portray a mood or a person with a single, well-chosen word. In "Gooseberries," he utilizes this technique as usual until Ivan Ivanich gives his speech on the evils of the world. At this point, Chekhov launches into a very uncharacteristic authorial sermon which catches the immediate attention of the reader, but which, at times, seems redundant.

Another Chekhovian technique, however, is carefully adhered to: the use of exaggeration of a human characteristic to prove a point. Chekhov wishes to portray the human ability to delude oneself and to settle for less than what one can achieve. In his portrayal of Nikolai Ivanich, Chekhov presents the reader with an absurd example of such a person, but not so absurd that the point is lost. Chekhov's immense talent permits him to exaggerate, but not go so far that the reader views the work as fantasy or comedy.

Philip Maloney

THE GOSPEL ACCORDING TO MARK

Author: Jorge Luis Borges (1899-1986)
Type of plot: Myth
Time of plot: March, 1928
Locale: The district of Junín, Argentina
First published: "El Evangelio según Marcos," 1970 (English translation, 1970)

Principal characters:
BALTASAR ESPINOSA, the protagonist, a medical student
THE GUTRE FAMILY, consisting of the father, a son, and a girl, caretakers of La Colorada ranch

The Story

Baltasar Espinosa, a medical student in Buenos Aires, is invited by his cousin Daniel to vacation at a ranch in the district of Junín in the final days of March, 1928. Gutre, who is the overseer of the premises, lives there with his son and a girl of questionable paternity. All three are notably primitive in appearance and in their ability to express themselves verbally. In that environment, Baltasar is to learn lessons about life which he has never before suspected.

A few days after arriving, Daniel must leave for the capital, but Baltasar chooses to stay behind with his textbooks. No sooner is Daniel gone than the stifling heat gives way to a cold rain and the river overflows its banks. Many animals are drowned, and when the overseer's quarters are threatened, Baltasar lodges him and his family in the main house. It is thus that the four come into close contact with one another. They eat together, but since communication is strained, Baltasar reads to them, first from Ricardo Güiraldes' work *Don Segundo Sombra* (1926; *Don Segundo Sombra: Shadows on the Pampas*, 1935) and the document of the Gutre family history, both of which they receive rather unenthusiastically, and later from the Bible, specifically the Gospel of Mark, which conversely sparks an unexplained interest.

In the meantime, Baltasar has become cognizant of certain changes in his own physiognomy and attitude that have taken place during his stay at the ranch. Matters which he would formerly have considered trivial have come to acquire significance. Furthermore, he grows nostalgic for Buenos Aires and his family, from which he feels increasingly separated.

One day, the girl brings to Baltasar an injured lamb which he cures using medicine rather than the spiderwebs she had intended to apply to the wound. Mysteriously, the family thereafter begins to follow Baltasar, both figuratively (they follow his orders) and literally (from room to room). They clean away his crumbs at the table, speak of him with respect, and provide him with coffee. When they ask him to reread the Gospel, he reflects that they have asked him to do so because they are like children who prefer repetition to variation and novelty.

On Tuesday, Baltasar dreams of the Flood, and on Thursday, the girl comes to him and loses her innocence. She says nothing to him nor does she kiss him. For some reason, he knows that he will not relate this episode to anyone in Buenos Aires. The following day, Friday, the father asks questions about Christ which Baltasar answers, albeit with uncertainty. After a final rereading of the Gospel and a sleep interrupted by hammering and vague premonitions, Baltasar is crucified by the three Gutres.

Themes and Meanings

In "The Gospel According to Mark," the passage of two thousand years is eradicated when a twentieth century man who travels to the country finds himself in the first century A.D. Baltasar Espinosa enters the world of the Gutre family, a primitive stage of human consciousness where reality takes place in the physical, literal dimension. There, he becomes the victim in an ancient ritual: human sacrifice.

Baltasar is a contemporary Christ figure: At thirty-three he faces the most important test of his life; through his medical studies, he has acquired the power to heal as demonstrated by the cure of the lamb; he possesses superior oratorical skills which he practices when reading parables to the Gutres; he is a courageous man whose goodness is nearly unlimited. At the same time, Baltasar, like his father, is a man of his times who knows too much to be able to believe wholeheartedly. His nightly prayers are more a matter of honor (keeping his promise to his mother) than faith. Furthermore, his attitude is not informed by the revolutionary's enlightened determination but rather by a complacency and an ambiguity of one who reconciles.

The Journey to La Colorada signifies a return to the inception of humankind, an age of innocence in the history of civilization. That place or time holds lessons for Baltasar about life and therefore death, its attraction for him being the eternal and the transcendent (versus the temporal sorts of interests of his cousin). The experience awaiting him at La Colorada is beyond doctrine, either scientific or religious; it is a return to an original source. As the floodwaters encroach upon the ranch, the protagonist moves farther and farther away from Buenos Aires society but closer to that mythological island somewhere in the Mediterranean.

The history of the Gutres traces a regression toward that source or beginning, paradoxically concurrent with the progress of time. Over the course of about a century in the New World, they forget how to write and how to speak languages; the species undergoes reversion instead of evolution. As he comes into closer proximity with the members of that family, Baltasar becomes aware of a correspondence between their almost savage appearance and their behavior described as a difficulty in verbalizing their experiences as well as an inability to remember, yet it is they who will lead him toward the goal of his quest. In a few days' time, contact with them and their environment produces a visible transformation in Baltasar, an outward sign of inner modifications: He is coming into the ultimate knowledge he seeks.

Indeed, the Gutres not only change Baltasar; they create him, or rather a god whose role he is to act out, from the words of the Evangelist Mark. While the writings themselves are ancient, they propose a new, mystical sort of concept to the Gutres: salvation from eternal damnation through a redeemer. In contrast to the other two texts read, which are merely different versions of their own actuality, the Gospel explains the stranger in their midst and directs their course of action: Baltasar is the healer, the shepherd, the teacher who is to be crucified as the Gutres re-create the Passion of Christ.

Style and Technique

In "The Gospel According to Mark," the author rewrites the myth of the return to the origin and, as is often the case with Borges, constructs his tale drawing on a literary model, here the Bible. At one point in the text, the narrator refers to the climax of St. Mark's account of the life of Christ—the Passion—as one of the two stories which men have repeated down through time. In fact, many structural and thematic elements found in "The Gospel According to Mark," especially those associated with the ranch, are of an archetypal nature: the eternal way of life at La Colorada; Baltasar's dreams about the Flood; the representation of the ranch as an island; the fanaticism and superstitions that the Gutres have in their blood; their identification with a primitive race of human beings; the circle of men strumming the guitar. Through these primordial references, Borges evokes the dark, forgotten beginnings of existence.

Another set of symbols in "The Gospel According to Mark" issues from Christian mythology and is related to Baltasar and his influence on the Gutre family. Curiously, he is not a confirmed believer and it is ironic not only that he should introduce to them the concept of faith in a savior but also that he himself should be the victim in the crucifixion. The chain of events leading up to that finish is seen to be no more than a series of accidents (how he arrives at La Colorada, Daniel's sudden departure, the rains that lead him to explore the house and find the Bible, his decision to practice translation by reading the Gospel, the cure of the lamb, even his casual answers to the father's questions). Thus, his experience becomes a nightmare based on mistaken interpretation, more akin to a trip to hell than a return to paradise.

Krista Ratkowski Carmona

GOSPEL SINGERS

Author: Langston Hughes (1902-1967)
Type of plot: Social commentary
Time of plot: The 1960's
Locale: Harlem
First published: 1965

> *Principal characters:*
> JESSE B. SEMPLE, nicknamed Simple, the protagonist, a black
>   Everyman
> BOYD, the narrator, a college-educated friend and companion
>   in the bar

The Story

"Gospel Singers" is not really a short story in the usual sense, nor a chapter in a novel, although Langston Hughes's books featuring the character called Simple are listed in bibliographies as novels. The story is found in *Simple's Uncle Sam* (1965), the last of several books devoted to a presumably average, relatively uneducated black man who speaks with a certain folk wisdom about Harlem and its denizens. His relationship to the black community seems somewhat analogous to that of Will Rogers to Midwestern rural and small-town white people of limited means. Simple's social commentary is more confined, perhaps, to strictly local conditions, those that beset urban blacks, late immigrants from the South.

Sketches about Jesse B. Semple, barroom philosopher, first appeared in 1943 in the Chicago *Defender*, perhaps the most widely read weekly newspaper among urban blacks. Semple, or Simple, as he was dubbed, became a kind of folk hero, speaking directly to the relatively unlettered people he commemorated in language that they could understand. Each short piece is a dialogue between Simple and the narrator, a college-educated friend named Boyd, whose somewhat stilted language contrasts effectively with Simple's colloquial dialect and direct approach. "Gospel Singers" is a typical piece of approximately five pages that might appear in the newspaper as a half-comic, half-serious commentary on contemporary life.

Though it has no plot in the sense of a causally connected set of actions, it has a plan which broaches a topic of conversation in the opening lines, explores the topic in the course of its five pages, and signs off with a minor rhetorical flourish. In this case, the opener is an observation about how many theaters are closing down in Harlem, to be reopened as churches with the names of ministers up in lights like those of film stars. There used to be storefront churches in Harlem; now there are theater-front churches. As Simple points out, "the box office has turned into a collection plate, and the choir is swinging gospel songs."

What follows is a discussion of the relative merits of gospel singing as well-paid entertainment. Simple points out sagely that the gospel singers are doing better than many a nightclub act. Boyd expresses the conventional objections to making religion a means for profit. With his usual sly humor, Simple describes gospel "shows" he has attended and, in effect, defends the pursuit of God and Mammon simultaneously, concluding that "good singers deserve their just rewards both in this world and the other."

The talk moves on to the subject of opera, which Simple's wife, Joyce, appreciates but he does not. Boyd defends opera. Simple went with Joyce to one black opera at Carnegie Hall. The program said it was sung in English, but Simple says, "it sounded to me like it were sung in Yiddish," and he asks Joyce, "did she "reckon all them colored singers had Jewish singing teachers?"

The conversation ends with a discussion of Marion Anderson at the Metropolitan Opera, and Boyd points out that Simple was sitting right there in the bar and cheering the loudest for Marion. Simple agrees heartily, but adds that now that she has retired from opera, Marion ought to take up gospel singing.

Themes and Meanings

"Gospel Singers" plays ironically with a number of commonly held assumptions about the proper role of religion. One of the distinctive capacities of Simple, which is presumably a strong tendency in urban black experience, is the ability to live comfortably amid contradictions and ambiguities. Hughes is not the only writer who deals with this ambivalence—witness Ralph Ellison's strange character, Rinehart, in the novel *Invisible Man* (1952), who is both a preacher and a procurer.

In one sense, the story is a defense of promoting happiness through religion, and a sly blow at the overly solemn view that religious worship should be steeped in the consciousness of sin and suffering. Black experience is no doubt adequately familiar with this world as a veil of tears without harping on that aspect of existence unnecessarily. Gospel singing, like jazz, that other quintessentially black contribution to American music, is a way to transcend the gloomier realities of ordinary life.

Simple also indirectly attacks the attitude, often given lip service by the pious, that religious people should despise money and prefer poverty as somehow good for the soul. The truly poverty-stricken are seldom aware of any great improvement in their souls attributable to their financial situation. They are more likely to suspect that goodness is a luxury for people who have enough to eat and shelter from the fierce extremes of Harlem weather.

The observations about opera are a comfortable reflection of unsophisticated tastes, directed to an audience of non-operagoers. Yet they are offered in such a way as to admit the possible virtues of that medium and suggest that black singers are also gaining recognition there. Even Simple, as unschooled as he is in highbrow music, knows a good voice when he hears one and applauds Marion Anderson.

Style and Technique

Hughes avoided the more illiterate dialect associated with so many literary black characters, sprinkled with "dis" and "dat" and "ain't no mo'." He tried to retain, however, the distinctive dialect of urban blacks, especially the characteristic "jive" talk and slang of Harlem, as evidenced in this exchange between Simple and Boyd:

> "I seed a poster outside a church last night. Sister Mamie Lightfoot and Her Gospel Show, and they were charging one dollar to come in, also programs cost a quarter, and you had to buy one to pass the door."
> "Did you go in?"
> "I did and it were fine! Four large ladies in sky-blue robes sung 'On My Journey Now,' sung it and swung it, real gone, with a jazz piano behind them that sounded like a cross between Dorothy Donegan and Count Basie. Them four sisters started slow, then worked it up, and worked it up, and worked it up until they came on like gang busters, led by Sister Lightfoot. . . ."

This example illustrates the role of Boyd, primarily as straight man to keep the attention on Simple's monologues. Occasionally, he functions as a somewhat pedantic repeater of platitudes, in order to emphasize his companion's greater vitality, as in this dull rejoinder to Simple's opinionated view of opera: "Just because you don't understand a thing, do not make fun of it too harshly, or be too critical of others for liking it. Tastes differ." The relationship between the two speakers seems to suggest that the process of indoctrinating the black into the standard speech patterns of white society results in a serious loss of rhetorical vigor.

Hughes has a characteristic way of closing these conversations—a witty twist that reinforces the impression of rather impudent common sense in the barroom orator who asserts his opinions with such gusto. He has just proclaimed that Marion Anderson could make a million dollars as a gospel singer. Boyd says, "Don't be ridiculous," to which Simple glibly returns, "When was money ever ridiculous?"

The main achievement of these dialogues is not so much the isolated opinions expressed in this or that conversation, but in the creation of a literary character who achieved the status of folk hero for urban blacks. Critic Saul Maloff describes Simple as

> the wry, ironic, crafty, folkloristic, garrulous, beer-swilling, homegrown barfly philosopher . . . a man who once he got his hands on your lapels, never let go, a

hilarious black Socrates of the neighborhood saloons who would at the drop of his hat discourse on anything from marital relations to international relations, lynching to lexicography, the foibles of mankind and follies of womankind. Whatever it was, Simple had the shrewd and loony answer.

Katherine Snipes

GRAPHOMANIACS
(A Story from My Life)

Author: Abram Tertz (Andrei Sinyavsky, 1925-   )
Type of plot: Parody
Time of plot: 1959
Locale: Moscow
First published: "Grafomany," 1961 (English translation, 1963)

> *Principal characters:*
> PAUL IVANOVICH STRAUSTIN, the narrator and protagonist, an
>   unsuccessful writer
> ZINAIDA, his wife
> PAUL, their six-year-old son
> SEMYON GALKIN, another unsuccessful writer, an acquaint-
>   ance of Straustin

The Story

The naïve, clichéd subtitle of this story suggests that its first-person narrator is rather inept, hardly a skilled writer. This impression is confirmed within the first page of the story when Paul Ivanovich Straustin, the narrator and protagonist, determines to memorize a phrase that has come to his mind: "the breath of an approaching thunderstorm could be sensed in the air." Oblivious to its excruciating banality, Straustin vows that he will use this phrase as the last sentence of his novel *In Search of Joy*, adding it "if necessary even at the proof stage." As the reader soon learns, however, this novel has been rejected for publication—the fate of all the other books which Straustin has written in twenty years of utter failure.

In the story's opening scene, Straustin meets another writer, Semyon Galkin, a poet translator rather than, like Straustin, a writer of fiction, but equally unsuccessful. Yet while they are both failures, Galkin's attitude toward his work and toward writing in general contrasts sharply with Straustin's, and this contrast is pivotal to the story.

In the common view, Galkin says, those who write year after year without so much as achieving publication, let alone the perquisites of the successful author, are simply sick. "Graphomania—it's a disease, the psychiatrists tell us, an incurable vicious urge to produce verses, plays and novels in defiance of the world." Yes, Galkin admits, writers such as he (and Straustin) are sick—but so also were William Shakespeare and Alexander Pushkin. They too were graphomaniacs, "graphomaniacs of genius." Straustin, however, rejects this appellation; it does not agree with his fanciful image of himself as a writer, and, worse, it emphasizes his kinship with Galkin and other unpublished scribblers.

After a futile visit to the offices of a publisher, an unpleasant surprise from his six-year-old son (whose first story, consisting of a few lines penciled in a drawing book, Straustin regards as competition), and an argument with his wife (who, sobbing, calls him a "maniac" and says that he needs treatment), Straustin goes to Galkin's apartment, where he stays for three days. Here, the contrast in their attitudes toward writing is further developed. Writing, Galkin says, is not a matter of "'expressing one's personality'"—quite the contrary: "we labor in the sweat of our brow and cover wagon-loads of paper with writing—in the hope of stepping aside, overcoming ourselves and granting access to thoughts from the air."

Far from sharing Galkin's awe at this process, Straustin hears the poet's declaration with great suspicion. If Galkin does not regard what he has written as his property, so Straustin reasons, then he must not respect the proprietary rights of others; in other words, he must be a plagiarist. Straustin finds confirmation for his suspicions in the wildly funny scene which follows. Graphomaniacs of all sorts gather in Galkin's apartment to read their work. Soon they are all reading at once, and in the surreal babble Straustin detects fragments of his own writings. Convinced that he has been the victim of massive plagiarism, he finds further evidence in books pulled at random from the shelf: Everyone, it seems, has been plagiarizing his unpublished works. He does not realize that the "incriminating" passages consist entirely of clichés.

This "discovery" sets him walking the streets of Moscow (an extraordinary number of which, he notes, are named for writers). After a hallucinatory night, he returns home and promises his wife, to her great delight, that he has given up writing. As soon as she leaves for work, however, he addresses his son as an accomplice and, swearing him to secrecy, welcomes him into the fellowship of graphomaniacs: For the first time, Straustin has accepted that designation for himself. Now the parenthetical subtitle takes on a new meaning, for the end of the story loops back to its beginning:

I took a fresh sheet and wrote on the top in capitals the title:

GRAPHOMANIACS

Then I thought for a moment and added in brackets:

(A Story from My Life)

Themes and Meanings

Andrei Sinyavsky, who wrote this story under the pen name Abram Tertz, has treated many of its themes in an essay entitled "The Literary Process in Russia." In that essay, Sinyavsky argues that "all true writing—even when no clash with authority is involved—is something forbidden, something reprehensible, and in this illicit element lies the whole excitement, the whole dilemma of being a writer." This view of writing conflicts not only with the dogma of socialist realism, which governs approved literature in the Soviet Union, but also with the prescriptions of the most famous Russian writer in exile, Alexander Solzhenitsyn.

At the beginning of "Graphomaniacs," Straustin is unwilling to admit that by spending his life writing, hunched over a piece of paper, he is doing something intrinsically shameful, illicit, whether or not the product of his labor meets with the world's approval. Despite his diatribes against the worship of the nineteenth century masters ("it's said that in Yalta Chekhov's dried-up spit has been collected in special little packets—yes, the actual spit of Anton Pavlovich Chekhov"), he measures writers and writing strictly in terms of conventional success. In his own writing, he aspires to literature with a vengeance, with grandiloquent phrases and lofty sentiments.

Sinyavsky, however, believes that true writing has nothing to do with "literature." It is only when Straustin abandons his pride and accepts his place among the graphomaniacs that he is able to write anything worthwhile. This is the cunning twist at the heart of "Graphomaniacs," for as one turns the last page one realizes that the author of the (mercifully unpublished) novels *In Search of Joy* and *The Sun Rises Above the Steppe* is also the "author" of the story which the reader has just finished reading.

Style and Technique

As one might expect from a writer who has said that "whenever I earn any money—and I earn it regularly from my literary works—I am amazed each time it happens and I carry the money away in haste, clutching my pocket, crouching slightly like a burglar," the style of "Graphomaniacs" is tricky, devious, playful. One notable example of this devious style is the manner in which Sinyavsky uses the character of Galkin.

Galkin is something of a buffoon—moreover, a buffoon seen through the eyes of the vain, spiteful Straustin. By using Galkin (instead of a more impressive figure) to express many of his own views on the nature of writing, Sinyavsky avoids a didactic or sententious tone. The same purpose is served by the description of Galkin in the grip of poetic inspiration. Straustin scornfully observes that, at such moments, Galkin would fall silent, sitting motionless for minutes on end. Complaining that these trances distracted him from his own work, Straustin relates that he "would drop some article on the floor—a pencil, a pair of scissors and once, for the sake of experiment, a heavy manuscript, the novel *In Search of Joy*"—but, having been lifted outside himself, "Galkin did not react. From his protuberant lower lip a strand of spittle hung down to his collar." Thus, Sinyavsky suggests that true writing is a selfless discipline in the service of transcendence—but deviously, with a smile.

John Wilson